THE GARDEN CONSERVANCY'S
OPEN DAYS DIRECTORY

The Guide to Visiting
America's Best Private Gardens

Foreword by Daryl Beyers
Assistant Editor of *Fine Gardening* magazine

2007
EDITION

Published and distributed by
The Garden Conservancy, Inc.

Distributed by The Garden Conservancy, Cold Spring, New York

Publisher's Cataloging-in-Publication
(provided by Quality Books, Inc.)
The Garden Conservancy's open days directory: the guide to visiting America's best private gardens, 2007 ed., 13th ed.
    p. cm.
    Includes index.
    ISSN: 1087-7738
    ISBN: 978-1-893424-20-3
1. Gardens—United States—Directories.
2. Botanical gardens—United States—Directories.
3. Arboretums—United States—Directories.
    I. Garden Conservancy
    II. Title: Open days directory
    SB466.U65G37 2007   712'.07473
                        QBI00-836

This book is printed on recycled paper
Manufactured in the United States

Cover and contents page photos: Mettawa Manor, Mettawa, IL. Photos by Allan Mandell.
Title page photo: Hilltop, North Salem, NY. Photo © 2005 Richard Felber.

CONTENTS

OUR SPONSORS

The Garden Conservancy gratefully
acknowledges W. Atlee Burpee & Co. for
their support of the Open Days Program
and the Garden Conservancy's work
towards increasing public awareness and
appreciation of America's gardens.

HERONSWOOD
N U R S E R Y

Visit Burpee's historic Fordhook Farm
during one of four Open Days this summer
featuring the Heronswood plant collection.

fine Gardening

Fine Gardening magazine
The National Media Sponsor of the
2007 Open Days Program.

We also extend our appreciation to the
fine garden businesses and public gardens
that support this publication
through their advertising.

*Photos from top to bottom: The Sheiling in Nantucket,
MA open June 28th; Garden at 413 Shore Road in York
County, ME open on June 23rd (Photo: Frank Wallace);
The McKenna Garden on Chicago's North Shore, IL open
June 24th.*

FOREWORD

Gardening is an act of faith. Gardeners see, shape, and plant the land with the future always in mind. As we perform each daily, weekly, or yearly task, we begin to recognize our inner nature reflected in our garden landscapes. To make and maintain a garden forms a union between people and nature, and that is why great gardens excite our admiration. As an art, a craft, a hobby, and a labor of love, gardening is a personal commitment to the creation of outdoor beauty through aesthetics, skill, pleasure, and passion. Experiences such as these are meant to be shared, because sharing the successes of challenging work is one of the greatest gifts anyone—including gardeners—can give.

The Garden Conservancy's Open Days program is vital to the gardening community because each year it invites hundreds of gardens to open their gates to thousands of visitors. Open Days serves the greater good of gardening by bringing people to places where horticultural experiences effectively shape the landscape into a more beautiful world we all can enjoy.

A visit to a great garden never fails to inspire and delight. It is where we realize that all gardens, including our own, are the result of dedication and devotion bestowed upon the land by the garden's creator. I recognized this truth as I wrote *Great Gardens*, a special publication of *Fine Gardening* magazine, in partnership with The Garden Conservancy. We observed the thought and attention lavished upon twelve amazing spaces, several included in the Open Days Program this year. These tours, through photography and words, inspired me to visit even more gardens in the hopes of replicating just a little bit of their magic on my own home ground.

The directory you hold in your hands is your guide to many moments of garden delight. I encourage you to accept the invitation to visit these gardens. You will remember the experience long after the gates have closed at the end of the day.

Daryl Beyers
Assistant Editor
Fine Gardening magazine

www.opendaysprogram.org

Don't forget to visit us online for updates on Open Days in your area and information on other Garden Conservancy programs and preservation projects. You may also register to receive weekly e-mail reminders and invitations to special events near you.

From the Chairman

Anyone who has taken up gardening will no doubt agree that it is a continuous learning experience. As gardeners, we are all familiar with the lessons of trial and error in our search to find the right combination of plants and design. We learn from our own experience and build on these lessons to grow as gardeners.

In addition to the "dirty work," we also look for inspiration. Whether it comes from our own experiences or those of others, inspiration is just as vital to a great garden as good soil and healthy plants.

This search for knowledge and inspiration is what compels hundreds of willing gardeners from coast to coast to open their gardens each year through the Garden Conservancy's Open Days Program. They want to share what they have learned through their own gardening experience and they want to learn from others. We are fortunate to have partners in W. Atlee Burpee & Co. and *Fine Gardening* magazine. Both of them are just as committed as we are to making you a better gardener.

In 2007, Burpee will host four Open Days at historic Fordhook Farm in Doylestown, Pennsylvania. Speakers, garden tours, and plants for sale from the extraordinary Heronswood Collection are well worth the trip. There will also be a rare opportunity to visit their gardens at Heronswood in Kingston, Washington this summer.

If you can't travel far this year, join us and *Fine Gardening* magazine for an armchair tour of twelve extraordinary private gardens from coast-to-coast-more than half of them are participating in Open Days this season. *Great Gardens* is beautifully illustrated by garden photographer Allan Mandell with interviews of their creators. We have provided a preview on page 20. Visit our website to buy your copy; part of the proceeds support the Open Days Program.

Enjoy the outstanding selection of gardens listed in this *Directory*. Your own garden will be better for it.

James DeGrey David
Chairman
Open Days Program

WELCOME TO OPEN DAYS

How is the Program Organized?

The Open Days Program would not be possible without the hard work and dedication of our volunteers. Each Open Day is organized locally by at least one Regional Representative who recruits private gardens and oversees the program in their area. Over the past twelve years, this roster of volunteers has grown to include more than 225 men and women. You will find a complete list of Regional Representatives in the appendix at the back of the directory. Regional Representatives active in 2007 are listed on page 24.

If you are interested in learning more about the organization of Open Days throughout the country and how you can become involved, please contact The Garden Conservancy's Open Days Program, P.O. Box 219, Cold Spring, NY 10516. Call us at (845) 265-5384 or e-mail us at info@gardenconservancy.org.

Admission

Proceeds from the Open Days Program support the national preservation work of the Garden Conservancy such as the rehabilitation of the gardens on Alcatraz Island, as well as local nonprofit organizations designated by our garden hosts.

A $5 admission fee is collected at each garden. Cash may be paid at the gate or visitors may purchase admission tickets at a discounted price.

Admission fees to the public gardens listed in the *Open Days Directory* are indicated in their listing. Open Days tickets may not be used at public gardens.

How to Use the *Directory*

Gardens and Open Days are cross-listed by date and by location beginning on page 25.

- To find out which gardens are open on particular dates, see "Open Days by Date."
- To find out when a particular region is holding an Open Day, see "Open Days by Location" (organized alphabetically by state).
- To find out when a particular garden will be open, look for the name of the garden (or gardener) in the index at the back of the book.

Garden descriptions, open hours, and directions will be found in the state chapters, which are ordered alphabetically. Within each state chapter, Open Days are then listed chronologically by Open Day. For each Open Day, listings are alphabetical by county, then town, then garden name. At the end of each state chapter, there is a listing and description of participating public gardens in that state.

Please be sure to check the Garden Conservancy's web site prior to your visit to note any last-minute schedule changes: www.opendaysprogram.org.

Etiquette in the Garden

Our Open Days Hosts spend countless hours preparing their gardens for your visit. Please reward their hard work by following these guidelines:

- Do not pick any plant or remove any part of a plant.
- Do not leave litter in the garden.
- Stay on the paths.
- Follow any posted signs or directions.
- Respect the privacy of the owners by not contacting them directly.
- Please leave all pets at home.
- Children must be supervised at all times.
- Park your car so others can enter and leave the parking area.
- Ask the owner's permission to take photographs; tripods are not permitted.
- Respect the listed dates and times of openings. To pursue special visiting arrangements, please contact the Garden Conservancy at (845) 265-5384.

Garden visitors tour Burpee's Fordhook Farm in Bucks County, PA during their 2006 Open Day event. See the ad on pg. 243 for details on Fordhook Farm's 2007 Open Days.

Lenkin Garden in Pasadena, CA is featured in Great Gardens by Taunton Press (see pg. 20) and will welcome visitors on April 29th this year. Photo: Allan Mandell.

AN OPEN INVITATION

Bringing People into Gardens

Here at the Garden Conservancy, we believe that the best way to learn about gardens and to appreciate them, is to simply spend more time in them. Whether it's your own garden, or your neighbor's, or the generous Garden Hosts across the country, we want you to be there. We invite you to explore examples of outstanding design and horticultural practice that are growing in America's gardens.

Since 1995, the Garden Conservancy's Open Days Program has unlocked the gates to hundreds of America's very best private gardens by working with volunteers coast to coast to coordinate schedules, collect information, and get it to you. Many of these gardens are rarely, if ever, otherwise open to the public.

The book you hold in your hands is your invitation to these Open Days treasures.

Hundreds of New Open Days Gardens

After twelve years, our beginning seems legendary. Our first gardens opened in 1995 when Garden Conservancy members and extraordinary gardeners Page Dickey and Penelope Maynard were inspired by England's National Gardens Scheme and its guidebook, *Gardens of England and Wales Open for Charity*, informally known as the Yellow Book. They came to the Garden Conservancy with 110 private gardens in hand,

> Since 1995, the Garden Conservancy's Open Days Program has unlocked the gates to hundreds of America's very best private gardens.

including theirs, that would open that first year.

The program was a resounding success. Since then, with the help of a network of volunteer regional representatives, the Garden Conservancy has expanded Open Days to the four corners of the country and has opened thousands of gardens. Each year, some 50 percent of the participating gardens are new to the program. The 2007 season features more than 350 gardens.

Mission of the Garden Conservancy

The Garden Conservancy is a national organization with a mission to preserve exceptional American gardens for public education and enjoyment. We seek to develop and deepen public appreciation of gardens as integral elements of our national artistic and cultural heritage. The Open Days Program serves as the primary educational outreach for the Conservancy and is a major component of this mission.

Right: The Smith Garden in Los Angeles, CA will be open on May 12th this year.

Garden visitors at Fitzpatrick's Hillhome in Berkshire County, MA. This garden will welcome guests again this year on July 22nd.

A couple admires the Japanese maples at the garden of Judy & Michael Steinhardt in Mount Kisco, NY during the 2006 fall Open Day. This garden will welcome guests in spring this year on May 6th.

Poth-Gill Garden in Austin, TX welcomed visitors during last year's popular Austin Open Day.

Cynthia's Urban Garden in Denver, CO will be open June 30th this year.

The Garden Conservancy at Work

Founded in 1989 by the distinguished American gardener Frank Cabot, the Garden Conservancy is now recognized as the leader of the growing national garden preservation movement. We work in partnership with individual garden owners and public and private organizations, and use our legal, financial, and horticultural resources to help secure the future of hundreds of gardens from across the country.

Hundreds of gardens across the United States have benefited from Garden Conservancy assistance.

Going Public
The preservation of a single garden requires technical supervision, master planning, fundraising, and the development of an organizational structure and boards of directors. We advise individuals as well as managers of existing public gardens.

Hundreds of gardens across the United States have benefited from our assistance. A limited few have been designated Garden Conservancy Projects. They are listed on the opposite page.

Conservation Easements
A conservation easement is a deed restriction that establishes specific requirements and limitations for the management of a private property. The restrictions are effective in perpetuity, and are monitored and enforced by the nonprofit organization to whom the easement is given. The easements prevent subdivision or further development and identify key garden elements that must be preserved. Provision is made for limited public access, but the properties remain in private ownership.

Making Connections
We are able to bring together garden advocates and professionals from a broad range of communities, such as our Pacific Northwest Garden Conservancy Forum. The Forum promotes communication, networking, and professional workshops for member gardens in that region.

Education and Training
We offer lectures and symposia to members and, for experienced horticulturists and landscape designers, internships at our preservation projects to learn the diversified skills required to run a public garden. We also publish a two-volume series, *Taking a Garden Public*, that outlines the issues and strategies involved in saving a garden.

Garden Conservancy Projects

Alcatraz Island,
San Francisco, CA

We are leading the effort to restore the gardens of Alcatraz in partnership with the National Park Service and the Golden Gate National Parks Conservancy by stabilizing and beginning the rehabilitation of these diverse gardens. See page 80 for visiting information.

The Chase Garden,
Orting, WA

This significant example of the Pacific Northwest, modernist garden style of the 1960s has been preserved through a conservation easement and the creation of The Friends of the Chase Garden. Together we raise funds to maintain the garden, plan for its future, and open it to the public. See page 276 for visiting information.

The Elizabeth Lawrence Garden,
Charlotte, NC

In 2001, we began working with local supporters to secure a Mecklenburg County Historic Landmark designation and a conservation easement to protect this property. We will continue to organize and oversee documentation of the garden and guiding principles for its preservation, along with maintenance standards for the house and garden. See their website for visiting information: www.elizabethlawrence.org

The Fells at the John Hay National Wildlife Refuge, Newbury, NH

Once the summer retreat of American statesman and author John Hay, the John Hay National Wildlife Refuge is becoming a regional center for conservation and horticulture. We managed the restoration and interpretation of the landscape for the state of New Hampshire. In 1997, we turned over the

Garden Conservancy Projects

management to a friends committee we helped to form. We continue to provide financial support and technical advice. See page 158 for visiting information.

Pearl Fryar's Topiary Garden,
Bishopville, SC

Pauline Laffitte

Recognized by art and botanical enthusiasts, the visually whimsical garden is maintained year-round by Fryar for visitors from around the world. The Friends of Pearl Fryar's Topiary Garden has been organized to help care for and preserve the garden and assist Pearl as he educates and inspires others to achieve their creative potential. See their website for visiting information: www.fryarstopiaries.com

Greenwood Gardens,
Short Hills, NJ

We are working closely with the Board of Directors and the staff of this twenty-

two-acre formal garden to oversee its extensive restoration, the development of the nonprofit organization, and the creation of what will become a valued horticultural resource for the New York metropolitan region. See page 170 for visiting information.

Hollister House—Garden of George Schoellkopf, Washington, CT

We worked closely with George Schoellkopf to plan for the garden's transition to nonprofit ownership and a new organization. Our 2006 Marco Polo Stufano Fellow was instrumental in documenting this garden. See page 115 for visiting information.

The John P. Humes Japanese Stroll Garden, Mill Neck, NY

The Humes Japanese Stroll Garden was nearly lost in 1993 when the foundation

Garden Conservancy Projects

that owned it ran low on funds and decided to close the garden. We responded to the emergency, taking over the management of the garden and overseeing its long-term preservation. Today it welcomes visitors and hosts a full schedule of tours and educational programs. See page 217 for visiting information.

LongueVue House & Garden,
Metarie, LA

A National Historic Landmark and regional resource and tourist destination, the garden is playing an important role in rebuilding a ravaged city of New Orleans. The Garden Conservancy first responded by sending a team of volunteers to assist in clean up and preparation for replanting. Today we are working with Longue Vue to replant damaged trees and shrubs. See their website for visiting information: www. longuevue.com

Montrose,
Hillsborough, NC

Montrose was once the location of the influential Montrose Nursery, closed since 1993. It was developed by renowned gardener, Nancy Goodwin, who continues to manage the property. We are assisting the Goodwins in planning for the future of Montrose as a public

garden and horticultural resource. See page 229 for visiting information.

Peckerwood Garden,
Hempstead, TX

In 1997 we began advising John Fairey on preservation strategies. One year later, the Peckerwood Garden Conservation Foundation was established and we continue to play a leadership role in the development of funding and programs to complete the transition of the Peckerwood Garden to public operations. See page 262 for visiting information.

Rocky Hills—The Garden of William & Henriette Suhr,
Mount Kisco, NY

We accepted a conservation easement to protect the property from development and steps are outlined for its eventual operation as a public garden, owned by the Westchester County Department

Garden Conservancy Projects

of Parks, Recreation and Conservation. The garden will ultimately become a horticultural education center for gardeners throughout Westchester County and New York State. See pages 182 and 185 for visiting information.

The Ruth Bancroft Garden,
Walnut Creek, CA

The Ruth Bancroft Garden was our first preservation project and the inspiration to our founder, Frank Cabot. In helping to protect this work of art, we created the first known conservation easement granted on a private garden. The garden now operates as a public garden owned

and supported by the Ruth Bancroft Garden, Inc. a local nonprofit organization we helped establish. See page 75 for visiting information.

Steepletop,
Austerlitz, NY

Other gardens we have assisted:

Abkhazi Garden, Vancouver, BC, Canada

Arthur Erickson House & Garden, Vancouver, BC, Canada

Ashintully, Tyringham, MA

Aullwood Garden, Dayton, OH

Beatrix Farrand Garden at Bellefield, Hyde Park, NY

Bellamy-Ferriday Garden, Bethlehem, CT

Blithewold, Bristol, RI

Brookwood Garden, Cooperstown, NY

Cohen-Bray House & Garden, Oakland, CA

Cross Estate, Bernardsville, NJ

Dumbarton Oaks Park, Washington, DC

Elk Rock, The Garden at the Bishop's Close, Portland, OR

Eudora Welty Garden, Jackson, MS

Garland Farm—The Last Garden of Beatrix Farrand, Mount Desert, ME

Gibraltar, Wilmington, DE

Harland Hand Memorial Garden, El Cerrito, CA

Garden Conservancy Projects

We are working with the Millay Society and their Friends group to develop a preservation planning process and a landscape master plan for Steepletop, the home and inspiration for poet Edna St. Vincent Millay. Steepletop is currently not open for visitation.

Van Vleck House & Gardens,
Montclair, NJ

We assist in the preservation, maintenance and interpretation of Van Vleck Gardens, working with the Montclair Foundation, owner of the property, and

the local Friends group. See page 169 for visiting information.

Yew Dell Gardens,
Crestwood, KY

We are assisting the Friends of Yew Dell by providing technical assistance in planning for the rehabilitation of the gardens, in listing the property on the National Register of Historic Places, and in the development of a master plan and funding strategy. See their website for visiting information: www. yewdellgardens.org

Historic Deepwood and the Lord & Schryver Conservancy, Salem, OR

The James Rose Center, Ridgewood, NJ

Justin Smith Morrill Homestead, Strafford, VT

Knoxville Botanical Garden & Arboretum, Knoxville, TN

Lee Memorial Garden, New Canaan, CT

Madoo Conservancy, Sagaponack, NY

Maudslay State Park, Newburyport, MA

McKee Botanical Garden, Vero Beach, FL

McLaughlin Garden, South Paris, ME

Moore-Turner Heritage Gardens, Spokane, WA

Morven Museum & Gardens, Princeton, NJ

Mukai Farm & Garden, Vashon Island, WA

Palm Cottage, Gotha, FL

Pavilion Gardens at the University of Virginia, Charlottesville, VA

Sonnenberg Gardens, Canandaigua, NY

Springside Landscape Restoration, Poughkeepsie, NY

Val Verde Estate, Montecito, CA

Great Gardens

Over the past twelve years, we have been working with volunteers, public gardens, and other like-minded organizations to make Open Days into a truly national garden-visiting program. Since 2003, we have partnered with *Fine Gardening* who has helped us spread the word to gardeners nationwide through their monthly magazine. Like Open Days, *Fine Gardening* encourages gardeners to learn from each other. The magazine is filled with articles written by great gardeners around the country and is filled with advice and practical information for the amateur and professional alike.

As a result of our growing relationship with *Fine Gardening*, we are especially pleased to be a part of this inspiring publication, *Great Gardens*. Many of the gardens that participate in Open Days have been featured over the years in *Fine Gardening*, including those you see here. We promise that within these pages, you will find gardens that will inspire and delight. They are personal visions by very talented gardeners ranging from a lush tropical garden on New York's Long Island, to a stately manor house north of Chicago surrounded by prairies and an oak-hickory forest, to an historic Italianate house in Los Angeles that sits amid formal, romantic gardens.

Best of all, you will have the opportunity to visit some of these gardens through Open Days. Order your copy today on our website, www.opendaysprogram.org, or by calling toll-free 1-888-842-2442. We'll send you a free admission ticket and a portion of the cover price ($7.99) supports the Open Days Program.

Above left: The garden of Buell Steelman and Rebecca Sams in Eugene, OR will be open on July 8th. Photo: Buell Steelman. Above right: The garden of Silas Mountsier in Nutley, NJ will be open on September 8th. Photo: Allan Mandell. Opposite page: The garden of Dennis Schrader & Bill Smith on Long Island, NY will be open on July 14th. Photo: Allan Mandell.

Notes From the Field

As a professional garden photographer my job is to immerse myself in the finest gardens on the planet and create images that reflect their beauty. Gardening is an art form, so I approach this task from the perspective of photographing art. I have a responsibility to the designer—who is often the garden owner—to tune in to what they are doing. Beyond this, what I count on is the consistency of my own artistic vision and the serendipity of natural light and bloom times.

I believe there is an essential experience to being in a garden. At its core a garden is not only a place of horticultural beauty but a gateway to an internal world that is private to you alone. It is similar to listening to music, at times you are trans-ported to a place within yourself. These kinds of inner/outer aesthetic experiences are plentiful in a well-designed garden. To me the success of a garden is determined by the intensity of these experiences, and my hope is to reflect these qualities in my photography.

What I see in the Open Days gardens is an exceedingly high level of passion and commitment to the art of garden-making. What is most interesting is the variety of ways this can be accomplished with such skill and taste. Every region I travel to offers creative examples of expert plantsmanship and inventive ways of sculpt-ing outdoor space. Whether it's a Midwest prairie, a high-altitude alpine retreat, a dramatic Los Angeles hillside, a sun-drenched wine-country spread, a lovingly cared-for chunk of Northwest forest, a Texan hill-country oasis, a sweeping vista across a posh estate or intimate details within a back yard gem, the cream rises.

Take a look for yourselves and see what is there for you. And in doing so you can help provide support for preserving some of the greatest gardens in existence today.

Allan Mandell
Garden Photographer

Above: W. Atlee Burpee & Co.'s Fordhook Farm in Bucks County, PA.
Opposite page bottom left: Visitors explore Fordhook Farm's grounds and gardens.
Opposite page top left and right: Garden enthusiasts peruse the selection of Heronswood plants for sale at last year's Fordhook Farm Open Days.

Invitation from Burpee

W. Atlee Burpee & Co., America's oldest and most trusted name in gardening, is once again teaming up with the Garden Conservancy's Open Days Program to bring gardeners together. Burpee provides a sponsorship donation that enables the Open Days to continue to invite gardeners around the country to open their gates to the public and to learn from each other in the process.

Heronswood Open Dates

HERONSWOOD
N U R S E R Y
Throughout 2007, Burpee will host four Open Days at historic Fordhook Farm in Doylestown, PA. These Open Days will feature guest speakers, garden tours, and plant sales.

April 20 & 21—Hellebores & Friends
May 18 & 19—Everything for Spring
August 3 & 4—Mid-summer Perennials
September 21 & 22—Viburnums

See the ad on page 243 for more information.

There will also be a rare opportunity to visit Heronswood Nursery in Kingston, Washington. See their listing on page 271.

You may also visit our website for more information: www.opendaysprogram.org

The Marek/Bernatz Garden in Santa Monica, CA will welcome visitors on May 12th this year. Photo: Joseph Marek

2007 Regional Representatives

Arizona: Tucson—*Lisa Lucking, Elizabeth Przygoda*

California: West Los Angeles—*Jeanne Anderson, Joseph Marek, Susan Keim*; Pasadena—*Martyn Belmont, Elena Shoch*; Sacramento—*Saul Wiseman*; San Diego—*Joanne Lee*; San Francisco Peninsula— *Mrs. Harvey D. Hinman, Joan Sanders*; Sebastopol—*Betsy Flack*

Colorado: Denver—*Laurie Brock, Suellen White*

Connecticut & Southeastern New York: *Page Dickey, Penelope Maynard, Francis Schell, Sara M. Knight*

Florida: Vero Beach—*Christine Hobart*

Illinois: Chicago's North Shore—*Mrs. Melville C. Hill, Jr.*; Western Chicago—*Betty Earl*

Maine: Hancock County—*Mrs. George H.P. Dwight*; Mid Coast—*Margaret P. Watson*; York County—*Mrs. Calvin Hosmer III*

Massachusetts: Berkshires—*Jytte Brooks, Diana Felber, Madeline & Ian Hooper, Honey Sharp*; Mid-Cape—*Mrs. Prescott Dunbar*; Nantucket—*Mrs. John A. Baldwin, Mrs. Coleman Burke, Caroline Ellis*

New Hampshire & Vermont: Upper Valley— *Mrs. John H. Hewitt*

New Jersey: Spring Lake—*Barbara Nelson*

New York: Bronx—*Marco Polo Stufano*; Eastern Long Island—*Lalitte Smith*; Ithaca— *Chrys Gardener*; Remsenburg—*Deonne Finkelstein*; Syracuse—*Michael Brennan*

North Carolina: Edenton—*Anne Rouse Edwards*; Raleigh—*Helen Yoest*

Oregon: Clackamas County—*Stephanie Butz, Y. Sherry Sheng, Lynn Swanson*, Eugene—*Diana Learner, Pam Perryman*; Portland—*Linda Ernst, Jill Schatz*

Pennsylvania: Philadelphia—*Diane Newbury, Susan Yeager*

Tennessee: Knoxville—*Jim McDonough*

Texas: Dallas—*Peter Schaar*; El Paso—*Maria Woody*; Fort Worth—*Ginger Bason*

Virginia: Charlottesville—*Candy Crosby, Mrs. Mario di Valmarana*

Washington: Bainbridge Island—*Karla Waterman*; Olympia—*Tam Crocker*

West Virginia: Charleston—*Marion Jones*

Open Days by Date

Saturday, April 7
FLORIDA
INDIAN RIVER COUNTY
Vero Beach
Drea's Garden, 10 a.m. to 4 p.m.
Marion's Garden, 10 a.m. to 4 p.m.
The Tropical Garden of Vero Beach
  Avenue, 10 a.m. to 4 p.m.

Saturday, April 14
NEW YORK
WESTCHESTER COUNTY
Lewisboro
The White Garden, 10 a.m. to 3 p.m.

Friday & Saturday
April 20 & 21
PENNSYLVANIA
BUCKS COUNTY
Doylestown
Heronswood Nursery Comes to Fordhook
  Farm of the W. Atlee Burpee & Co.,
  10 a.m. to 4 p.m.

Saturday, April 21
NORTH CAROLINA
CHOWAN COUNTY
Edenton
Beverly Hall Gardens, 10 a.m. to 4 p.m.
Homestead Garden, 10 a.m. to 4 p.m.
Mary's Garden at the Brown-Elliott House,
  10 a.m. to 4 p.m.
The Paine House Garden, 10 a.m. to
  4 p.m.
Rose Cottage, 10 a.m. to 4 p.m.
Skinner-Paxton House, 10 a.m. to 4 p.m.

Sunday, April 22
CALIFORNIA
SAN DIEGO COUNTY
El Cajon
Rick & Joyce Dentt's Garden, 10 a.m. to
  4 p.m.
Steve & Susie Dentt's Garden, 10 a.m. to
  4 p.m.
La Mesa
Hillside Jungle Garden, 10 a.m. to 4 p.m.
Nugent Garden, 10 a.m. to 4 p.m.
San Diego
Oak Park Secret Garden, 10 a.m. to 4 p.m.

CONNECTICUT
FAIRFIELD COUNTY
Weston
Toscairn, Guided tours at 10 a.m. &
  12 p.m.

Saturday, April 28
CALIFORNIA
SACRAMENTO COUNTY
Sacramento
New England Style Landscaping, 10 a.m.
  to 4 p.m.
Santa Barbara Villa, 10 a.m. to 4 p.m.
Split-level Sculpture Garden, 10 a.m. to
  4 p.m.
Tropical Caribbean Resort, 10 a.m. to
  4 p.m.
The Wells Garden, 10 a.m. to 4 p.m.
The Wise Garden, 10 a.m. to 4 p.m.

SAN DIEGO COUNTY
Poway
Arnold Garden, 10 a.m. to 4 p.m.
Casterline Garden, 10 a.m. to 4 p.m.

Cattolico Garden, 10 a.m. to 4 p.m.
Les Belles Fleurs, 10 a.m. to 4 p.m.
Moore Garden, 10 a.m. to 4 p.m.
Wits End West, 10 a.m. to 4 p.m.

NEW JERSEY
MONMOUTH COUNTY
Atlantic Highlands
Mrs. Sverre Sorensen, 10 a.m. to 4 p.m.

NEW YORK
SUFFOLK COUNTY
East Hampton
Abby Jane Brody, 10 a.m. to 4 p.m.
Margaret Kerr, 10 a.m. to 2 p.m.
Wainscott
Biercuk/Luckey Garden, 10 a.m. to 4 p.m.

Sunday, April 29
CALIFORNIA
LOS ANGELES COUNTY
Pasadena
574 Bellefontaine Street, 10 a.m. to 4 p.m.
La Casita del Arroyo Garden, 9:30 a.m. to
   3:30 p.m.
Linda Baisley & Lenny Amato Garden,
   10 a.m. to 4 p.m.
Bennett-DeBeixedon Garden, 10 a.m. to
   4 p.m.
Susan & Doug Kranwinkle, 10 a.m. to
   4 p.m.
Lenkin Garden, 10 a.m. to 4 p.m.
The Florence Yoch-Designed Ira Bryner
   Garden, 10 a.m. to 4 p.m.
The Zasa Garden, 10 a.m. to 4 p.m.

NEW YORK
PUTNAM COUNTY
Cold Spring
Stonecrop Gardens, 10 a.m. to 5 p.m.

Saturday, May 5
CALIFORNIA
ALAMEDA COUNTY
Berkeley
Cathleen's Garden, 10 a.m. to 4 p.m.
The Harmon Garden, 10 a.m. to 4 p.m.
Our Own Stuff Gallery Garden, 10 a.m. to
   4 p.m.

NEW YORK
SUFFOLK COUNTY
Cutchogue
Jacqueline Penney Art Gallery & Studio,
   10 a.m. to 4 p.m.
Manfred & Roberta Lee, 10 a.m. to 4 p.m.

WESTCHESTER COUNTY
Bedford
Mr. & Mrs. Coleman Burke, 10 a.m. to
   4 p.m.
Penelope & John Maynard, 10 a.m. to
   6 p.m.
Bedford Hills
Sandra & Roger Goldman, 10 a.m. to
   2 p.m.
Phillis Warden, 10 a.m. to 6 p.m.
Larchmont
Forest Court—Joanna & Mark Friedman,
   10 a.m. to 4 p.m.

Saturday & Sunday May 5 & 6
TEXAS
EL PASO COUNTY
El Paso
Azar Garden, 10 a.m. to 4 p.m.
Beltran Family Garden, 10 a.m. to 4 p.m.
Brandt Garden, 10 a.m. to 4 p.m.
Dodd Garden, 10 a.m. to 4 p.m.
Stewart Garden, 10 a.m. to 4 p.m.

Sunday, May 6
NEW YORK
WESTCHESTER COUNTY

Mount Kisco
Judy & Michael Steinhardt, 10 a.m. to
4 p.m.
Rocky Hills—The Garden of William &
Henriette Suhr, 12 p.m. to 4 p.m.

Saturday, May 12
CALIFORNIA
LOS ANGELES COUNTY

Los Angeles
The O'Neill Garden, 10 a.m. to 4 p.m.

Pacific Palisades
The Smith Garden, 10 a.m. to 4 p.m.

Santa Monica
The Edna May Garden, 10 a.m. to 4 p.m.
Lidow Residence, 10 a.m. to 4 p.m.
Marek/Bernatz Garden, 10 a.m. to 4 p.m.
Mayer Residence, 10 a.m. to 4 p.m.
Merrihew's Sunset Gardens, 9:30 a.m. to
3:30 p.m.

NEVADA COUNTY

Grass Valley
Shenoa, 10 a.m. to 4 p.m.

Penn Valley
The Gardens at Troll Knoll, 10 a.m. to
4 p.m.

PLACER COUNTY

Auburn
Sally's Garden, 10 a.m. to 4 p.m.
Stonegarden, 10 a.m. to 4 p.m.

CONNECTICUT
NEW HAVEN COUNTY

Middlebury
John N. Spain, 10 a.m. to 4 p.m.

NEW JERSEY
BERGEN COUNTY

Ridgewood
The Handley Garden, 10 a.m. to 4 p.m.

Woodcliff Lake
Wiebke & Jan Hinsch, 10 a.m. to 4 p.m.

NEW YORK
DUTCHESS COUNTY

Amenia
Broccoli Hall—Maxine Paetro, 10 a.m. to
4 p.m.
Mead Farm House Garden, 10 a.m. to
4 p.m.

OREGON
MULTNOMAH COUNTY

Portland
Heims Garden, 10 a.m. to 4 p.m.
June's Garden, 10 a.m. to 4 p.m.
The Narizny Garden, 10 a.m. to 4 p.m.
The Jane Platt Garden, 10 a.m. to 4 p.m.

WASHINGTON COUNTY

Portland
Barbara Blossom Ashmun, 10 a.m. to
4 p.m.

Sunday, May 13
CALIFORNIA
SONOMA COUNTY

Occidental
Misty Ridge, 10 a.m. to 4 p.m.
Western Hills Nursery, 10 a.m. to 4 p.m.

Sebastopol
Arnold Garden, 10 a.m. to 4 p.m.
Paeonia, 10 a.m. to 4 p.m.
Olive Oaks, 10 a.m. to 4 p.m.
A Mother's Day Rose Garden, 10 a.m. to
4 p.m.

CONNECTICUT
NEW HAVEN COUNTY

Middlebury
John N. Spain, 10 a.m. to 4 p.m.

NEW YORK
PUTNAM COUNTY

Cold Spring
Stonecrop Gardens, 10 a.m. to 5 p.m.

Friday & Saturday
May 18 & 19

PENNSYLVANIA
BUCKS COUNTY

Doylestown
Heronswood Nursery Comes to Fordhook
Farm of the W. Atlee Burpee & Co.,
10 a.m. to 4 p.m.

Saturday, May 19

CALIFORNIA
SANTA CLARA COUNTY

Los Altos
Sun Acres, 10 a.m. to 4 p.m.
Los Altos Hills
Eclectic Estate Garden, 10 a.m. to 4 p.m.
The Smith Garden, 10 a.m. to 4 p.m.

NEW YORK
TOMPKINS COUNTY

Trumansburg
Hitch Lyman's Garden, 10 a.m. to 4 p.m.

PENNSYLVANIA
BUCKS COUNTY

Doylestown
Carter van Dyke & Lynn Reynolds,
10 a.m. to 4 p.m.
Wrightstown
Hortulus Farm, 10 a.m. to 4 p.m.

VIRGINIA
ALBEMARLE COUNTY

Charlottesville
Balge-Crozier Garden, 10 a.m. to 4 p.m.
The Frierson Garden, 10 a.m. to 4 p.m.
The Frischkorn Garden, 10 a.m. to 4 p.m.
Howard Garden, 10 a.m. to 4 p.m.
Tank Hut, 10 a.m. to 4 p.m.

WASHINGTON
KING COUNTY

Federal Way
Powellswood, A Northwest Garden,
10 a.m. to 4 p.m.

Saturday & Sunday
May 19 & 20

TENNESSEE
KNOX COUNTY

Knoxville
Bush Garden, Saturday, 10 a.m. to 5 p.m.;
Sunday, 1 p.m. to 5 p.m.
GATOP, Saturday, 10 a.m. to 5 p.m.;
Sunday, 1 p.m. to 5 p.m.
Hill Top Farm, Saturday, 10 a.m. to 5 p.m.;
Sunday, 1 p.m. to 5 p.m.

VIRGINIA
ALBEMARLE COUNTY

Free Union
Bird Hill—C. Colston Burrell & D. Bruce
Ellsworth, 10 a.m. to 4 p.m.
Galvin Garden, 10 a.m. to
4 p.m.
The Gardens at Waterperry Farm, 10 a.m.
to 4 p.m.

Sunday, May 20

MASSACHUSETTS
BERKSHIRE COUNTY

Housatonic
Under the Hemlocks, 10 a.m. to 4 p.m.
Lenox
Foothill Farm, 10 a.m. to 4 p.m.
Richmond
Black Barn Farm, 10 a.m. to 4 p.m.

NEW JERSEY
ESSEX COUNTY

Short Hills
Greenwood Gardens, 12 p.m. to 4 p.m.
Garden of Dr. & Mrs. George E. Staehle,
10 a.m. to 2 p.m.

Union County
Summit
Regina Carlson (with help from Kenneth Carlson), 10 a.m. to 4 p.m.

NEW YORK
Suffolk County
Remsenburg
Little Birdstone—Mr. & Mrs. Howard Finkelstein, 10 a.m. to 4 p.m.
The Gardens of Fred & Monica Meyer, 10 a.m. to 4 p.m.
Mara J. Urshel and Ronald R. Rothstein, 10 a.m. to 4 p.m.

Westchester County
Ossining
The Wildflower Island at Teatown Lake Reservation, 11 a.m. to 3 p.m.

Saturday, May 26
NEW YORK
Westchester County
Mount Kisco
Rocky Hills—The Garden of William & Henriette Suhr, 2 p.m. to 6 p.m.

Sunday, May 27
NEW YORK
Westchester County
Armonk
Cobamong Pond, 10 a.m. to 4 p.m.

Saturday, June 2
CONNECTICUT
Fairfield County
Fairfield
Nancy & Tom Grant, 10 a.m. to 4 p.m.
Greenwich
Stonybrooke—Sandra Fales Hillman, 10 a.m. to 4 p.m.
Ridgefield
Garden of Ideas, 10 a.m. to 4 p.m.

Riverside
Susan & Bruce Cohen, 12 p.m. to 4 p.m.
Weston
Toscairn, Guided tours at 10 a.m. & 12 p.m.
Westport
Susan Lloyd, 10 a.m. to 4 p.m.
Wilton
"Seven Gardens, Three Frogs", 10 a.m. to 4 p.m.

NEW JERSEY
Hunterdon County
Califon
Frog Pond Farm, 10 a.m. to 4 p.m.

Somerset County
Bedminster
River Run Farm, 10 a.m. to 4 p.m.

WEST VIRGINIA
Kanawha County
Charleston
"Her Garden" Paula Vasale Memorial Garden, 10 a.m. to 4 p.m.
Westwind Way Gardens, 10 a.m. to 2 p.m.
Elkview
The Fuqua Garden, 10 a.m. to 4 p.m.
The Garden of Paula & Roger Shafer, 10 a.m. to 4 p.m.

Sunday, June 3
CONNECTICUT
Hartford County
Burlington
The Salsedo Family Garden, 10 a.m. to 4 p.m.
Canton
Preminger Garden, 12 p.m. to 4 p.m.
East Windsor Hill
Patricia Porter, 10 a.m. to 4 p.m.
Plantsville
The Kaminski Garden, 10 a.m. to 4 p.m.

NEW JERSEY
ESSEX COUNTY
Short Hills
George Sternlieb, 10 a.m. to 2 p.m.

HUNTERDON COUNTY
Califon
Frog Pond Farm, 10 a.m. to 4 p.m.

MONMOUTH COUNTY
Spring Lake
McMullen Garden, 10 a.m. to 4 p.m
Richard & Barbara Nelson, 10 a.m. to
   4 p.m
Jules and Jane Plangere, 10 a.m. to 4 p.m

Saturday, June 9
CONNECTICUT
NEW HAVEN COUNTY
Meriden
Jardin des Brabant, 12 p.m. to 5 p.m.
Sabbatical Garden, 12 p.m. to 5 p.m.

NEW HAMPSHIRE
MERRIMACK COUNTY
Elkins
Cottage Rock, 10 a.m. to 4 p.m.
New London
The Gardens of Carolyn & Peter Hager,
   10 a.m. to 4 p.m.
The Hewitt Garden, 10 a.m. to 4 p.m.

SULLIVAN COUNTY
Cornish
Northcôte, 10 a.m. to 4 p.m.

NEW YORK
TOMPKINS COUNTY
Danby
Myers Gardens, 10 a.m. to 4 p.m.
Ithaca
Hospicare, 10 a.m. to 4 p.m.
Jim Eavenson, 10 a.m. to 4 p.m.
Posner Garden, 10 a.m. to 4 p.m.

Newfield
Medicine Tree Farm, 10 a.m. to 4 p.m.

ULSTER COUNTY
New Paltz
Lee Reich, 10 a.m. to 4 p.m.
Saugerties
Riverhill Garden—Joe & Tamara
   DiMattio, 10 a.m. to 4 p.m.

VERMONT
WINDSOR COUNTY
Bridgewater
The Shackleton Garden, 10 a.m. to 4 p.m.
Woodstock
Indian Tree Hill—The Highberg Garden,
   10 a.m. to 2 p.m.
The Garden of Fiona & Bob McElwain,
   10 a.m. to 4 p.m.

Sunday, June 10
DELWARE
NEW CASTLE COUNTY
Wilmington
Eve & Per Thyrum, 11 a.m. to 5 p.m.

NEW YORK
PUTNAM COUNTY
Cold Spring
Stonecrop Gardens, 10 a.m. to 5 p.m.
Garrison
Manitoga/The Russel Wright Design
   Center, 10 a.m. to 12 p.m.
Ross Gardens, 10 a.m. to 4 p.m.

SUFFOLK COUNTY
St. James
Head of the Harbor—Alexandra
   Leighton's Garden, 10 a.m. to 4 p.m.

WESTCHESTER COUNTY
Bedford
High and Low Farm, 10 a.m. to 4 p.m.
Keith & Susan Kroeger—Pook's Hill,
   10 a.m. to 4 p.m.

Michael & Katherine Takata, 10 a.m. to
    4 p.m.
Bedford Hills
Phillis Warden, 10 a.m. to 6 p.m.
Cortlandt Manor
Vivian & Ed Merrin, 10 a.m. to 2 p.m.
Mount Kisco
Barbara & John Schumacher, 10 a.m. to
    4 p.m.
North Salem
Artemis Farm—Carol & Jesse Goldberg,
    10 a.m. to 4 p.m.
Page Dickey & Francis Schell—Duck Hill,
    10 a.m. to 6 p.m.
Keeler Hill Farm, 10 a.m. to 4 p.m.

PENNSYLVANIA
CHESTER COUNTY
Downingtown
David Culp, 11 a.m. to 5 p.m.
West Chester
Inta Krombolz, 11 a.m. to 5 p.m.

DELAWARE COUNTY
Chadds Ford
WynEden, 11 a.m. to 5 p.m.
Glen Mills
Jim & Conny Parsons, 11 a.m. to 5 p.m.

Saturday, June 16
NEW JERSEY
BERGEN COUNTY
Maywood
Dail & Tony's Garden, 10 a.m. to 4 p.m.
Ridgewood
The Handley Garden, 10 a.m. to 4 p.m.
River Edge
Anthony "Bud" & Virginia Korteweg,
    8 a.m. to 4 p.m.
Tenafly
Linda Singer, 10 a.m. to 4 p.m.

NEW YORK
COLUMBIA COUNTY
Claverack
Peter Bevacqua & Stephen King, 10 a.m.
    to 4 p.m.
Copake Falls
Margaret Roach, 10 a.m. to 4 p.m.
East Taghkanic
Grant & Alice Platt, 10 a.m. to 4 p.m.
Germantown
Tailings—Robert Montgomery, 10 a.m. to
    2 p.m.
Hillsdale
Shale Hill—Douglas Hunt, 10 a.m. to
    4 p.m.
Hudson
Hudson Bush Farm, 10 a.m. to 4 p.m.
Antony Nagelmann & Helen Faraday
    Young, 10 a.m. to 4 p.m.
Livingston
River School Farm—Owen Davidson &
    Mark Prezorski, 10 a.m. to 4 p.m.
West Taghkanic
Arcadia—Ronald Wagner & Timothy Van
    Dam, 10 a.m. to 4 p.m.

DUTCHESS COUNTY
Amenia
Broccoli Hall—Maxine Paetro, 10 a.m. to
    4 p.m.

OREGON
CLACKAMAS COUNTY
Lake Oswego
Mike & Linda Darcy, 10 a.m. to 4 p.m.
Walt Hodges, 10 a.m. to 4 p.m.
Oregon City
Sharon McCauley & Dean Dikeman,
    10 a.m. to 4 p.m.
Smith's Solitude, 10 a.m. to 4 p.m.
West Linn
Bonnie's Garden, 10 a.m. to 4 p.m.
Foxglove Point, 10 a.m. to 4 p.m.
Y. Sherry Sheng Garden, 10 a.m. to 4 p.m.

Saturday, June 23

CONNECTICUT

LITCHFIELD COUNTY

Falls Village
Nancy McCabe, 10 a.m. to 4 p.m.
Bunny Williams, 10 a.m. to 4 p.m.

Sharon
Lee Link, 10 a.m. to 4 p.m.
Sally Pettus, 10 a.m. to 4 p.m.

Washington
Linda Allard, 10 a.m. to 4 p.m.
Hollister House—The Garden of George
    Schoellkopf, 3 p.m. to 6 p.m.
Charles Raskob Robinson & Barbara Paul
    Robinson, 2 p.m. to 6 p.m.

West Cornwall
Michael Trapp, 10 a.m. to 4 p.m.

MASSACHUSETTS

BERKSHIRE COUNTY

Williamstown
260 Northwest Hill Road, 10 a.m. to
    4 p.m.
Ilona Bell's Garden, 10 a.m. to 4 p.m.
The Weber Garden, 10 a.m. to 4 p.m.

MAINE

YORK COUNTY

Cape Neddick
413 Shore Road, 10 a.m. to 4 p.m.
Cragmere, 10 a.m. to 4 p.m.
Sealedges, 10 a.m. to 4 p.m.
Wind Acre, 10 a.m. to 4 p.m.

Ogunquit
Mayfair, 10 a.m. to 4 p.m.

NEW JERSEY

MONMOUTH COUNTY

Rumson
Beliza Ann Furman, 10 a.m. to 4 p.m.
King & Leigh Sorensen, 10 a.m. to 4 p.m.

NEW YORK

BRONX COUNTY

Bronx
Byrns Garden, 12 p.m. to 4 p.m.

Riverdale
The Weinroth Gardens at Quarrytop,
    12 p.m. to 4 p.m.

Riverside
Morgenthau, 12 p.m. to 4 p.m.

SUFFOLK COUNTY

East Hampton
Abby Jane Brody, 10 a.m. to 4 p.m.
Garden of Arlene Bujese, 10 a.m. to 2 p.m.
Margaret Kerr, 10 a.m. to 2 p.m.
Carol Mercer, 10 a.m. to 4 p.m.

Sunday, June 24

CONNECTICUT

HARTFORD COUNTY

Glastonbury
The Murray Gardens, 10 a.m. to 4 p.m.

Harwinton
Archer-Chiarmonte Garden, 10 a.m. to
    4 p.m.

Simsbury
Skyflower-Ingram Garden, 10 a.m. to
    4 p.m.

LITCHFIELD COUNTY

Bridgewater
Maywood Gardens, 10 a.m. to 2 p.m.

New Hartford
Jillian Gardens, 10 a.m. to 4 p.m.

NEW LONDON COUNTY

Stonington
Mr. & Mrs. Juan O'Callahan, 10 a.m. to
    2 p.m.
Mrs. Frederic C. Paffard, Jr., 10 a.m. to
    4 p.m.

ILLINOIS
COOK COUNTY
Barrington Hills
Peggy & Eric Olsen, 10 a.m. to 4 p.m.
Evanston
McKenna Garden, 10 a.m. to 4 p.m.
Winnetka
Liz & Bob Crowe, 10 a.m. to 4 p.m.
Mr. & Mrs. Edgar D. Jannotta, 10 a.m. to
  4 p.m.

LAKE COUNTY
Highland Park
Markus Collection and Garden, 10 a.m.
  to 4 p.m.

Thursday, June 28
MASSACHUSETTS
NANTUCKET COUNTY
Nantucket
Nantucket Wildflower Farm, 9 a.m. to
  5 p.m.
Siasconset
"Barnagain", 10 a.m. to 4 p.m.
Hedged About—Charlotte & Macdonald
  Mathey, 10 a.m. to 4 p.m.
Linda & George Kelly—"Up All Night",
  10 a.m. to 4 p.m.
Alan & Janet Morell, 10 a.m. to 4 p.m.
"None Too Big", 10 a.m. to 4 p.m.
The Powerhouse, 10 a.m. to 4 p.m.
Siasconset Union Chapel, 10 a.m. to
  4 p.m.
The Sheiling, 10 a.m. to 4 p.m.
Summer Salt, 10 a.m. to 4 p.m.

Saturday, June 30
COLORADO
DENVER COUNTY
Denver
Cynthia's Urban Garden, 10 a.m. to 4 p.m.
Gedrose Family Garden, 10 a.m. to 4 p.m.
El Puesto de Paz—Jon Snyder & Becca
  Robinson, 10 a.m. to 4 p.m.
Susan Mathews Garden, 10 a.m. to 4 p.m.

Scharfenaker Garden, 10 a.m. to 4 p.m.
White Garden, 10 a.m. to 4 p.m.

Saturday, July 7
NEW YORK
ULSTER COUNTY
Bearsville
Gayle Burbank Garden, 10 a.m. to 4 p.m.
West Hurley
Bebe & Dan Turck, 10 a.m. to 4 p.m.

Sunday, July 8
CONNECTICUT
NEW HAVEN COUNTY
Guilford
Angelwood—Mary Anne & Dale
  Athanas, 10 a.m. to 4 p.m.
Meriden
Jardin des Brabant, 12 p.m. to 5 p.m.
Sabbatical Garden, 12 p.m. to 5 p.m.
The Stankevich Garden, 12 p.m. to 4 p.m.
George Trecina, 12 p.m. to 4 p.m.

OREGON
LANE COUNTY
Eugene
The Alba Garden, 10 a.m. to 4 p.m.
Circles in Thyme, 10 a.m. to 4 p.m.
The Hewitt Garden, 10 a.m. to 4 p.m.
The Bernard Levine Garden, 10 a.m. to
  4 p.m.
Buell Steelman & Rebecca Sams, 10 a.m.
  to 4 p.m.
The Garden of Monica Tallerday and
  Gene Humphreys, 10 a.m. to 4 p.m.

Friday, July 13
MAINE
KNOX COUNTY
Rockland
Nina Scott-Hansen, 1 p.m. to 4 p.m.
Rockport
Nonesuch Farm, 1 p.m. to 4 p.m.

Oyster River Farm Garden, 1 p.m. to
4 p.m.

Saturday, July 14
ILLINOIS
COOK COUNTY

Glencoe
Litowitz Garden, 10 a.m. to 4 p.m.

Glenview
Windmill, 10 a.m. to 4 p.m.

Wilmette
The Drucker Garden, 10 a.m. to 4 p.m.

Winnetka
Nantucket Garden, 10 a.m. to 4 p.m.
Taylor Garden, 10 a.m. to 4 p.m.

LAKE COUNTY

Highland Park
Magic Garden, 10 a.m. to 2 p.m.

Lake Forest
Old Mill Farm, 10 a.m. to 4 p.m.

MAINE
WALDO COUNTY

Belfast
39 Battery Road, 1 p.m. to 5 p.m.

Islesboro
Homan's Garden, 12 p.m. to 4 p.m.

Lincolnville
Shleppinghurst, 10 a.m. to 4 p.m.

NEW YORK
SUFFOLK COUNTY

Cutchogue
Conni Cross Garden Designer, 10 a.m. to
2 p.m.

Mattituck
Maurice Isaac & Ellen Coster Isaac,
10 a.m. to 4 p.m.
Dennis Schrader & Bill Smith, 10 a.m. to
4 p.m.

Southold
Milford Garden, 10 a.m. to 4 p.m.

TOMPKINS COUNTY

Danby
Myers Gardens, 10 a.m. to 4 p.m.

Freeville
Ann M. & Carlton J. Manzano Garden,
10 a.m. to 4 p.m.

Ithaca
Cayuga Daylilies, 10 a.m. to 4 p.m.
Roseanne & Joe Moresco, 10 a.m. to
4 p.m.
Mount Garden, 10 a.m. to 4 p.m.

Lansing
Lion Garden, 10 a.m. to 4 p.m.

Sunday, July 15
MAINE
KNOX COUNTY

North Haven
The Anchorage, 10 a.m. to 12 p.m.

WALDO COUNTY

Belfast
133 Miller Street, 10 a.m. to 4 p.m.

Southport
Rabbit Point Gardens, 1 p.m. to 4 p.m.

NEW YORK
PUTNAM COUNTY

Cold Spring
Stonecrop Gardens, 10 a.m. to 5 p.m.

WESTCHESTER COUNTY

Valhalla
The Lady Bird Johnson and the Stone
Cottage Demonstration Garden—The
Native Plant Center, 12 p.m. to 4 p.m.

SUFFOLK COUNTY

East Hampton
Alexandra Munroe & Robert Rosenkranz
Gardens, 11 a.m. to 4 p.m.
Bob & Mimi Schwarz, 10 a.m. to 2 p.m.

Montauk
Richard Kahn & Elaine Peterson, 10 a.m.
to 2 p.m.

Saturday, July 21

CONNECTICUT
FAIRFIELD COUNTY

Redding
Stone Orchard, 10 a.m. to 4 p.m.

Weston
Birgit Rasmussen Diforio, 10 a.m. to 4 p.m.

NEW LONDON COUNTY

North Stonington
Blue Flag Farm, 10 a.m. to 4 p.m.

NEW YORK
DUTCHESS COUNTY

Amenia
Jade Hill—Paul Arcario & Don Walker,
    10 a.m. to 4 p.m.
Mead Farm House Garden, 10 a.m. to
    4 p.m.

Millbrook
309 Route 343, 12 p.m. to 4 p.m.
Belinda & Stephen Kaye, 8:30 a.m. to
    4 p.m.

Millerton
Hyland/Wente Garden, 10 a.m. to 4 p.m.

Pawling
The Brine Garden—Duncan & Julia
    Brine, 2 p.m. to 6 p.m.

Stanfordville
Ellen & Eric Petersen, 12 p.m. to 4 p.m.

WASHINGTON
KITSAP COUNTY

Bainbridge Island
Little and Lewis, 10 a.m. to 3 p.m.
McFarlane Gardens, 10 a.m. to 3 p.m.
The Skyler Garden, 10 a.m. to 3 p.m.

Sunday, July 22

CONNECTICUT
HARTFORD COUNTY

Avon
Green Dreams—Garden of Jan Nickel,
    10 a.m. to 4 p.m.

Bloomfield
Terrace Hill Farm, 10 a.m. to 4 p.m.

LITCHFIELD COUNTY

New Hartford
Jillian Gardens, 10 a.m. to 4 p.m.

Sharon
Lynden Miller's Garden, 10 a.m. to 2 p.m.

West Cornwall
Garden of Roxana & Ledlie Laughlin,
    12 p.m. to 4 p.m.

MASSACHUSETTS
BERKSHIRE COUNTY

Richmond
Chelsea Woods, 10 a.m. to 4 p.m.
Thomas Gardner, 10 a.m. to 4 p.m.

Stockbridge
Fitzpatrick's Hillhome, 11 a.m. to 3 p.m.

NEW YORK
COLUMBIA COUNTY

Canaan
Rockland Farm, 10 a.m. to 4 p.m.

WESTCHESTER COUNTY

Bedford Hills
Phillis Warden, 10 a.m. to 6 p.m.

Katonah
Michael Fuchs, 10 a.m. to 4 p.m.

Larchmont
Premium Pond Garden, 10 a.m. to 2 p.m.

North Salem
Hilltop, 10 a.m. to 4 p.m.

Scarsdale
Fran & Alan Zimbard, 10 a.m. to 4 p.m.

Saturday, July 28

MASSACHUSETTS
BARNSTABLE COUNTY

Brewster
Gardens at the McLoud House, 10 a.m. to
    4 p.m.

Chatham
Behind the Hedges—Peggy & Bob Black,
    10 a.m. to 4 p.m.

The Cotnam Garden, 10 a.m. to 4 p.m.
The Gnomerie—Sarah & Prescott Dunbar
    Garden, 10 a.m. to 4 p.m.
Harwichport
Pillar to Post—Don & Cele Milbier,
    10 a.m. to 4 p.m.
North Chatham
Amanda's Garden, 10 a.m. to 4 p.m.

Sunday, July 29
ILLINOIS
LAKE COUNTY
Lake Forest
Camp Rosemary, 10 a.m. to 4 p.m.
Lake Forest Country Gentleman's Farm,
    10 a.m. to 4 p.m.
Mettawa
Mettawa Manor, 10 a.m. to 4 p.m.

MASSACHUSETTS
BARNSTABLE COUNTY
East Orleans
Clairvue, 10 a.m. to 4 p.m.
Harwichport
Pillar to Post—Don & Cele Milbier,
    10 a.m. to 4 p.m.

BERKSHIRE COUNTY
Alford
RavenTree, 10 a.m. to 4 p.m.
Great Barrington
Aston Magna, 10 a.m. to 4 p.m.
Seekonk Farm—Honey Sharp's Garden,
    10 a.m. to 4 p.m.

Friday & Saturday August 3 & 4
PENNSYLVANIA
BUCKS COUNTY
Doylestown
Heronswood Nursery Comes to Fordhook
    Farm of the W. Atlee Burpee & Co.,
    10 a.m. to 4 p.m.

Saturday, August 4
PENNSYLVANIA
BUCKS COUNTY
Perkasie
Carol A. Pierce, 11 a.m. to 5 p.m.
Point Pleasant
The Gardens at Mill Fleurs, Guided tours
    at 10 a.m., 12 p.m. & 2 p.m.

Sunday, August 5
CONNECTICUT
LITCHFIELD COUNTY
Taconic
Rivendell, 10 a.m. to 4 p.m.

ILLINOIS
DU PAGE COUNTY
West Chicago
The Gardens at Ball, 10 a.m. to 4 p.m.

MASSACHUSETTS
BERKSHIRE COUNTY
Sheffield
Good Dogs Farm, 10 a.m. to 4 p.m.

MAINE
HANCOCK COUNTY
Mt. Desert Island
Garland Farm—The Last Garden of
    Beatrix Farrand, 10 a.m. to 4 p.m.
Judith S. Goldstein, 10 a.m. to 4 p.m.
Northeast Harbor
Westward Way, 10 a.m. to 4 p.m.
Southwest Harbor
Alexandra's Cottage, 10 a.m. to 4 p.m.

Saturday, August 11
NEW JERSEY
BERGEN COUNTY
Tenafly
Linda Singer, 10 a.m. to 4 p.m.

MORRIS COUNTY
Randolph
Jones Garden, 10 a.m. to 4 p.m.

WASHINGTON
PIERCE COUNTY
DuPont
Froggy Bottom, 10 a.m. to 4 p.m.

THURSTON COUNTY
Olympia
The Hatten Garden, 10 a.m. to 4 p.m.
The Koi Garden, 10 a.m. to 4 p.m.
Phillips Garden, 10 a.m. to 4 p.m.
Stanford Garden, 10 a.m. to 4 p.m.

Tenino
Golden Leaf Acres, 10 a.m. to 4 p.m.

Sunday, August 12
CONNECTICUT
HARTFORD COUNTY
Plantsville
The Kaminski Garden, 10 a.m. to 4 p.m.

NEW HAVEN COUNTY
Meriden
George Trecina, 12 p.m. to 4 p.m.

NEW YORK
PUTNAM COUNTY
Cold Spring
Stonecrop Gardens, 10 a.m. to 5 p.m.

Saturday, September 8
NEW JERSEY
ESSEX COUNTY
Nutley
Graeme Hardie, 10 a.m. to 4 p.m
Silas Mountsier, 10 a.m. to 4 p.m

Short Hills
Greenwood Gardens, 1 p.m. to 3 p.m.
George Sternlieb, 10 a.m. to 2 p.m.

Sunday, September 9
NEW YORK
COLUMBIA COUNTY
Ancram
Adams-Westlake, 10 a.m. to 4 p.m.

Claverack
Loomis Creek–Gardens of Andrew
   Beckman & Bob Hyland, 10 a.m. to
   4 p.m.

Copake Falls
Margaret Roach, 10 a.m. to 4 p.m.

Craryville
Susan Anthony & Richard Galef, 10 a.m.
   to 4 p.m.

Millerton
Helen Bodian, 2 p.m. to 6 p.m.

DUTCHESS COUNTY
Rhinebeck
Cedar Heights Orchard—William &
   Arvia Morris, 10 a.m. to 4 p.m.

WESTCHESTER COUNTY
Lewisboro
The White Garden, 10 a.m. to 3 p.m.

Sunday, September 16
CONNECTICUT
FAIRFIELD COUNTY
Greenwich
Topiary Fancies—Garden of Lucy & Nat
   Day, 10 a.m. to 4 p.m.

Riverside
172 Indian Head Road, 10 a.m. to 4 p.m.

HARTFORD COUNTY
Avon
Green Dreams—Garden of Jan Nickel,
   10 a.m. to 4 p.m.

Farmington
Kate Emery & Steve Silk, 12 p.m. to
   4 p.m.

Glastonbury
The Murray Gardens, 10 a.m. to 4 p.m.

Wethersfield
Idyll Haven—Sue & Tom Webel, 10 a.m.
to 4 p.m.

MASSACHUSETTS
BERKSHIRE COUNTY
Great Barrington
Seekonk Farm—Honey Sharp's Garden, 10
a.m. to 4 p.m.
Wheelbarrow Hill Farm, 10 a.m. to 4 p.m.
Housatonic
Under the Hemlocks, 10 a.m. to 4 p.m.

NEW YORK
ONONDAGA COUNTY
Jamesville
McAuliffes' Garden, 10 a.m. to 4 p.m.
Lafayette
Pagoda Hill—Michael Brennan & Robert
Moss, 10 a.m. to 4 p.m.
Solvay
Dr. & Mrs. Charles Mango, 10 a.m. to
4 p.m.
Westvale
Tortuga—Ellen & David Suarez, 10 a.m.
to 4 p.m.

WESTCHESTER COUNTY
Bedford
Penelope & John Maynard, 10 a.m. to
6 p.m.
North Salem
Dick Button—Ice Pond Farm, 10 a.m. to
4 p.m.
Pound Ridge
John & Melanie Danza, 10 a.m. to 4 p.m.
Waccabuc
James & Susan Henry, 10 a.m. to 4 p.m.

Friday & Saturday
September 21 & 22
PENNSYLVANIA
BUCKS COUNTY
Doylestown
Heronswood Nursery Comes to Fordhook
Farm of the W. Atlee Burpee & Co.,
10 a.m. to 4 p.m.

Saturday, September 22
CONNECTICUT
FAIRFIELD COUNTY
Westport
Judith & Charles Kiernan Garden, 2 p.m.
to 7 p.m.

Saturday & Sunday
September 22 & 23
NORTH CAROLINA
WAKE COUNTY
Raleigh
The Bromhal Garden, Saturday 11 a.m. to
4 p.m.; Sunday 1 p.m. to 4 p.m.
The Davies Garden, Saturday 11 a.m. to
4 p.m.; Sunday 1 p.m. to 4 p.m.
The Hanson Garden, Saturday 11 a.m. to
4 p.m.; Sunday 1 p.m. to 4 p.m.
A Plant Collector's Paradise, Saturday
11 a.m. to 4 p.m.; Sunday 1 p.m. to
4 p.m.
Mrs. Alton B. Smith, Saturday 11 a.m. to
4 p.m.; Sunday 1 p.m. to 4 p.m.

Sunday, September 23
CONNECTICUT
FAIRFIELD COUNTY
Westport
Judith & Charles Kiernan Garden, 2 p.m.
to 7 p.m.

NEW YORK

PUTNAM COUNTY

Cold Spring
Stonecrop Gardens, 10 a.m. to 5 p.m.

Saturday, September 29

ARIZONA

PIMA COUNTY

Tucson
Bamboo Ranch, 10 a.m. to 3 p.m.
Chestnut Sanctuary, 10 a.m. to 3 p.m.
Southwest Retreat, 10 a.m. to 3 p.m.

Sunday, October 14

TEXAS

TARRANT COUNTY

Arlington
Debbie Duncan & Randy Jordan, 10 a.m.
    to 4 p.m.
Mary Nell's Garden, 10 a.m. to 4 p.m.

Fort Worth
Mr. & Mrs. Fred Cauble, 10 a.m. to 4 p.m.
Gardens of Little Castle—Bill & Donna
    Vance, 10 a.m. to 4 p.m.
The Moncrief Garden, 10 a.m. to 4 p.m.
Sherrod-Pool Garden, 10 a.m. to 4 p.m.

Saturday, October 20

TEXAS

DALLAS COUNTY

Dallas
Angelica's Four Season Garden, 10 a.m.
    to 4 p.m.
Chantilis Garden, 10 a.m. to 4 p.m.
Newport Garden, 10 a.m. to 4 p.m.
Peter & Julie Schaar, 10 a.m. to 4 p.m.
Sewell Garden, 10 a.m. to 4 p.m.
Waisanen, 10 a.m. to 4 p.m.

Open Days by Location

ARIZONA
PIMA COUNTY

Tucson
Bamboo Ranch, Saturday, September 29
Chestnut Sanctuary, Sunday,
     September 29
Southwest Retreat, Saturday,
     September 29

CALIFORNIA
ALAMEDA COUNTY

Berkeley
Cathleen's Garden, Saturday, May 5
The Harmon Garden, Saturday, May 5
Our Own Stuff Gallery Garden, Saturday,
     May 5

LOS ANGELES COUNTY

Los Angeles
The O'Neill Garden, Saturday, May 12
Pacific Palisades
The Smith Garden, Saturday, May 12
Pasadena
574 Bellefontaine Street, Sunday, April 29
Linda Baisley & Lenny Amato Garden,
     Sunday, April 29
Bennett-DeBeixedon Garden, Sunday,
     April 29
Susan & Doug Kranwinkle, Sunday,
     April 29
La Casita del Arroyo Garden, Sunday,
     April 29
Lenkin Garden, Sunday, April 29
The Florence Yoch-Designed Ira Bryner
     Garden, Sunday, April 29
The Zasa Garden, Sunday, April 29
Santa Monica
The Edna May Garden, Saturday, May 12
Lidow Residence, Saturday, May 12

Marek/Bernatz Garden, Saturday, May 12
Mayer Residence, Saturday, May 12
Merrihew's Sunset Gardens, Saturday,
     May 12

NEVADA COUNTY

Grass Valley
Shenoa, Saturday, May 12
Penn Valley
The Gardens at Troll Knoll, Saturday,
     May 12

PLACER COUNTY

Auburn
Sally's Garden, Saturday, May 12
Stonegarden, Saturday, May 12

SACRAMENTO COUNTY

Sacramento
New England Style Landscaping, Saturday,
     April 28
Santa Barbara Villa, Saturday, April 28
Split-level Sculpture Garden, Saturday,
     April 28
Tropical Caribbean Resort, Saturday,
     April 28
The Wells Garden, Saturday, April 28
The Wise Garden, Saturday, April 28

SAN DIEGO COUNTY

El Cajon
Steve & Susie Dentt's Garden, Sunday,
     April 22
Rick & Joyce Dentt's Garden, Sunday,
     April 22
La Mesa
Hillside Jungle Garden, Sunday, April 22
Nugent Garden, Sunday, April 22
Poway
Arnold Garden, Saturday, April 28

Casterline Garden, Saturday, April 28
Cattolico Garden, Saturday, April 28
Les Belles Fleurs, Saturday, April 28
Moore Garden, Saturday, April 28
Wits End West, Saturday, April 28
San Diego
Oak Park Secret Garden, Sunday, April 22

SANTA CLARA COUNTY
Los Altos
Sun Acres, Saturday, May 19
Los Altos Hills
Eclectic Estate Garden, Saturday, May 19
The Smith Garden, Saturday, May 19

SONOMA COUNTY
Occidental
Misty Ridge, Sunday, May 13
Western Hills Rare Plant Nursery, Sunday, May 13
Sebastopol
Arnold Garden, Sunday, May 13
A Mother's Day Rose Garden, Sunday, May 13
Paeonia, Sunday, May 13
Olive Oaks, Sunday, May 13

COLORADO
DENVER COUNTY
Denver
Cynthia's Urban Garden, Saturday, June 30
Gedrose Family Garden, Saturday, June 30
El Puesto de Paz—Jon Snyder & Becca Robinson, Saturday, June 30
Susan Mathews Garden, Saturday, June 30
Scharfenaker Garden, Saturday, June 30
White Garden, Saturday, June 30

CONNECTICUT
FAIRFIELD COUNTY
Fairfield
Nancy & Tom Grant, Saturday, June 2
Greenwich
Topiary Fancies—Garden of Lucy & Nat Day, Sunday, September 16

Stonybrooke—Sandra Fales Hillman, Saturday, June 2
Redding
Stone Orchard, Saturday, July 21
Ridgefield
Garden of Ideas, Saturday, June 2
Riverside
172 Indian Head Road, Sunday, September 16
Susan & Bruce Cohen, Saturday, June 2
Weston
Birgit Rasmussen Diforio, Saturday, July 21
Toscairn, Sunday, April 22, Saturday, June 2
Westport
Judith & Charles Kiernan Garden, Sunday, September 22
Susan Lloyd, Saturday, June 2
Wilton
"Seven Gardens, Three Frogs", Saturday, June 2

HARTFORD COUNTY
Avon
Green Dreams—Garden of Jan Nickel, Sunday, July 22, Sunday, September 16
Bloomfield
Terrace Hill Farm, Sunday, July 22
Burlington
The Salsedo Family Garden, Sunday, June 3
Canton
Preminger Garden, Sunday, June 3
East Windsor Hill
Patricia Porter, Sunday, June 3
Farmington
Kate Emery & Steve Silk, Sunday, September 16
Glastonbury
The Murray Gardens, Sunday, June 24, Sunday, September 16
Harwinton
Archer-Chiarmonte Garden, Sunday, June 24

Plantsville
The Kaminski Garden, Sunday, June 3,
Sunday, August 12

Simsbury
Skyflower-Ingram Garden, Sunday,
June 24

Wethersfield
Idyll Haven—Sue & Tom Webel, Sunday,
September 16

LITCHFIELD COUNTY
Bridgewater
Maywood Gardens, Sunday, June 24

Falls Village
Nancy McCabe, Saturday, June 23
Bunny Williams, Saturday, June 23

New Hartford
Jillian Gardens, Sunday, June 24, Sunday,
July 22

Sharon
Lee Link, Saturday, June 23
Lynden Miller's Garden, Sunday, July 22
Sally Pettus, Saturday, June 23

Taconic
Rivendell, Sunday, August 5

Washington
Linda Allard, Saturday, June 23
Hollister House—The Garden of George
Schoellkopf, Saturday, June 23
Charles Raskob Robinson & Barbara Paul
Robinson, Saturday, June 23

West Cornwall
Garden of Roxana & Ledlie Laughlin,
Sunday, July 22
Michael Trapp, Saturday, June 23

NEW HAVEN COUNTY
Guilford
Angelwood—Mary Anne & Dale
Athanas, Sunday, July 8

Meriden
Jardin des Brabant, Saturday, June 9,
Sunday, July 8
Sabbatical Garden, Saturday, June 9,
Sunday, July 8
The Stankevich Garden, Sunday, July 8

George Trecina, Sunday, July 8, Sunday,
August 12
Middlebury
John N. Spain, Saturday & Sunday, May
12 & 13

NEW LONDON COUNTY
North Stonington
Blue Flag Farm, Saturday, July 21

Stonington
Mr. & Mrs. Juan O'Callahan, Sunday,
June 24
Mrs. Frederic C. Paffard, Jr., Sunday,
June 24

DELWARE
NEW CASTLE COUNTY
Wilmington
Eve & Per Thyrum, Sunday, June 10

FLORIDA
INDIAN RIVER COUNTY
Vero Beach
Drea's Garden, Saturday, April 7
Marion's Garden, Saturday, April 7
The Tropical Garden of Vero Beach
Avenue, Saturday, April 7

ILLINOIS
COOK COUNTY
Barrington Hills
Peggy & Eric Olsen, Sunday, June 24

Evanston
McKenna Garden, Sunday, June 24

Glencoe
Litowitz Garden, Saturday, July 14

Glenview
Windmill, Saturday, July 14

Wilmette
The Drucker Garden, Saturday, July 14

Winnetka
Liz & Bob Crowe, Sunday, June 24
Mr. & Mrs. Edgar D. Jannotta, Sunday,
June 24
Nantucket Garden, Saturday, July 14
Taylor Garden, Saturday, July 14

DU PAGE COUNTY
West Chicago
The Gardens at Ball, Sunday, August 5

LAKE COUNTY
Highland Park
Magic Garden, Saturday, July 14
Markus Collection and Garden, Sunday,
   June 24
Lake Forest
Camp Rosemary, Sunday, July 29
Lake Forest Country Gentleman's Farm,
   Sunday, July 29
Old Mill Farm, Saturday, July 14
Mettawa
Mettawa Manor, Sunday, July 29

MAINE
HANCOCK COUNTY
Mt. Desert Island
Garland Farm—The Last Garden of
   Beatrix Farrand, Sunday, August 5
Judith S. Goldstein, Sunday, August 5
Northeast Harbor
Westward Way, Sunday, August 5
Southwest Harbor
Alexandra's Cottage, Sunday, August 5

KNOX COUNTY
North Haven
The Anchorage, Sunday, July 15
Rockland
Nina Scott-Hansen, Friday, July 13
Rockport
Nonesuch Farm, Friday, July 13
Oyster River Farm Garden, Friday, July 13

WALDO COUNTY
Belfast
133 Miller Street, Sunday, July 15
39 Battery Road, Saturday, July 14
Islesboro
Homan's Garden, Saturday, July 14
Lincolnville
Shleppinghurst, Saturday, July 14

Southport
Rabbit Point Gardens, Sunday, July 15

YORK COUNTY
Cape Neddick
413 Shore Road, Saturday, June 23
Cragmere, Saturday, June 23
Sealedges, Saturday, June 23
Wind Acre, Saturday, June 23
Ogunquit
Mayfair, Saturday, June 23

MASSACHUSETTS
BARNSTABLE COUNTY
Brewster
Gardens at the McLoud House, Saturday,
   July 28
Chatham
Behind the Hedges—Peggy & Bob Black,
   Saturday, July 28
The Cotnam Garden, Saturday, July 28
The Gnomerie—Sarah & Prescott Dunbar
   Garden, Saturday, July 28
East Orleans
Clairvue, Sunday, July 29
Harwichport
Pillar to Post—Don & Cele Milbier,
   Saturday & Sunday, July 28 & 29
North Chatham
Amanda's Garden, Saturday, July 28

BERKSHIRE COUNTY
Alford
RavenTree, Sunday, July 29
Great Barrington
Aston Magna, Sunday, July 29
Seekonk Farm—Honey Sharp's Garden,
   Sunday, July 29, Sunday, September 16
Wheelbarrow Hill Farm, Sunday,
   September 16
Housatonic
Under the Hemlocks, Sunday, May 20,
   Sunday, September 16
Lenox
Foothill Farm, Sunday, May 20

Richmond
Black Barn Farm, Sunday, May 20
Chelsea Woods, Sunday, July 22
Thomas Gardner, Sunday, July 22
Sheffield
Good Dogs Farm, Sunday, August 5
Stockbridge
Fitzpatrick's Hillhome, Sunday, July 22
Williamstown
260 Northwest Hill Road, Saturday,
    June 23
Ilona Bell's Garden, Saturday, June 23
The Weber Garden, Saturday, June 23

NANTUCKET COUNTY
Nantucket
Nantucket Wildflower Farm, Thursday,
    June 28
Siasconset
"Barnagain", Thursday, June 28
Hedged About—Charlotte & Macdonald
    Mathey, Thursday, June 28
Linda & George Kelly—"Up All Night",
    Thursday, June 28
Alan & Janet Morell, Thursday, June 28
"None Too Big", Thursday, June 28
The Powerhouse, Thursday, June 28
Siasconset Union Chapel, Thursday,
    June 28
The Sheiling, Thursday, June 28
Summer Salt, Thursday, June 28

NEW HAMPSHIRE
MERRIMACK COUNTY
Elkins
Cottage Rock, Saturday, June 9
New London
The Gardens of Carolyn & Peter Hager,
    Saturday, June 9
The Hewitt Garden, Saturday, June 9

SULLIVAN COUNTY
Cornish
Northcôte, Saturday, June 9

NEW JERSEY
BERGEN COUNTY
Maywood
Dail & Tony's Garden, Saturday, June 16
Ridgewood
The Handley Garden, Saturday, May 12,
    Saturday, June 16
River Edge
Anthony "Bud" & Virginia Korteweg,
    Saturday, June 16
Tenafly
Linda Singer, Saturday, June 16, Saturday,
    August 11
Woodcliff Lake
Wiebke & Jan Hinsch, Saturday, May 12

ESSEX COUNTY
Nutley
Graeme Hardie, Saturday, September 8
Silas Mountsier, Saturday, September 8
Short Hills
Greenwood Gardens, Sunday, May 20,
    Saturday, September 8
Garden of Dr. & Mrs. George E. Staehle,
    Sunday, May 20
George Sternlieb, Sunday, June 3,
    Saturday, September 8

HUNTERDON COUNTY
Califon
Frog Pond Farm, Saturday & Sunday,
    June 2 & 3

MONMOUTH COUNTY
Atlantic Highlands
Mrs. Sverre Sorensen, Saturday, April 28
Rumson
Beliza Ann Furman, Saturday, June 23
King & Leigh Sorensen, Saturday, June 23
Spring Lake
McMullen Garden, Sunday, June 3
Richard & Barbara Nelson, Sunday, June 3
Jules and Jane Plangere, Sunday, June 3

MORRIS COUNTY
Randolph
Jones Garden, Saturday, August 11

SOMERSET COUNTY
Bedminster
River Run Farm, Saturday, June 2

UNION COUNTY
Summit
Regina Carlson (with help from Kenneth Carlson), Sunday, May 20

NEW YORK
BRONX COUNTY
Bronx
Byrns Garden, Saturday, June 23
Riverdale
The Weinroth Gardens at Quarrytop, Saturday, June 23
Riverside
Morgenthau, Saturday, June 23

COLUMBIA COUNTY
Ancram
Adams-Westlake, Sunday, September 9
Canaan
Rockland Farm, Sunday, July 22
Claverack
Peter Bevacqua & Stephen King, Saturday, June 16
Loomis Creek–Gardens of Andrew Beckman & Bob Hyland, Sunday, September 9
Copake Falls
Margaret Roach, Saturday, June 16, Sunday, September 9
Craryville
Susan Anthony & Richard Galef, Sunday, September 9
East Taghkanic
Grant & Alice Platt, Saturday, June 16
Germantown
Tailings—Robert Montgomery, Saturday, June 16

Hillsdale
Shale Hill—Douglas Hunt, Saturday, June 16
Hudson
Hudson Bush Farm, Saturday, June 16
Antony Nagelmann & Helen Faraday Young, Saturday, June 16
Livingston
River School Farm—Owen Davidson & Mark Prezorski, Saturday, June 16
Millerton
Helen Bodian, Sunday, September 9
West Taghkanic
Arcadia—Ronald Wagner & Timothy Van Dam, Saturday, June 16

DUTCHESS COUNTY
Amenia
Broccoli Hall—Maxine Paetro, Saturday, May 12, Saturday, June 16
Jade Hill—Paul Arcario & Don Walker, Saturday, July 21
Mead Farm House Garden, Saturday, May 12, Saturday, July 21
Millbrook
309 Route 343, Saturday, July 21
Belinda & Stephen Kaye, Saturday, July 21
Millerton
Hyland/Wente Garden, Saturday, July 21
Pawling
The Brine Garden—Duncan & Julia Brine, Saturday, July 21
Rhinebeck
Cedar Heights Orchard—William & Arvia Morris, Sunday, September 9
Stanfordville
Ellen & Eric Petersen, Saturday, July 21

ONONDAGA COUNTY
Jamesville
McAuliffes' Garden, Sunday, September 16
Lafayette
Pagoda Hill—Michael Brennan & Robert Moss, Sunday, September 16

Solvay
Dr. & Mrs. Charles Mango, Sunday,
September 16
Westvale
Tortuga—Ellen & David Suarez, Sunday,
September 16

PUTNAM COUNTY
Cold Spring
Stonecrop Gardens, Sundays, April 29,
May 13, June 10, July 15, August 12,
September 23
Garrison
Manitoga/The Russel Wright Design
Center, Sunday, June 10
Ross Gardens, Sunday, June 10

SUFFOLK COUNTY
Cutchogue
Conni Cross Garden Designer, Saturday,
July 14
Jacqueline Penney Art Gallery & Studio,
Saturday, May 5
Manfred & Roberta Lee, Saturday, May 5
East Hampton
Abby Jane Brody, Saturday, April 28,
Saturday, June 23
Garden of Arlene Bujese, Saturday,
June 23
Margaret Kerr, Saturday, April 28,
Saturday, June 23
Carol Mercer, Saturday, June 23
Alexandra Munroe & Robert Rosenkranz
Gardens, Sunday, July 15
Bob & Mimi Schwarz, Sunday, July 15
Mattituck
Maurice Isaac & Ellen Coster Isaac,
Saturday, July 14
Dennis Schrader & Bill Smith, Saturday,
July 14
Montauk
Richard Kahn & Elaine Peterson, Sunday,
July 15
Remsenburg
Little Birdstone—Mr. & Mrs. Howard
Finkelstein, Sunday, May 20

The Gardens of Fred & Monica Meyer,
Sunday, May 20
Mara J. Urshel & Ronald R. Rothstein,
Sunday, May 20
Southold
Milford Garden, Saturday, July 14
St. James
Head of the Harbor—Alexandra
Leighton's Garden, Sunday, June 10
Wainscott
Biercuk/Luckey Garden, Saturday,
April 28

TOMPKINS COUNTY
Danby
Myers Gardens, Saturday, June 9, Saturday,
July 14,
Freeville
Ann M. & Carlton J. Manzano Garden,
Saturday, July 14
Ithaca
Cayuga Daylilies, Saturday, July 14
Jim Eavenson, Saturday, June 9
Hospicare, Saturday, June 9
Roseanne & Joe Moresco, Saturday,
July 14
Mount Garden, Saturday, July 14
Posner Garden, Saturday, June 9
Lansing
Lion Garden, Saturday, July 14
Newfield
Medicine Tree Farm, Saturday, June 9
Trumansburg
Hitch Lyman's Garden, Saturday, May 19

ULSTER COUNTY
Bearsville
Gayle Burbank Garden, Saturday, July 7
New Paltz
Lee Reich, Saturday, June 9
Saugerties
Riverhill Garden—Joe & Tamara
DiMattio, Saturday, June 9
West Hurley
Bebe & Dan Turck, Saturday, July 7

WESTCHESTER COUNTY
Armonk
Cobamong Pond, Sunday, May 27
Bedford
Mr. & Mrs. Coleman Burke, Saturday, May 5
Penelope & John Maynard, Saturday, May 5, Sunday, September 16
Keith & Susan Kroeger—Pook's Hill, Sunday, June 10
High and Low Farm, Sunday, June 10
Michael & Katherine Takata, Sunday, June 10
Bedford Hills
Sandra & Roger Goldman, Saturday, May 5
Phillis Warden, Saturday, May 5, Sunday, June 10, Sunday, July 22
Cortlandt Manor
Vivian & Ed Merrin, Sunday, June 10
Katonah
Michael Fuchs, Sunday, July 22
Larchmont
Forest Court—Joanna & Mark Friedman, Saturday, May 5
Premium Pond Garden, Sunday, July 22
Lewisboro
The White Garden, Saturday, April 14, Sunday, September 9
Mount Kisco
Barbara & John Schumacher, Sunday, June 10
Judy & Michael Steinhardt, Sunday, May 6
Rocky Hills—The Garden of William & Henriette Suhr, Sunday, May 6, Saturday, May 26
North Salem
Artemis Farm—Carol & Jesse Goldberg, Sunday, June 10
Dick Button—Ice Pond Farm, Sunday, September 16
Page Dickey & Francis Schell—Duck Hill, Sunday, June 10
Hilltop, Sunday, July 22

Keeler Hill Farm, Sunday, June 10
Ossining
The Wildflower Island at Teatown Lake Reservation, Sunday, May 20
Pound Ridge
John & Melanie Danza, Sunday, September 16
Scarsdale
Fran & Alan Zimbard, Sunday, July 22
Valhalla
The Lady Bird Johnson and the Stone Cottage Demonstration Garden—The Native Plant Center, Sunday, July 15
Waccabuc
James & Susan Henry, Sunday, September 16

NORTH CAROLINA
CHOWAN COUNTY
Edenton
Beverly Hall Gardens, Saturday, April 21
Homestead Garden, Saturday, April 21
Mary's Garden at the Brown-Elliott House, Saturday, April 21
The Paine House Garden, Saturday, April 21
Rose Cottage, Saturday, April 21
Skinner-Paxton House, Saturday, April 21

WAKE COUNTY
Raleigh
The Bromhal Garden, Saturday & Sunday, September 22 & 23
The Davies Garden, Saturday & Sunday, September 22 & 23
The Hanson Garden, Saturday & Sunday, September 22 & 23
A Plant Collector's Paradise, Saturday & Sunday, September 22 & 23
Mrs. Alton B. Smith, Saturday & Sunday, September 22 & 23

OREGON
CLACKAMAS COUNTY
Lake Oswego
Mike & Linda Darcy, Saturday, June 16

Walt Hodges, Satruday, June 16
Oregon City
Sharon McCauley & Dean Dikeman,
    Saturday, June 16
Smith's Solitude, Saturday, June 16
West Linn
Bonnie's Garden, Saturday, June 16
Foxglove Point, Saturday, June 16
Y. Sherry Sheng Garden, Saturday, June 16

LANE COUNTY
Eugene
The Alba Garden, Sunday, July 8
Circles in Thyme, Sunday, July 8
The Hewitt Garden, Sunday, July 8
The Bernard Levine Garden, Sunday,
    July 8
Buell Steelman & Rebecca Sams, Sunday,
    July 8
The Garden of Monica Tallerday & Gene
    Humphreys, Sunday, July 8

MULTNOMAH COUNTY
Portland
Heims Garden, Saturday, May 12
June's Garden, Saturday, May 12
The Narizny Garden, Saturday, May 12
The Jane Platt Garden, Saturday, May 12

WASHINGTON COUNTY
Portland
Barbara Blossom Ashmun, Saturday,
    May 12

PENNSYLVANIA
BUCKS COUNTY
Doylestown
Heronswood Nursery Comes to Fordhook
    Farm of the W. Atlee Burpee & Co.,
    Fridays and Saturdays, April 20 &
    21, May 18 & 19, August 3 & 4,
    September 21 & 22
Carter van Dyke & Lynn Reynolds,
    Saturday, May 19
Perkasie
Carol A. Pierce, Saturday, August 4

Point Pleasant
The Gardens at Mill Fleurs, Saturday,
    August 4
Wrightstown
Hortulus Farm, Saturday, May 19

CHESTER COUNTY
Downingtown
David Culp, Sunday, June 10
West Chester
Inta Krombolz, Sunday, June 10

DELAWARE COUNTY
Chadds Ford
WynEden, Sunday, June 10
Glen Mills
Jim & Conny Parsons, Sunday, June 10

TENNESSEE
KNOX COUNTY
Knoxville
Bush Garden, Saturday & Sunday,
    May 19 & 20
GATOP, Saturday & Sunday,
    May 19 & 20
Hill Top Farm, Saturday & Sunday,
    May 19 & 20

TEXAS
DALLAS COUNTY
Dallas
Angelica's Four Season Garden, Saturday,
    October 20
Chantilis Garden, Saturday, October 20
Newport Garden, Saturday, October 20
Peter & Julie Schaar, Saturday, October 20
Sewell Garden, Saturday, October 20
Waisanen, Saturday, October 20

EL PASO COUNTY
El Paso
Azar Garden, Saturday & Sunday, May 5
    & 6
Beltran Family Garden, Saturday &
    Sunday, May 5 & 6
Brandt Garden, Saturday & Sunday,
    May 5 & 6

Dodd Garden, Saturday & Sunday,
    May 5 & 6
Stewart Garden, Saturday & Sunday,
    May 5 & 6

TARRANT COUNTY

Arlington
Debbie Duncan & Randy Jordan, Sunday,
    October 14
Mary Nell's Garden, Sunday, October 14
Fort Worth
Mr. & Mrs. Fred Cauble, Sunday,
    October 14
Gardens of Little Castle—Bill & Donna
    Vance, Sunday, October 14
The Moncrief Garden, Sunday,
    October 14
Sherrod-Pool Garden, Sunday, October 14

VERMONT
WINDSOR COUNTY

Bridgewater
The Shackleton Garden, Saturday, June 9
Woodstock
Indian Tree Hill-The Highberg Garden,
    Saturday, June 9
The Garden of Fiona & Bob McElwain,
    Saturday, June 9

VIRGINIA
ALBEMARLE COUNTY

Charlottesville
Balge-Crozier Garden, Saturday, May 19
The Frierson Garden, Saturday, May 19
The Frischkorn Garden, Saturday, May 19
Howard Garden, Saturday, May 19
Tank Hut, Saturday, May 19

Free Union
Bird Hill—C. Colston Burrell & D. Bruce
    Ellsworth, Saturday & Sunday, May 19
    & 20
Galvin Garden, Saturday & Sunday, May
    19 & 20
The Gardens at Waterperry Farm,
    Saturday & Sunday, May 19 & 20

WASHINGTON
KING COUNTY

Federal Way
Powellswood, A Northwest Garden,
    Sunday, May 20

KITSAP COUNTY

Bainbridge Island
Little and Lewis, Saturday, July 21
McFarlane Gardens, Saturday, July 21
The Skyler Garden, Saturday, July 21

PIERCE COUNTY

DuPont
Froggy Bottom, Saturday, August 11

THURSTON COUNTY

Olympia
The Hatten Garden, Saturday, August 11
The Koi Garden, Saturday, August 11
Phillips Garden, Saturday, August 11
Stanford Garden, Saturday, August 11
Tenino
Golden Leaf Acres, Saturday, August 11

WEST VIRGINIA
KANAWHA COUNTY

Charleston
"Her Garden" Paula Vasale Memorial
    Garden, Saturday, June 2
Westwind Way Gardens, Saturday, June 2
Elkview
The Fuqua Garden, Saturday, June 2
The Garden of Paula & Roger Shafer,
    Saturday, June 2

ARIZONA
Tucson Open Day
Saturday, September 29
PIMA COUNTY

TUCSON
Bamboo Ranch
1901 North Avenida Azahar

One of Arizona's hidden treasures, Bamboo Ranch has the most comprehensive collections of bamboo in the desert southwest. The Finstroms have converted the three-quarter-acre property into a lush bamboo garden with more than 140 types in cultivation. Bamboo Ranch is the headquarters of the Tierra Seca Chapter of the American Bamboo Society of which Matt Finstrom is the chapter president. The chapter collection is also maintained at the property. The groves are situated along winding paths and are marked with interpretive signs. Sturdy footwear is recommended. **NEW**

Hours: 10 a.m. to 3 p.m.

From I-10, go west on Grant Road about 2 miles and turn left onto Saddlewood Ranch (just west of intersection at Greasewood). Go 3 blocks and turn right onto Avenida Azahar. Follow around curve, about 1.5 blocks, to #1901 on right. Look for a black mailbox and a jungle. Please park on street.

Proceeds shared with The American Bamboo Society

Chestnut Sanctuary
5185 North Mesquite Canyon Place

Desert Streams and Waterfalls, Inc. was brought in to make this concept work—a desert sanctuary with a waterfeature that makes you feel as if you have entered a different world. They built a waterfall and pad to accommodate the large rock necessary to create a miniature "natural lake." cut out of rock outcroppings, littered with waterfalls and a romantic private cove that has a swim-in cave with a waterfall curtain.

Hours: 10 a.m. to 3 p.m.

Go north on Houghton Road to end at stop sign on Snyder Road. Turn right. Go tu second street, Saguaro Hills Drive, and turn left. It is a gated community (Saguaro Hills Estates) and there is a rammed earth wall around the gate entrance. Once through the gate drive to the stop sign. Turn left onto Windsong and drive ahead to the second left. Ours is the first house on the left, #5185.

Proceeds shared with Parent Project Muscular Dystrophy

Southwest Retreat
3330 North El Camino Rinconado

This beautiful house is located as far east as you can get but well worth the drive. The Santa Fe style-house and casita are gorgeous, set in naturally landscaped surroundings. This house has been compared to a mini Tohono Chul Park, except with a swimming pool. Lots of native plants with amazing Mediterranean sitting areas. This site has a place for everyone, designed for functionality and beauty. Wander through this garden and be captivated.

Hours: 10 a.m. to 3 p.m.

From Bamboo Ranch at 1901 North Avenida Azahar, head northeast on North Avenida Azahar for 0.2 miles. Turn left onto North Saddlewood Ranch Drive. Go 0.4 miles and turn right onto West Ironwood Hill Drive. Go 0.6 miles and the road becomes West Grant Road. Go 9.6 miles and turn left onto East Tanque Verde Road. Go 7.9 miles and the road becomes East Redington Road. Go 1 mile and turn left onto North El Camino Rinconado to #3330.

Proceeds shared with The Haven

Public Gardens
PIMA COUNTY

TUCSON
Tohono Chul Park
7366 North Paseo del Norte,
(520) 742-6455, www.tohonochulpark.org

Tohono Chul Park is a hidden oasis of southwestern flora, fauna, and culture. We feature dramatic views from our nature trails full of

---

native and arid-adapted plants, regional art, cultural exhibits, beautiful gardens reflecting local history, an arid-adapted plant-specialized greenhouse, plus southwestern cuisine from our famous Tea Room.

Hours: Year round, daily, 8 a.m. to 5 p.m.

Admission: $5 adults, $4 seniors, $3 students, $2 children 5 to 12, children under 5 free

From Ina Road, go 1 block west of Oracle Road and turn north onto Paseo del Norte to entrance on right.

From I-10, take Ina Road exit, go east about 5 miles (after La Cañada traffic light), and turn left at next light to entrance on right.

CALIFORNIA
San Diego Area Open Day
Sunday, April 22
SAN DIEGO COUNTY

EL CAJON
Rick & Joyce Dentt's Garden
1184 Coco Palms Drive

Our love for the French countryside has been the inspiration for our house and garden. As you meander through the four acres there are formal and informal borders bursting with roses, perennials, fountains, and antique statuary. Our outdoor kitchen and dining structure, surrounded by citrus trees and grapevines, invites you to enjoy the view of our lake and cascading waterfall. **NEW** ♿

Hours: 10 a.m. to 4 p.m.

Take I-5 south to I-805 south to I-8 east to El Cajon Boulevard turnoff. Veer right onto Chase Avenue, left onto Grove Road, left onto Coco Palms Drive.

Proceeds shared with Christian Community Theater

Steve & Susie Dentt's Garden
1470 Grove Road

Our garden has been considered a little bit country, a little bit English, a little bit rustic, and a whole lot charming. The garden is on a broad acre. There are various seating areas inviting you to view the garden filled with perennials and roses combined with whimsical and interesting objects. **2003**

Hours: 10 a.m. to 4 p.m.

From Los Angeles, take I-5 south to I-805 south to I-8 east. Go about 15 miles and take El Cajon Boulevard. Veer right onto Chase Avenue and go about 3.5 miles. Turn left onto Grove Road.

From I-15 south, take I-8 east and proceed as directed above. Please park on Coco Palms Drive.

Proceeds shared with the Susan G. Komen Breast Cancer Foundation

LA MESA
Hillside Jungle Garden
7979 Lemon Circle

Overlooking the village of La Mesa, which is known as "the jewel of the hills," this free-form garden offers tranquility amid a frenzy of established, luxurious tropical plantings. Always eclectic, the garden is a juxtaposition of koi ponds, a Zen garden, statuary, hidden meandering paths, several micro-climates, and even an Indian elephant! There are several hundred bamboo and bromeliads, many rare cycads and palms, angel trumpets, passion vines, and other exotics—even a surprise or two. An extensive collection of potted specimen plants encircle the house. Always a work in progress, this is truly a gardener's garden. **NEW**

Hours: 10 a.m. to 4 p.m.

Take I-8 Freeway east from San Diego to La Mesa (5 miles). Exit at Spring Street. Proceed 0.5 mile on Spring Street south and turn right onto La Mesa Boulevard (crossing trolley). Go about 3 blocks and turn left at traffic light at La Mesa Boulevard and Normal Street (on right is Vons Shopping Center). Go one half block up hill and turn right onto Lemon Circle. Number 7979 is third house on left. Please park on street.

Nugent Garden
4705 Maple Avenue

Step into a lush, park-like atmosphere brimming with hundreds of colorful and unusual annuals and perennials. The garden reflects our continuing passion for English cottage-style garden design and aesthetics, punctuated with meandering pathways, borders, and beds. This fully landscaped one-third acre property also provides a haven for a variety of butterflies and birds. Additionally, it incorporates an eclectic blend of exotic bamboo, vines, and succulents, as well as African, Australian, Asiatic, Mediterranean, and South American trees and shrubs. **2004** ♿

Hours: 10 a.m. to 4 p.m.

From I-8, take 70th Street/Lake Murray Boulevard exit. Head south on 70th Street about 0.25 mile to El Cajon Boulevard. Turn

♿ indicates parts of garden are handicapped accessible

left and go east 1 mile. Turn right onto Maple Avenue (located just before entrance to Auto Zone parking lot) and follow south 3 blocks. Garden is on left with street number painted on curb. Please park along street and enter garden through redwood arbor located in center of front yard.

Proceeds shared with The San Diego Horticultural Society

SAN DIEGO
Oak Park Secret Garden
5211 South Thorn Street

Nestled in a community of 1950s bungalows, this garden oasis evolved from my long commitment to bring young and old together in a place that both could enjoy. This is a private garden, a secret garden, but everybody is welcome here. I've always wanted to create a setting that was inviting. The garden is a series of smaller gardens each with its own theme. In front, there is a rose-framed courtyard which features a large Amish playhouse. There is also a Japanese garden (with koi pond), an English garden, a French café, a terraced organic vegetable garden, and a grass and cobblestone amphitheatre complete with cypresses and a stone fireplace for outdoor plays, concerts, and other community events. Throughout, one will find a lush variety of trees, plants, and roses. **NEW** ⅊

Hours: 10 a.m. to 4 p.m.

Take I-805 south and merge onto CA-94 east and go 1.4 miles. Take Exit 4A/Euclid Avenue onto the Euclid Avenue north ramp. Merge onto Euclid Avenue and go 0.3 mile. Veer slightly to right onto 54th Street and go 1.1 miles. Turn left onto Redwood Street and then right onto 53rd Street. Turn left onto South Thorn Street and end as road begins to curve at #5211. Garden is 10 minutes from downtown San Diego.

Sacramento Area Open Day Saturday, April 28

SACRAMENTO COUNTY

SACRAMENTO
New England Style Landscaping
3661 Winding Creek Road

Explore this newly rebuilt house and landscape reminiscent of the Cape Cod-style. The front bluestone-and-brick walk surrounds a stone planter filled with a grove of little gem magnolias and white carpet roses. The rear bluestone and brick patio leads to a covered loggia with an outdoor rock-faced fireplace and an outdoor kitchen with barbeque, sink, refrigerator, and granite counter. The landscape is a moonlight garden, a white garden with blooming little gem magnolias, white crape myrtles, white carpet and iceberg roses, and varieties of lavender and boxwoods. The newly renovated swimming pool becomes a focal point for the upper terrace and is flanked by a spacious lawn. The plantings add beauty and elegance to this truly beautiful Michael Glassman design. **NEW** ⅊

Hours: 10 a.m. to 4 p.m.

From Sacramento, take Highway 50 toward South Lake Tahoe/Watt Avenue Exit. Take Arden Creek Road and turn right onto Winding Creek Road. Number 3661 Winding Creek Road is on left.

Proceeds shared with River City Community Services

Santa Barbara Villa
4061 Riding Club Lane

Michael Glassman has created a truly one-of-a-kind landscape. Reminiscent of an Old World Santa Barbara estate, this magnificent landscape has French limestone patios and walkways, hand-painted Tunisian tile accents, and lush planters filled with palms and gardenias. The front courtyard has a beautiful, bubbling cobalt-blue urn fountain with scented flowering plants inside to dazzle the senses. The pool house has both an amazing hand-painted

mural and a one-of-a-kind three-tier wall fountain made from original hand-painted Tunisian
tiles. The property has a covered loggia with
a limestone patio, an outdoor fireplace and
kitchen, a large lawn area and tennis court, a
swimming pool and spa—all creating an ideal
landscape for entertaining. **NEW** ♿

Hours: 10 a.m. to 4 p.m.

Take Freeway 50 towards South Lake Tahoe. Take Howe Avenue Exit and go left over
freeway. Go 2.6 miles, turn right onto Arden
Way. Go 0.2 mile and turn left onto Cathay
Way. Riding Club Lane is 489 feet on left.

*Proceeds shared with The Sacramento Food
Bank*

Split-level Sculpture Garden
3720 Winding Creek Road

Our multi-level Mediterranean-style garden
has evolved gradually over the last thirty-five
years. As you step down, the property unfolds to
reveal a private garden previously undetected.
The street level, dominated by California
natives, descends to a trellised adobe terrace
bordered by stone retaining walls, lavender,
citrus, figs, olives, and grapes. Meandering
pathways lead in every direction to an organic
vegetable garden, perennial hill, natives, herbs,
dogwoods, viburnums, and California poppies.
Steps lead to a lawn area with oranges, mature
trees, a chestnut-shaded petanque court, and
sheltered creekside. Our water-efficient refuge
has become a natural backdrop for numerous
sculptures, from small to monumental, mostly
by Helen Post. **NEW** ♿

Hours: 10 a.m. to 4 p.m.

From Highway 50, take Watt Avenue Exit,
north. Continue about 3 miles, crossing the
American River, to Winding Creek Road. Turn
right, go 0.5 mile and garden is on right before
second bridge.

From Highway 80, take Watt Avenue Exit,
south. Continue about 2.5 miles to Winding
Creek Road and turn left. Proceed 0.5 mile to
house on right. Please park along street with
caution, there are no sidewalks.

*Proceeds shared with Fair Oaks Horticulture
Center*

Horticultural Seminars at The Ruth Bancroft Garden

Lectures • Plant Walks
Plant Sales • Garden Tours

**Presented by
The Garden Conservancy &
The Ruth Bancroft Garden**

Mark your calendar:
**Friday, July 20, Walnut Creek
Saturday, July 21, Study Tour**

Influence of South America on the California Garden

* A second 2007 Ruth Bancroft
Garden seminar and tour is
planned for October 19 & 20.

Cornerstone Garden Design Lecture Series

**Summer Season 2007 Presented
by The Garden Conservancy**

At Cornerstone Festival of
Gardens, Highway 121, Sonoma,
CA. *Dates and Programs TBA.*

To register or for
additional information
about these and other
Garden Conservancy
programs in California, contact:
The Garden Conservancy
1014 Torney Ave #1
San Francisco, CA 94129.
(415)561-7895
wcprog@gardenconservancy.org,
www.gardenconservancy.org.

♿ indicates parts of garden are handicapped accessible

Tropical Caribbean Resort
3771 Random Lane

Vacation is in your own backyard! This unique backyard, designed by Michael Glassman, gives one the feeling of a Caribbean resort. A rock-lined spa cascades into a stream that flows into a three-tiered swimming pool flanked with large boulders and accented with glass tile. The upper terrace is a large tile patio that flows from inside the house. Walk down the tile steps to a beautiful flagstone patio and walkways that are enhanced with an arched wood trellis covered with bamboo poles. A rustic cabana equipped with a bathroom, kitchen, and outdoor barbeque area, and an outdoor fireplace and sheeting fountain create a vacation-like setting. The night lighting is truly magical. Queen palms, red-hot pokers, red carpet roses, large bird of paradise, cannas lilies, fan palms, and angel trumpets create an image of a tropical paradise. **NEW**

Hours: 10 a.m. to 4 p.m.

From Sacramento, this garden is 15 minutes from Freeway 1. Take Freeway 50 toward South Lake Tahoe. Exit at Watt Avenue North and turn right onto Maplewood Lane. Turn left to stay on Maplewood Lane. Then turn right onto Random Lane. Number 3771 is about a 10-minute drive from freeway.

Proceeds shared with The Sacramento Food Bank

The Wells Garden
631 Morse Avenue

Designed and planted by Marc Askew in 1990, tended and loved by Jim and Patricia Wells in the intervening seventeen years, the garden has grown with abandon. The basic design was meant to give one the feeling of discovering a mountain stream among the aspens. White birches were used in place of aspens and the dark blue green of the pool was chosen to approximate the color of the south fork of the Yuba River. The feelings we want you to experience in the garden are serenity and peace. **NEW** ♿

Hours: 10 a.m. to 4 p.m.

From downtown Sacramento, drive west and north on J Street or H Street until they join and become Fair Oaks Boulevard. Continue to Morse Avenue traffic light and turn left. The house is 1.25 blocks down Morse Avenue on west side, about 5 to 6 miles from the Capitol.

From Highway 50 West, take the Watt Avenue exit north to Fair Oaks Boulevard. Turn left and then right at first traffic light onto Morse Avenue. Go 1.25 blocks. Garden is on west side.

From Highway 80 West, take the Watts Avenue Exit to Fair Oaks Boulevard. Turn right and continue to first traffic light at Morse Avenue. Turn right. There is a bike lane on Morse Avenue. Please park on side streets, Laurel and Barberry.

Proceeds shared with Heifer Project International

The Wise Garden
601 Laurel Drive

Sited on almost one and one-half acres, this six-year-old Mediterranean-influenced, water-efficient garden is a collaboration between landscape architect David Gibson and the owners. Olive trees grace both the front and back of the house. Boxwood hedges (800+ plants!) provide structure, lining the driveway and surrounding beds of roses, bulbs, and perennials. The garden includes a formal lily pond, bocce court, fountains, fruit trees, a table-grape vineyard, and an allée of zinfandel grapevines. There is no turf grass in this landscape; open areas, including walkways, are covered by gravel or bark mulch. This is a gardener's garden—every plant was selected, planted, and is maintained by the gardener! **NEW**

Hours: 10 a.m. to 4 p.m.

From Highway 50, exit at Watt Avenue going north. Go about 1 mile to first traffic light at Fair Oaks Boulevard; turn left. At next traffic light turn right onto Morse Avenue. Go 1 block to Laurel Drive; turn right. The garden is at northeast corner. Please park on street.

Proceeds shared with Fair Oaks Horticulture Center

2007 California Garden Conservancy Seminars
On Garden History and Design

Friday, March 30, 2007
The Presidio, San Francisco
8:30 a.m. to 5 p.m.

Gardens of the Mind: landscapes that excite the intellect and the emotions

Fifth in the *Gardens to Match Your Architecture* series. Co-sponsored by *Pacific Horticulture*

Fee: $125 Garden Conservancy members
    $145 general admission

A garden study tour will follow on Saturday, March 31. Fee for both is $255 for Garden Conservancy members, $285 general admission.

Magical gardens come about in a variety of ways: *Tony Duquette Garden, Malibu Ranch.*
sometimes, there is a garden-maker living out his
or her fantasy; sometimes the fantasy is created in the mind of the viewer. How these gardens translate from the mind to the ground is the great wonder.

Seminar speakers include landscape designer **Laura Morton** and architect **David Hertz** from the Los Angeles area; landscape designer and professor of literature **James Yoch**, University of Oklahoma; Bay Area artist **Marcia Donahue** and landscape designers **Cevan Forristt** and **Shirley Watts**. The study tour will include both public and private gardens and the work of San Francisco landscape architect **Cheryl Barton, Marcia Donahue**, and Shirley Watts.

September 28 – 30, Los Angeles
California Japanese Style Gardens: traditions & practice

A conference and annual meeting of The California Garden & Landscape History Society featuring lectures, exhibit, and garden tours.

Co-hosted by the Japanese American National Museum, the Garden Conservancy, and the Los Angeles Conservancy.

To register or for additional information about these and other Garden Conservancy programs in California, contact: The Garden Conservancy, 1014 Torney Ave #1, San Francisco, CA 94129. (415)561-7895, wcprog@gardenconservancy.org, www.gardenconservancy.org.

San Diego Area Open Day Saturday, April 28

SAN DIEGO COUNTY

POWAY

Arnold Garden
15638 Boulder Mountain Road

Our nineteen-acre, boulder-strewn, hilltop property is a combination botanical garden and nature preserve. The overall theme of the garden and property is, "In balance with nature," and careful attention has been paid to the use of massive boulders, natural slopes, and native plants. The botanical portion of the property is an extensive collection of hundreds of tropical and subtropical plants from around the world, including more than eighty palm and fifty cycad species, as well as flowering trees, aloes, proteas, orchids, bromeliads, and ferns. More than fifteen acres of our property is highly diverse, undisturbed coastal chaparral, which will be in peak bloom in April and May. **2003** ♿

Hours: 10 a.m. to 4 p.m.

From I-15, go east on Rancho Bernardo Road 1.75 miles (it becomes Espola Road after 0.81 mile). Turn right onto Martincoit Road and go 1.27 miles. Turn right onto Orchard Gate Road and go 0.32 mile. Turn left onto Lime Grove Road and go 0.25 mile. Turn right onto Arroya Vista Road for 0.14 mile. Turn left onto Boulder Mountain Road and go straight through gate for 0.53 mile. Please park along wide road on property and walk or take shuttle up narrow driveway to gardens and trails.

Casterline Garden
16291 Martincoit Road

Our long, steep driveway includes an island of boulders and interesting plant material. One side features a huge orange pincushion protea, a bush poppy, and a naked coral tree. My husband, Paul, tends his roses at the top. Ahead is a rustic gate to the Santa Fe-style garden room. Formerly the garage, it has been pictured in national magazines. Flower beds inside the fence frame a pool with a vanishing edge fac-

ing a big view of nearby mountains. Continue on the wandering paths and you will pass an incredible variety of trees and shrubs, eventually reaching a secluded garden on the other side of the house. Recently we have removed old avocado trees to open up a sunny area in a grove. This space has been landscaped and it is being called "The Australian Garden". After a wildflower tour of western Australia, we have combed the nurseries in search of grevilleas, banksias, and wax flowers. If they all reach their potential size it will be something to see. These Aussies are not shy. **2003**

Hours: 10 a.m. to 4 p.m.

From I-15, take Rancho Bernardo Road exit and go east about 3 miles (name will change to Espola Road). Continue to Martincoit Road, where you must turn right. About 0.75 mile will bring you to #16291 on left. Please park on right shoulder and walk up driveway. If driveway looks too strenuous, you may walk or drop off from next driveway up hill and enter through arch.

Proceeds shared with The San Dieguito River Valley Land Conservancy

Cattolico Garden
15706 Boulder Mountain Road

Our three-quarter-acre property, deemed to be unbuildable, was a challenge that spurred my husband to build a Colonial-style house in 1998. My task was to design a garden complementing the long and narrow terrain. To accomplish this, the hardscape was engineered and implemented (retaining walls, Trex decks and stairs, stamped-concrete paths, trellises). Existing native plants were then incorporated with specimen trees, a variety of perennials, shrubs, and vines. We are now enjoying paths lined with roses and flowers, vine-covered arbors, a shade garden, a waterfall, and bird baths frequented by birds and butterflies. Whimsical ornaments and a birdhouse collection (featured in *Sunset* magazine) add to the charm. Recently a new deck was constructed capturing the panoramic view of the mountains and valley below. **2003** ♿

Hours: 10 a.m. to 4 p.m.

Take I-15 to Rancho Bernardo Road exit and go east. Rancho Bernardo Road turns into Espola Road. Turn right at traffic light onto Martincoit Road (Stoneridge Country Club is on left and Prudential Realty on right). The preceding road is Valle Verde. Go 1 mile to top of hill. Turn right onto Orchard Gate. Turn left onto Lime Grove (preceding road is Ranch Hallow). Turn right onto Arroya Vista and left onto Boulder Mountain Road. Distance from I-15 to Boulder Mountain Road is 4 miles. Our house is third on right, white Colonial style. Please park on either side of street, leaving driveway clear.

Les Belles Fleurs
13003 Avenida la Valencia

Les Belles Fleurs occupies an acre of fertile soil adjacent to a creek and equestrian trail. This is a new home for us and we have only just begun to find all the hidden treasures. Included on the property is a peaceful lily pond with a waterfall, a chicken coop, and a critter-proof organic potager. The previous owner set up this perennial organic garden loaded with roses to always have beauty in bloom. We welcome guests to share names of plants we have not yet identified. The garden has previously been in several publications including *Better Homes & Gardens* and *Sunset* magazines. We welcome your visit. **2003** ♿

Hours: 10 a.m. to 4 p.m.

From I-15, take the Rancho Bernardo Road exit. From the north, turn left off the exit; from the south turn right. Pass traffic lights at Pomerado Road and Summerfield Road. Turn right onto Avenida Florenzia (there is no traffic light or stop sign at this turn). Go to the third stop sign and turn left onto Avenida la Valencia. Our garden is ninth on right.

Proceeds shared with The San Diego Horticultural Society

Moore Garden
15615 Boulder Ridge Lane

The Moore Garden is a two and one-half acre oasis of palms and other tropical plants, meandering streams and pathways, and water gardens. The garden contains nearly 300 spe-cies of palms that Mr. Moore has collected during his world travels. A highlight is the climate-controlled conservatory containing rare palms and other tropical plants requiring a year-round humid and warm climate. A box-wood hedge-lined formal garden of sixty-five rose varieties provides color and fragrance. A nursery is maintained on the property for seed germination and plant production. **NEW** ♿

Hours: 10 a.m. to 4 p.m.

From I-15 in Rancho Bernardo, exit at Rancho Bernardo Road and go east for 3 miles. The road bends to right and becomes Espola Road in Poway. At first traffic light after bend, turn right onto Lake Poway Road. Go west for 3 miles to turnaround. Beyond is private road of Green Valley Summit. Go 1 block and turn right onto Boulder Ridge Lane. The Moore Garden is first property on right.

Proceeds shared with The San Diego Museum of Man

Wits End West
13639 Jackrabbit Road

Wits End West is a riparian, woodland garden that uses native and non-native trees, shrubs, and flowers to offer respite from the Southern California heat. The natural stone outcroppings in the garden and its surroundings lend the area great charm and character. Ours is a woodland garden that relies on the varying vertical aspects of large native oaks and ornamental flowering trees and shrubs to provide four different canopy habitat levels as well as a series of smaller compartmentalized spaces that offer intimacy and privacy. A variety of plants from around the world has helped to create this woodland paradise, which is enjoyed by us and a large number of the local fauna. **2003** ♿

Hours: 10 a.m. to 4 p.m.

From I-15, take Rancho Bernardo Road east for about 2 miles. (Just after crossing Pomerado Road, the name changes to Espola Road.) Turn right onto Orchard Bend South about 0.25 mile after Martincoit Road traffic light. Third street on right is Jackrabbit Road. Wits End West is at #13639, second house on left with red mailbox. Please park on street.

♿ indicates parts of garden are handicapped accessible

Pasadena Open Day
Sunday, April 29

Maps and discounted admission tickets will be available at La Casita del Arroyo Garden in Pasadena from 9:30 a.m. to 3:30 p.m. See page 78 for directions.

LOS ANGELES COUNTY

PASADENA
574 Bellefontaine Street
574 Bellefontaine Street

In 1979 when we moved into our Sylvanus Marston-designed Craftsman-style house, we began to work on the garden immediately. We removed overgrown shrubs and planted a camellia woods under our two large Chinese elms. We hung a swing from one of the elm branches. We planted a grove of Japanese maples for privacy on the porch and birches and liquidambars for autumn color. Nine years later Victor Lang, a professional gardener, came to help us, and he is still here lending his vision and inspiration. When our venerable oak fell during a major winter storm, he transformed what had been a shade garden into an English-style border. Three years ago he developed a path through the now grown-up camellia woods. Our son was married in the front garden and escorted his bride along the camellia path to a reception on the back terrace. Now a swing hangs again from the elm for our little grandson. Our garden gives us beauty from every window, provides flowers for our rooms, vegetables for our table, and shelter from the harshness of modern life. The house is on the National Register of Historic Places. **NEW** ♿

Hours: 10 a.m. to 4 p.m.

From 210 or 134 Freeway, exit at Orange Grove Boulevard. Turn south and go to Bellefontaine Street. Turn right. Number 574 is on the corner of Bellefontaine Street and Bellefontaine Place. The entrance to garden is on Bellefontaine Place.

From Pasadena Freeway/110 Freeway, exit at Orange Grove Boulevard. Turn north and go to Bellefontaine Street. Turn left. The entrance to garden is on Bellefontaine Place.

Linda Baisley & Lenny Amato Garden
470 Prospect Terrace

When we moved here five years ago, the garden consisted of twelve sickly roses, dead grass, two ugly palms, and unlimited potential. We asked landscape designer Mark Bartos to draw up a plan that would give us a beautiful, low-maintenance garden to surround our Wallace Neff-designed 1929 Italian Revival-style house. Mark found enough space on the lot for several garden rooms, lots of interesting plants, two fountains, a welcoming drought-tolerant front garden with great potted olive trees, and a lovely patio with an outdoor fireplace looking out to a swimming pool. We enjoy sitting outside on the patio, watching the sunset with a glass of wine and listening to the birds and soothing sound of the water fountain that runs into the pool. The overall design is so good that we are able to enjoy the entire landscape with a weekly visit from Naturescape, our garden/maintenance service. **NEW** ♿

Hours: 10 a.m. to 4 p.m.

Drive north on Orange Grove after exiting the 210 Freeway. Turn left onto Rosemont. Turn right onto second street on right, Prospect Terrace, and drive to #470.

Proceeds shared with The Los Angeles Arboretum Foundation

Bennett-DeBeixedon Garden
645 Bradford Street

Hidden away at the end of a long gravel drive, our magical garden was created in 2003 on a lot previously abandoned for fifty years. Wrapping around a newly built northern European-style cottage, the site utilizes the sloped and rocky terrain to create a two-level slate patio with riverrock walls and steps. Surrounded by major oak trees and bordered by vines and climbing roses on all four sides, the garden is divided into rooms, including a sunny cottage garden, a shade garden under the oaks, and a culinary garden. **NEW** ♿

Hours: 10 a.m. to 4 p.m.

From the Pasadena Freeway/110 Freeway, exit north onto Orange Grove Boulevard and drive about 1mile. Turn left onto Bradford Street. Cross South Grand Avenue. Our house is on right with long driveway. Please park on street.

From 134 Freeway, exit south onto Orange Grove Boulevard and go 1 mile. Turn right onto Bradford Street. Proceed as directed above.

Susan & Doug Kranwinkle
691 La Loma Road

We have lived in our 1907 Craftsman-style house for forty years. The previous owner, gardening legend Georgie Van de Kamp, spent years personally collecting rocks from the nearby arroyo to form the "bones" of the garden. A friend has told me that my garden looks like a "miniature park" with its miniature trees, beds of perennials, blowsy bushes and busy birds, bees, and insects. I am more a farmer than a gardener and am often inspired at nurseries to bring home interesting plants to plant, move about, and sometimes later edit—some plants have lived in every corner of my garden! I am also an inveterate collector of many things and during my travels and on eBay. I look for antique watering cans of all shapes and sizes which give my deck a wonderful old-fashioned look. **NEW** ♿

Hours: 10 a.m. to 4 p.m.

From the south, take Pasadena Freeway/110 to Pasadena. Exit at Orange Grove Boulevard and turn left. Go to fourth traffic light, about 1 mile, to California Boulevard. Turn left and go 2 blocks to stop sign at Grand Avenue. Turn left and go 1 block to La Loma Road. Go half a block to #691.

Proceeds shared with La Casita del Arroyo Foundation

Lenkin Garden
1112 Lagunita Road

Carved out of an acre of hillside during the last eighteen years, the twenty-one individual gardens on this property surround an historic

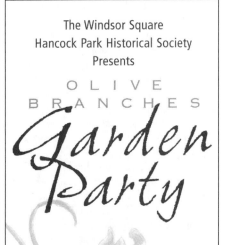

The Windsor Square
Hancock Park Historical Society
Presents

OLIVE BRANCHES
Garden Party

Tour 6 private gardens in this historic area of Los Angeles and enjoy food provided by local restaurants

All proceeds go toward creating more green space in Los Angeles

Sunday
June 10, 2007
Noon to 5pm

Visit
www.wshphs.org
or call
213.243.8182
for more
information

♿ indicates parts of garden are handicapped accessible

Italianate-style 1923 house designed by Webber, Staunton, and Spaulding. A forty-foot tented area, fountains, arbors, statuary, lighting, orchid house, and waterfall combine to create a series of enchanting spaces. The garden space in the front of the property is formal. The formality gives way to untailored, romantic gardens that make their way around to the hillside behind and give the impression of an untamed but lush and dramatic landscape. Three golden retrievers, two cats, and an African gray parrot live here. Please bring dog biscuits! This garden won *Garden Design* magazine's 2006 Golden Trowel Award, honoring America's best gardens. It is also featured in *Fine Gardening* magazine's 'Great Gardens' (February 2007), *Garden Design* (January 2006), and *Cottage Living* (April 2007). **2006** ♿

Hours: 10 a.m. to 4 p.m.

Take I-210 to Route 34 west. Go to exit on right for San Rafael/Linda Vista. Turn left onto bridge over freeway. Turn right onto Colorado Boulevard which is first street after bridge. Turn left onto South San Rafael. Turn right at fork onto Lagunita Road. Go to fourth house on left.

From south of Pasadena, take I-10 to I-110 north. Take exit for Orange Grove Boulevard. Turn left, then left again onto Colorado. Proceed as directed above. Please park on street.

Proceeds shared with The Los Angeles Arboretum Foundation

The Florence Yoch-Designed Ira Bryner Garden
494 Bradford Street

In 1929, Florence Yoch prepared a garden for Ira Bryner on a sloping lot with a view to the hills above the arroyo in Pasadena. The drive divides the space in two: an upper level with the house and its terraces perched obliquely to catch the view, and a lower area where paths entwine through green and flowered garden rooms. This landscape, in a suburban lot of less than two-fifths of an acre, combines the sweeping drive, arbor, parterre, and citrus grove of an Italian villa with an English manor's rose garden, orchard, lawn, and summerhouse

(with thanks to *James C. Yoch: Landscaping the American Dream*). We purchased the property after long-time owner, Harriet Doerr, died in 2003. We want to maintain the integrity of the garden as one of the best remaining Florence Yoch designs. The garden has recently been designated as a historical landmark. **NEW**

Hours: 10 a.m. to 4 p.m.

From Pasadena Freeway/110 Freeway, exit north onto Orange Grove Boulevard and drive about 1 mile. Turn left onto Bradford Street.

From 134 Freeway, exit south on Orange Grove Boulevard and drive slightly more than 1 mile. Turn left onto Bradford Street and go to #494. Please park on Bradford Street only.

The Zasa Garden
315 Bellefontaine Street

The Zasa family has belonged to this 1933 house and garden for fourteen years. We first landscaped the rear garden to accommodate our active family by adding a pool and spa. We updated entertaining spaces near the house and installed fountains to add the sound of water. Gradually we created outdoor rooms with hedges. One room has a parterre of flowering pear trees, another hedged-in area uses citrus trees to give privacy to a home office. We covered a pergola with climbing roses to create a reading nook. The original six rose beds have been restored and replanted and we concentrate much of our gardening energy on the roses. The front garden has evolved as we removed grass and widened the planting beds along the path and around the front door. Our increasing interest in Mediterranean gardening has led us to plant more drought-tolerant perennials in these front beds. We hope you enjoy your visit to our garden. **NEW** ♿

Hours: 10 a.m. to 4 p.m.

From Los Angeles, take the 110 Freeway east and exit at Orange Grove Boulevard. Turn left and drive north. Third traffic light is Bellefontaine Street. Turn left to #315.

From 134 Freeway east, exit at Orange Grove Boulevard. Turn right and drive south. Fourth traffic light is Bellefontaine Street. Turn left to #315.

From 210 Freeway west, follow signs toward Del Mar and the 710 Freeway. Exit at California and go straight through light, traveling south on St. John. Next light is Bellefontaine Street. There is a right turn only lane. Turn right and go to #315. There is ample street parking.

Proceeds shared with Descanso Gardens

Berkeley Open Day
Saturday, May 5

ALAMEDA COUNTY

BERKELEY
Cathleen's Garden
37 Poplar Street

This eclectic cottage garden has evolved over the past twenty years from a barren hillside lot into a textured botanical tapestry. The steep slope, carved into broad terraces and anchored with chunks of recycled concrete, is now covered with rosemary. Flower beds alternate with lawn on different levels, each a composition of my favorite perennials, shrubs, and specimen trees. A huge stone Buddha gazes enigmatically out at the panoramic view of the San Francisco Bay and the luscious Berkeley Hills landscape. **NEW**

Hours: 10 a.m. to 4 p.m.

From I-80 east, take the Buchanan Street exit. Buchanan becomes Marin Avenue after crossing San Pablo Avenue. Stay on Marin Avenue into the hills. Turn left onto Euclid Avenue, then left onto Poplar Street, and #37 is on right. Take steps up to terrace and garden.

The Harmon Garden
726 Euclid Avenue

In collaboration with designer Brandon Tyson, Amy and Cyrus Harmon have created a hillside oasis to complement their restored Santa Barbara-style house. This garden showcases Tyson's signature style with its myriad of bold forms and vibrant color combinations using rare palms, cycads, proteas, aloes, and agaves. Drought-tolerant and succulent plants are a special focus, particularly in the curbside plantings. The garden also features a tile fountain by Diana Watson and the ceramic art of Marcia Donahue, another Open Days participant. **NEW** ♿

Hours: 10 a.m. to 4 p.m.

The garden is best reached via the Buchanan Street exit to Albany (from Highway 80 South and Highway 580 East) and the Cleveland Avenue exit to Albany (from Highway 80 North). Take Buchanan Street east toward the hills, which will turn into Marin Avenue. Continue up the 2.2 miles; cross the circle with the fountain. Turn left onto Euclid Avenue and go north 0.3 mile. Garden is on the bay side of street. Parking is limited. Please do not park in driveway.

Our Own Stuff Gallery Garden
3017 Wheeler Street

My small urban garden has, over the past twenty-seven years, become mature—that is to say, way over my head—an oasis, and a world of

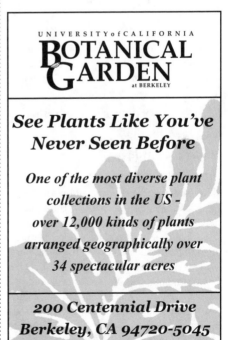

♿ indicates parts of garden are handicapped accessible

its and our own. Unusual subtropical plants still intermingle with sculptures in steel, stone, and ceramic, which Mark Bulwinkle, Sara Floor, and I have made. I have added a "beach," a *faux* eroded landfill of pebbles and shards. The ex-driveway is now The Big Beauty Garden, where strong colors and bold foliage embrace a ten-foot-tall ceramic, beatific female figure. The National Collection of Bambusa Ceramica continues to increase in size and varieties. The garden never holds still. **2006**

Hours: 10 a.m. to 4 p.m.

From I-80/I-580 by San Francisco Bay, take Ashby Avenue/Berkeley exit. After 1.5 miles, look for Shattuck Avenue. There are 2 gas stations at that intersection. Cross Shattuck and turn right onto Wheeler Street. Look for fourth house on left, #3017. Please park on Wheeler or Emerson Street.

Proceeds shared with San Francisco Botanical Garden Society at Strybing Arboretum

West Los Angeles Area Open Day
Saturday, May 12

Maps and discounted admission tickets will be available at Merrihew's Sunset Gardens in Santa Monica from 9:30 a.m. to 3:30 p.m. See page 79 for directions.

LOS ANGELES COUNTY

LOS ANGELES
The O'Neill Garden
1007 *Wellesley Avenue*

This garden expresses the passion for the unusual and unexpected that was the signature of Donna O'Neill. Starting in front, boulders are set into a native plant garden featuring manzanita, artemisia, Cleveland sage, buckwheat, and verbena. Aromas reminiscent of the coastal foothills of California pervade the air year round. The back garden is reached through a small garage—an unlikely passage to an expansive garden with a surprising vista. The upper deck garden runs the length of the house and features an indoor/outdoor

living room and a collection of rare potted plants. Broken concrete is used to create steps leading to the lower deck garden, where it is used informally as paving. The lower deck is actually a roof garden that boasts an eclectic mix of trees, succulents, grasses, and perennials and offers a view of both the tilted grass roof and the tropical garden below. The tropical garden has several mature stands of bamboo, two small water elements, and plantings that include palms, succulents, heliconias, various ligularias, and hellebores. Boulders hug the steps that lead to the woodland garden patio and its view of the natural creek below. A walk down the stairs reveals a small pool created by strategically placed boulders that enhance the sound of running water. From this serene retreat, one can easily forget that Wilshire Boulevard is merely blocks away. A path winds from the patio to the top of the woodland garden where roses surround a fountain and a hedge frames a secret garden door that leads back to the roof garden. **NEW**

Hours: 10 a.m. to 4 p.m.

The garden is located about 2 blocks north of Wilshire Boulevard and 2 blocks west of Bundy Drive. From the 405, exit at Wilshire Boulevard and go west for about 2 blocks. Turn north onto Wellesley Avenue.

PACIFIC PALISADES
The Smith Garden
850 *Muskingum Avenue*

This half-acre garden was conceived to blend with the architecture of the house. The inspiration of the house was based on the early California architect Irving Gill. Gill's theory was that nature should be seen from all windows in the house. The front is an environmental nature center that includes a stream-like water feature. Many varieties of wildlife are welcome. There are a large number of California and Australian natives. The back yard features many unusual plants and heirloom roses. There are also many antique pots and urns, along with an outdoor kitchen and rock tiled pool. **NEW**

Hours: 10 a.m. to 4 p.m.

From the 10 Freeway go west to Pacific Coast Highway. Turn right onto Temescal Canyon. Turn left onto Sunset Boulevard. Turn right at first traffic light which is El Medio. Turn left onto Muskingum Avenue. Garden is on left.

From the 405 Freeway, exit at Sunset and go west about 5 miles. Turn right onto El Medio. Turn left onto Muskingum Avenue. Garden is on left. Please do not block neighboring driveways when parking.

Santa Monica
The Edna May Garden
1101 Yale Street

Designer Lisa Moseley created outdoor rooms on what was a flat plot of grass and weeds, giving the family places to play, relax, and entertain. A pergola is shaded by an ancient and rare lilac bougainvillea, white buddleia attracts an array of butterflies and various fruit trees offer treats throughout the year. A charming vegetable garden, a sitting area, and a "white garden" are other attractions. The garden is organized and structured yet very relaxing. **NEW** ♿

Hours: 10 a.m. to 4 p.m.

From the 405 Freeway exit at Wilshire Boulevard. Go west to Yale Street. Turn right and go 1 half block north on east side of street.

From 10 East, exit at the 405 Freeway North and proceed as directed above.

Proceeds shared with The Tuberous Sclerosis Alliance

Lidow Residence
665 East Channel Road

The original grand sycamore trees set the stage for the development of the house and the lower gardens. To maximize the rest of this hillside property, landscape architect W. Garett Carlson has created a series of paths and gardens leading up the hill. The lap pool is sited midway where its stone terrace captures the sun. Very simple plantings with decomposed granite pathways seem to go on forever. The hillside provides an ever-present visual and is enjoyed from the house at all times of the day and night

and through all seasons. The steep climb to the top rewards visitors with a remarkable view of Santa Monica Canyon. Please be aware that there are no handrails on the paths, so caution is advised. **NEW**

Hours: 10 a.m. to 4 p.m.

From the 10 Freeway West, exit at Lincoln Boulevard and go north to San Vincente Boulevard and turn left. Turn right onto Seventh Street and go down hill to San Lorenzo Street and turn right. Turn left onto Esparta Way. Turn right onto East Channel Road and park along street. The garden is at end of this dead-end street, on left. It may be necessary to park on San Lorenzo Street and walk to garden.

From the 405 Freeway, exit at Wilshire Boulevard West and go to San Vincente Boulevard West. At Seventh Street turn right and continue down hill, turning right onto San Lorenzo Street. Turn left onto Esparta Way. Turn right onto East Channel Road and park along street. The garden is at end, on left. It may be necessary to park on San Lorenzo Street and walk to garden. Please note that the entrance to both

♿ indicates parts of garden are handicapped accessible

the Lidow Garden and the Mayer Garden is on East Channel Road.

Marek/Bernatz Garden
2252 25th Street

When John Bernatz and Joseph Marek purchased this house ten years ago, it was a rather plain bungalow. The gardens were nonexistent, with the front yard consisting of a lawn and foundation plantings common to this neighborhood and to so many. Also typical was the lack of a front entry path, leaving guests no option but to walk up the driveway. A new stone path now leads you to the entry courtyard with a checkerboard sandstone "carpet" and a bubbling fountain made from old Spanish tiles. The front garden, inspired by the gardens of Old California, Italy, and the American South, is surrounded by a juniper hedge and filled with aloes, agaves, lavenders, golden yellow roses, and olive trees dripping with Spanish moss. Through the gates are the potting garden, outdoor dining room, and a new gravel and pebble terrace leading to Marek's design studio. A mighty Chinese elm tree dominates the lower garden, which had been completely covered by concrete when the couple bought the house. Goldchip gravel now covers the ground, with the tree giving shade and dappled light to the new back gardens and outdoor living spaces. The back gardens were inspired by landscapes in England, Mexico, and the Tropics, with brightly colored walls and lush plantings of hot-colored cannas, birds of paradise, gingers, and Marek's ever-increasing collection of tillandsias and staghorn ferns. At the back of the property are the vegetable, herb, and rose gardens, used for bringing color, fragrance, and flavor into the house as well. The gardens were designed by the owner, landscape architect Joseph Marek. The gardens and house have been featured in *House Beautiful, Horticulture,* and the *Los Angeles Times* magazine. **2004** ♿

Hours: 10 a.m. to 4 p.m.

From the 10 West, take Cloverfield Boulevard exit. At top of exit ramp, turn left. At traffic light, turn left onto Pico Boulevard. Go 2 blocks to 25th Street and turn right. House is fifth on right.

From the 10 East, take 20th Street exit. Turn right onto 20th Street. Turn left onto Pico. Go to 25th Street and turn right. House is fifth on right. Please park on street.

Mayer Residence
14198 Alisal Lane

Over a thirty-year period, landscape architect W. Garett Carlson transformed this Santa Monica Canyon garden from its original avocado grove into a hillside garden of towering trees, meandering paths, and restful vantage points. The original garden encompassed only the entry and the pool area at the base of the hill—it is now home to soaring redwoods and mature tree ferns. The current owner purchased the property in 1993 and the hillside development began in 2001. Remnants of the avocado grove still exist, but now pathways lead to the top of the hill. Broken concrete walls now terrace the hillside and the whole is planted in a very natural way. The goal was to create an interesting way to travel the property for exercise and enjoyment. The hillside has taken on a magic of its own with a feeling that it has been there forever. Please note that there are no handrails on the paths, so caution is advised. **NEW**

Hours: 10 a.m. to 4 p.m.

From the 10 West, exit at Lincoln Boulevard, go north to San Vincente Boulevard and turn left. Turn right onto Seventh Street and continue down hill to San Lorenzo Street and turn right. Turn left onto Esparta Way. Turn right onto East Channel Road and park. The garden is at end of this street on left. Public parking is prohibited on Alisal Lane.

From the 405, exit at Wilshire Boulevard West and continue to San Vincente Boulevard West. At Seventh Street turn right and continue down the hill, turning right onto San Lorenzo Street. Turn left onto Esparta Way. Turn right onto East Channel Road and park. The garden is at end of this dead-end street on left. It may be necessary to park on San Lorenzo Street and walk to the garden. Public parking is prohibited on Alisal Lane. Please note that the entrance to both the Mayer Garden and the Lidow Garden is on East Channel Road.

Sacramento Area Open Day Saturday, May 12

NEVADA COUNTY

GRASS VALLEY
Shenoa
14165 Talking Pines Road

"Shenoa" (a peaceful retreat) describes this garden nestled into the rolling hills and heavily wooded site in the Sierra Nevada foothills. The gardens were designed by Carolyn Singer, Grass Valley designer and garden writer. They include a vegetable and flower garden with rock walls, an Irish potting shed, a swimming pool garden, and grasses and ground covers around the large pond containing more rock walls and a waterfall. The emphasis is on seasonal change and an integration of house and garden. The paths through the main gardens invite walking and lingering, and a close look at the many unusual specimens. **NEW** ♿

Hours: 10 a.m. to 4 p.m.

From I-80 South take Exit 135/Colfax/ Highway 174. Follow Highway 174 signs (turning more than 360 degrees from exit). Go 5.3 miles. Turn left onto Talking Pines Road and go 0.3 mile.

From Highway 49 South take Exit 182A/ Highway 174/Colfax and stay on Highway 174 for 7.5 miles. Turn right onto Talking Pines Road and go 0.3 mile.

PENN VALLEY
The Gardens at Troll Knoll
10148 Oak Canyon Drive

Troll Knoll speaks to a way of living. It expresses ideas through the garden vistas across the Sacramento Valley to the coastal mountains and east to the rim of Lake Tahoe. Paths, overlooks, and trails lead through more than sixty featured areas and gardens—each enough to please the viewer. There are roses and perennials everywhere. Orchards, potagers, a swamp, a train garden, a vineyard maze, golf course, mining town, and Pinky's Trailer Park

are the work of Ann and John Morris to share with visitors and gardeners. **NEW** ♿

Hours: 10 a.m. to 4 p.m.

From the east at intersection of Highways 49 & 20, take Highway 20 west 9.7 miles. Turn left at the intersection of Penn Valley Drive, Oak Canyon Drive, and Highway 20. Turn right and go up Oak Canyon Drive 0.2 mile. The entrance is on right.

From the west, take Highway 20 from Marysville past Smartville on left (Melody Lane, Poker Flat, and a sign for Indian Springs Road are on right). Just past sign for Indian Springs Road, turn right onto Penn Valley Drive and then right onto Oak Canyon Drive. Go up hill 0.2 mile to entrance on right.

PLACER COUNTY

AUBURN
Sally's Garden
1621 Hidden Valley Lane

This is a collector's garden with a wide variety of carefully selected and placed shrubs and trees to provide year-round interest. Many paths wander through the different gardens. Wide steps, flanked by trellised clematis, enter the terraced woodland shade garden that contains azaleas, rhododendrons, hydrangeas, columbine, dogwood, and viburnums. The extensive rose garden has ramblers on an inner fence and rows of hybrid teas. The perennial gardens host peonies, dahlias, and much, much more. Sally's vegetable garden is near the house. **NEW**

Hours: 10 a.m. to 4 p.m.

From I-80 West, exit at Dry Creek Road. Turn right. Turn left onto Dry Creek Road. Turn right at stop sign onto Christian Valley Road. Go 1.6 miles and turn right onto Hidden Valley Road. Go to #1621 on left.

From I-80 East, exit at Dry Creek Road. Turn left. Turn right onto Christian Valley Road. Go 1.6 miles and turn right onto Hidden Valley Road. Go to #1621 on left. Please park along street.

Proceeds shared with The Auburn Garden Club

♿ indicates parts of garden are handicapped accessible

Stonegarden
1480 Merry Knoll Road

This garden began when the original stone house was built in the 1920s. Much of the work in developing the garden involved uncovering old stone walls and pathways and reviving original plantings including climbing roses, spirea, agapanthus, and fruit trees. A large pond has been restored and other water features added. Using the original garden as a guide, we added a greenhouse, arbors, a gazebo, rose garden, small vineyard, and orchard. Blackberries and weeds have been pushed back to reclaim the original planting areas. The garden is approximately one and one-half acres and includes five distinct ecosystems including two shade gardens near the house, a pond with surrounding rock walls, a gazebo, and azaleas and rhododendrons. There is also a large rose garden, an annual and vegetable garden, and a small orchard/vineyard. **NEW**

Hours: 10 a.m. to 4 p.m.

From San Francisco Bay Area, take I-80 East then take the CA-49 Exit toward Grass Valley/Placerville. Turn left onto CA-49. Continue on CA-49, then turn left onto Palm Avenue. Palm Avenue becomes Mount Vernon Road. Turn right onto Merry Knoll Road, and stay right at the "Y". Continue to #1480.

From Grass Valley take Highway 49 South, then turn right onto Nevada Street. Turn right onto Mount Vernon Road. Turn right onto Merry Knoll Road; stay right at "Y". Continue to #1480.

Proceeds shared with Homeward Bound

Sebastopol Area Open Day Sunday, May 13

A Mother's Day Rose Garden in Sebastopol and Western Hills Nursery in Occidental are also open today for visitors.
See their listings on pages 82 & 83.

SONOMA COUNTY

OCCIDENTAL
Misty Ridge
17650 Willow Creek Road

The gardens of Misty Ridge are surrounded by redwoods, neighboring vineyards, and a distant ocean view. Barbara and Bob Costa bought their 1970s house in 2004 after selling their bed and breakfast in the Gold Country. They came from a historic house with a century-old garden to a very dark and foreboding house with minimal landscaping. They have spent the last three years redesigning their garden under the tutelage of designer Maile Arnold. The garden abounds with native trillium, fern, and iris, as well as hellebores, hydrangeas, roses, and foxgloves that confirm the Costa's love of cottage gardens in a coastal environment and is a new and fun experience for them. **NEW**

Hours: 10 a.m. to 4 p.m.

From Highway 101, take the Rohnert Park/Sebastopol Exit. Take Route 116 west for 7.4 miles to Sebastopol. Turn left onto Bodega Highway and go 6.4 miles. Turn right onto Bohemian Highway, go through Freestone and continue 3.7 miles to Occidental. At four-way stop, turn left onto Coleman Valley Road and go 1.5 miles to Willow Creek Road (first right turn past Western Hills Nursery and school bus stop sign). Continue 1.1 miles to #17650 on right. See signs for parking.

SEBASTOPOL
Arnold Garden
5876 Lone Pine Road

This garden is a laboratory and work of art for Maile Arnold who is a landscape designer in Sonoma County. In it are many hundreds of plant species, which are grown organically and with minimal attention except for an annual pruning and addition of compost. Irrigation is by in-line drip emitter tubing that waters the entire planting bed rather than the individual plant. This sustainable garden is located on five and one-half acres and is teeming with insect and bird life. It includes large trees, shrubs, perennials, several hundred rose plants and a habitat garden. Annuals are allowed to reseed. Compost, created from grass clippings and food waste from a local organic restaurant, contributes to the tremendous productivity of this garden with its domestic orchard and vegetable garden. **2005** ♿

Hours: 10 a.m. to 4 p.m.

From Highway 101 north take Rohnert Park/Sebastopol exit at Cotati (Highway 116 West/Gravenstein Highway). Allow about an hour driving time to the exit from San Francisco. The exit road ends at a traffic light. Turn left and drive west on Highway 116 toward Sebastopol. Go about 5 miles, turn left onto Lone Pine Road (look for left turn sign and Lander's Automotive and Lone Pine Antique Shop.) At 0.75 mile, turn right onto private gravel road marked by a post listing five house numbers, including #5876. The Arnold Garden is second house on left. Look for parking signs. (NOTE: do not turn up the road that lists #5874/#5878 and the name Sisson at the entrance.)

From Santa Rosa or Healdsberg, take Highway 101 south to Route 12 West/Sebastopol/Bodega Highway exit. After Route 12 narrows from 4 lanes to 2 lanes past Fulton Road, turn left onto Llano Road (a turning lane and sign announces the turn). This is a shortcut between Route 12 and Highway 116. From Llano turn right onto Todd Road at the stop sign. Turn left briefly onto Old Gravenstein Highway at the stop sign. Turn left at the next stop sign onto Highway 116 and turn right onto Lone Pine Road. Proceed as directed above.

From central Sebastopol, take Highway 116 east toward Highway 101. Turn right onto Lone Pine Road soon after the Red Antique Shop. Proceed as directed above.

Rose and Thorn

10050 Bodega Highway
Sebastopol, CA, 707/823-9467

Located on Bodega Highway, 3 miles west of Sebastopol near Grandview Road.

Hours: 11 – 5:30 p.m.
Thursday – Monday
Open year round

On the day of the Sebastopol Open Day, show the owner and hostess Carole Coler-Dark your Open Days ticket stub and she will fill your cup with lemonade, offer you cookies, picnic grounds and restroom facilities. **A 15% discount may be applied to any purchases made during the month of May.**

Rose and Thorn, a retail shop that offers garden accessories, gifts, and items for home décor, is the backyard garden of your dreams—not fancy, but certainly fun and full of whimsy. This country shop and gardens is a magical sanctuary in a park-like setting—one that is pesticide free and friendly for people and critters alike. Garden salvage art adds a playful touch to the bird and sitting garden, while maintaining an unruliness of "organized chaos" and shelter for wildlife. Picnicking is encouraged—bird houses, benches galore, roses and unique treasures in every corner. Children are especially invited to meet the tiny friendly goats and exotic chickens—a joyous place for all! This one-acre garden farm is always growing, always changing, always moving. Come visit.

♿ indicates parts of garden are handicapped accessible

Olive Oaks

1305 Ferguson Road

This two-acre property is located on the western slope of the Atascadero Creek arroyo across from Ragle Ranch Park. It is nestled within a beautiful woodland of mature valley oaks and has a pleasant view across a neighboring vineyard. Originally a family farm with orchards, a dairy, and chickens, its 1897 farmhouse was restored in 1989 and an extensive garden was planted that included manzanitas and olives. The present owners, with the help of garden designer and builder Tod Rimrodt from Oakland, have recently reworked the garden plantings and graveled the extensive meandering paths. A new entry, low stone walls and steps, several comfortable outdoor sitting areas, and an unobtrusive chlorine-free pool, complete this informal country garden. The new plantings were designed to be simple—to force the eye to go immediately to the view—and to continue a Mediterranean and relatively low-maintenance theme. Several mature olive trees were added, as well as succulents, roses, white hydrangeas, heirloom bearded iris, sheets of lavender and ornamental grasses, and a woodland walk with native ferns and hellebores. **NEW**

Hours: 10 a.m. to 4 p.m.

From Highway 101 take Rohnert Park/Sebastopol exit at Cotati and continue west on Highway 116/Gravenstein Highway. Travel about 8 miles to central Sebastopol. Turn left at traffic light onto Highway 12/Bodega Highway and continue straight approximately 2.3 miles. Turn right onto Ferguson Road at bottom of a large "S" curve and go about 0.9 mile. Turn right onto Ferguson Court and go about 0.2 mile and turn right onto a private lane. After lane swings to left, continue 100 yards down hill. Parking areas will be marked and managed.

Paeonia

190 Montgomery Road

Paeonia is a private garden and small nursery inspired by the tranquil aspects of the Far East and dedicated to the peony. Hidden behind a Japanese fence and gates, you will enjoy strolling through the Buddha's Weeping Willow Allée and the labyrinth of paths between peony beds and other specialty plants such as cryptomeria, Japanese maples, magnolias, Atlantic cedars, and dwarf conifers. There is ample opportunity to see rare and unusual fragrant, herbaceous, tree, and Itoh hybrid peonies, in traditional and surprisingly "hot" colors unavailable in garden centers. Observing their growth habits will aid your success in determining which type you can take home to enjoy and grow these in your own garden. Along one edge of the garden is a pleasant woodland garden walk planted with natives and a large garden viewing deck with semitropical plants and pool. **NEW**

Far West Trading Company and TeaBar from Graton, California (www.farwesttrading-company.com) will be serving White Peony Tea and other loose-leaf teas for total immersion in the peony experience. The garden is open only to participants in The Garden Conservancy's Open Days on this date, otherwise during the months of May and June, by appointment only (paeonia-nursery@sbcglobal.net).

Hours: 10 a.m. to 4 p.m.

From Highway 101 take Rohnert Park/Sebastopol exit at Cotati and continue west on Highway 116/Gravenstein Highway. Travel about 8 miles to central Sebastopol. Turn left at traffic light onto Highway 12/Bodega Highway and continue straight approximately 2.5 miles. Pass Ferguson Road and turn right onto Montgomery Road just after the large "S" curve. Go about 100 yards, over a small bridge and look for signs to the parking area on left.

San Francisco Peninsula Open Day
Saturday, May 19

SANTA CLARA COUNTY

Los Altos

Sun Acres

18 Bridgton Court

This elegant, edible garden features a central gazebo and arbor, which serve as the fulcrum around which a colorful wheel of raised beds produce bountiful harvests throughout the season. A terraced play lawn and flower garden surround a large brick patio and wildflowers are grown among the fruit trees to attract beneficial insects and butterflies. A newly planted fence of espaliered apple and pear trees promises future delicious harvests and delicate spring blossoms as the garden settles in for another glorious season of productive beauty. **NEW** &

Hours: 10 a.m. to 4 p.m.

From Highway 280, take El Monte Avenue to Los Altos. Turn left onto Foothill Expressway. Turn right onto Edith Avenue. Take immediate left onto Los Altos Avenue. Turn right onto Mount Hamilton Avenue. Turn left onto Bridgton Court. Garden is on left near cul-de-sac.

From Highway 101, take San Antonio Road to Los Altos. Continue about 3 miles then turn right onto Mount Hamilton Avenue. Turn right onto Bridgton Court. Garden is on left near cul-de-sac. Please park on Mount Hamilton Avenue and walk short distance to garden.

Los Altos Hills
Eclectic Estate Garden
27570 Altamont Road

This private estate garden is rarely open to the public. Its one-acre garden was originally created in the early 1980s, but was replanted and renovated with several new gardens added by landscape architect Jarrod Baumann in 2006. This eclectic estate garden is a garden on many levels and includes many different rooms: the Balinese Black Bamboo Garden, the Black and White Labyrinth with its lush tropical backdrop, the New Zealand Garden with its succulents, and the majestic and mature Redwood Allée that links the gardens. This garden is a must see! **NEW**

Hours: 10 a.m. to 4 p.m.

From 280 Freeway, take Page Mill Exit. Travel west into Los Altos Hills, approximately 2 miles, and turn left onto Altamont Road. The garden is second drive on right. Park carefully on street or at Menalto

The Smith Garden
12791 Normandy Lane

Originally built for the Steinhart family in 1927, the Old World grandeur of this estate was luxuriously updated once in the 1990s and last year by the current owners. Upon entering the grounds through wrought-iron gates, the entry turret of this French Normandy-style manor beckons with its mullioned windows and an atmosphere of stately elegance embraces you. A grand oak presides out front and the side garden boasts one of the largest copper beech trees in the Bay area, with a myriad of other trees rising throughout the gardens to create a sense of peace and privacy. In 1997, garden designer Mary Kaye refurbished the front garden, and in the summer of 2006, garden designer Laurie Callaway established garden "rooms" behind the main house and enhanced garden areas around the craft house, sports court, pool, and guest house. Each area has a distinct purpose and personality, fulfilling the needs for formal business entertaining while maintaining a comfortable atmosphere for the young children and their friends. Noted features Laurie designed are the Children's Garden with a tree house overlooking the property and plentiful flowers in the cutting garden growing among the butterflies and fairies to remind the family of their time living in New Zealand; the Woodland Walk, where a gated trellis leads to a private area facing the pool; the pool section with a pergola and seating area around the new fireplace; and the parterre garden that catches the sun and focuses it on a large urn spilling with roses. The hardscape on the property was designed to reflect the Normandy-style architecture by using field stone and adding balustrades. Finally, an outdoor dining room is surrounded by matching wrought-iron gates. The "walls" are vines trained on wires that match the pattern of the original lead glass windows and provide a lovely fragrance that encourages lingering over a morning cup of coffee. **NEW**

Hours: 10 a.m. to 4 p.m.

From I-280 take El Monte east and turn left onto O'Keefe, then left again onto Normandy Lane. Number 12791 is second house on right.

From I-101 take South San Antonio west and turn left onto Foothill Expressway. Turn right onto El Monte and then right again onto O'Keefe. Turn left onto Normandy Lane. Number 12791 is second house on right.

Public Gardens

ALAMEDA COUNTY

BERKELEY

University of California Botanical Garden at Berkeley

200 Centennial Drive, (510) 643-2755, http://botanicalgarden.berkeley.edu

The University of California Botanical Garden is a living museum, its premier collection ranks among the world's leaders in the quality and diversity of its plants and their scientific importance. The garden's collection of more than 12,800 different kinds of plants, collected from the wild, includes a large number of rare and endangered species. The collection is displayed in beautiful, naturalistic plantings arranged by geographic region: California, Asia, southern Africa, the Mediterranean region, South America, Australasia, Mexico, and Central America, the New World deserts, and eastern North America. Greenhouse collections include cacti and succulents, carnivorous plants, ferns, and orchids. Ethnobotanical collections include heritage roses, European herbs, Chinese medicinal herbs, and crops of the world. The garden is a national leader in developing environmental education curricula and is building a program in plant conservation. Established in 1890, the garden moved in 1925 to its current thirty-four-acre location in Strawberry Canyon, with panoramic views of the San Francisco Bay.

Hours: Year round, daily, 9 a.m. to 5 p.m. Closed first Tuesday of every month and some holidays. Free docent-led tours, Thursday, Saturday and Sunday, 1:30 p.m.

Admission: $5 adults, $3 seniors, $1 children 3 to 18, children under 3 free.

From I-80, exit at University Avenue and go east to Oxford Street. Turn left. Turn right onto Hearst and go east to second traffic light, Gayley Road. Turn right. Go to first stop sign, and turn left onto Stadium Rim Way. Go to first stop sign. Turn left onto Centennial Drive. Garden is 0.75 mile up hill on right. Parking lot is 100 yards further up hill.

OAKLAND

Cohen-Bray House & Garden

1440 29th Avenue, (510) 536-1703, www.cohen-brayhouse.info

This distinctive Victorian residence with a formal front garden and a working backyard provides the visitor with the rare opportunity to imagine home life as it was a century ago. In 2001, the Garden Conservancy recognized the significance of the Cohen-Bray landscape and extended preservation assistance to the Victorian Preservation Center of Oakland. In a short amount of time the organization has done a remarkable job of protecting this outstanding remnant of California's garden and agrarian history and planning for its restoration.

Hours: Special tours for interested groups including school children are welcomed and can be arranged by calling in advance.

Admission: $5

From Highway 880 take Fruitvale exit. Go 3 blocks parallel to freeway and turn left onto Fruitvale Avenue. Then turn left onto International Boulevard (formerly East 14th). Turn right onto 29th Avenue. The Cohen-Bray House is third on right.

From Walnut Creek, take Highway 24 to Route 980 to Route 880 and follow directions above.

From south, take Route 880 north and exit at 29th Avenue. Continue east to #1440.

Dunsmuir Historic Estate

2960 Peralta Oaks Court, (510) 615-5555, www.dunsmuir.org

John McLaren, designer of Golden Gate Park in San Francisco, is said to have assisted in designing the gardens at the Dunsmuir Estate for the Hellman family, which owned it from

1906 until the late 1950s. Today, its fifty acres are still graced with a wide variety of trees that surround the turn-of-the-century neoclassical Revival-style mansion.

Hours: February through October, Tuesday through Friday, 10 a.m. to 4 p.m., also open the first Sunday of each month, May through September, 10 a.m. to 3 p.m.

Admission: Free

From I-580 east, take 106th Avenue exit. Make three quick left turns to cross freeway, then turn right onto Peralta Oaks Drive. Follow signs to Dunsmuir.

From I-580 west, exit at Foothill/MacArthur Boulevard and veer right onto Foothill Boulevard. Turn right onto 106th Avenue and turn right again onto Peralta Oaks Drive. Follow signs to Dunsmuir.

Kaiser Center Roof Garden
300 Lakeside Drive, (510) 271-6197

Kaiser Center Roof Garden is a three-and-one-half-acre park located four floors above street level on top of the Kaiser Center garage. Despite its urban setting, boundary hedges, winding paths, bermed plantings, and a reflecting pond give the garden a quiet, oasis-like quality. Specimen trees, shrubs, perennials, and annuals provide year-round horticultural interest.

Hours: Year round, weekdays, 8 a.m. to 5 p.m.

Admission: Free

From San Francisco, take Bay Bridge to I-580 south towards Hayward. One mile past bridge, take Harrison Street exit and turn right onto Harrison. Go through three traffic lights. Lake Merritt is on left and Kaiser Building is ahead on right. Continue straight on Harrison and get into right lane. Turn right onto 20th Street and make immediate right into parking garage. There is also street parking. Take garage elevator to Roof Garden level.

CONTRA COSTA COUNTY

KENSINGTON
The Blake Garden of the University of California
70 Rincon Road, (510) 524-2449

This ten-and-one-half-acre garden was given to the University of California in the early 1960s by the Blake family. The garden was established when the house was designed and built in the 1920s. It has a large display of plants ranging from drought-tolerant to more moisture-loving plants.

Hours: Year round, weekdays, 8 a.m. to 4:30 p.m. Closed on University holidays.

Admission: Free

From I-80, take Buchanan Street exit east. Follow Buchanan, which turns into Marin Avenue, to a traffic circle with a fountain. Take fourth exit off circle onto Arlington Avenue. Travel 1.8 miles to Rincon Road on left. Blake Garden is #70.

WALNUT CREEK
The Ruth Bancroft Garden
1500 Bancroft Road, (925) 210-9663, *www.ruthbancroftgarden.org*

A PROJECT OF THE GARDEN CONSERVANCY

The Ruth Bancroft Garden is an exceptional demonstration of the art of garden design. Working primarily with the dramatic forms of her beloved succulents, Mrs. Bancroft has created bold and varied compositions in which the colors, textures, and patterns of foliage provide a setting for the sparkle of floral color.

Hours: Group tours Wednesday through Saturday. Docent-led tours on Friday and Saturday. Self-guided tours on Friday and Sunday. All tours by reservation only. Reserve online or by phone.

Admission: $7 adults, $5 students, free to Garden Conservancy members.

Located just north of Highway 24; exit I-680 onto Ygnacio Valley Road. Go 2 to 3 miles to Bancroft Road. Turn left and pass Stratton. Take the second driveway on the right at #1500.

♿ indicates parts of garden are handicapped accessible

LOS ANGELES COUNTY

ARCADIA
Los Angeles County Arboretum & Botanic Garden
301 North Baldwin Avenue,
(626) 821-3222, www.arboretum.org

The arboretum is a 127-acre horticultural and botanical museum with plants from around the world blooming in every season. The arboretum staff has introduced more than 100 flowering plants to the California landscape and boasts tree collections from many countries.

Hours: Year round, daily, 9 a.m. to 4:30 p.m.

Admission: $6 adults, $4 seniors/students, $1.50 children 5 to 12, children under 5 free

From I-210, exit onto Baldwin Avenue. Arboretum is in San Gabriel Valley, close to downtown Los Angeles and next to Pasadena.

BEVERLY HILLS
Greystone Estate
905 Loma Vista Drive, (310) 550-4796,
www.beverlyhills.org

Edward Lawrence Doheny was the original proprietor of Greystone Estate. In 1956, the City of Beverly Hills purchased the estate and dedicated the site as a public park in 1971. In 1976, Greystone Estate was recognized as a historic landmark and placed on the National Register of Historic Places. Visitors may peek through select windows of the mansion. The formal garden is a lush and tranquil area with a variety of vegetation, slated walkways, and a fountain. The inner courtyard is surrounded by Greystone Mansion and features a fountain, flower beds, and slated grounds. The former pool area provides a beautiful setting with a pool house façade and lush greens. The Terrace has breathtaking views of the city, a slated surface, and rests between the mansion, a grassy knoll, a pond, and an oak tree.

Hours: Year round, daily, 10 a.m. to 5 p.m.

Admission: Free

From the Los Angeles area or the I-405, take Sunset Boulevard to Foothill Road. Go north on Foothill Road which curves to the right and becomes Doheny Road. Turn left onto Loma Vista Drive and left again into the first driveway at #905.

Virginia Robinson Garden
1008 Elden Way, (310) 276-5367, ext. 100

You will find six and one-half acres of display gardens, including a terrace rose garden, Italian terrace garden, the formal mallarca, and an extensive palm garden.

Hours: Tours by appointment only, Tuesday through Friday.

Admission: $10 adult, $5 seniors, $3 children 12 and under.

Take Sunset Boulevard to Crescent Drive north to Elden Way north. Parking available on property; no street parking available.

CLAREMONT
Rancho Santa Ana Botanic Garden
1500 North College Avenue,
(909) 625-8767, www.rsabg.org

This garden was the first botanical garden established in California devoted to the study of native flora. eighty-six acres are organized by plant communities—desert, coastal, woodland, riparian with special manzanita, ceonothus, conifer and wildflower displays. The garden includes an extensive herbarium, seed bank, a leading research center and library, affiliated with the Claremont Colleges. Visit website for calendar of events, including garden walks, lectures, and plant sales.

Hours: Year round, daily, 8 a.m. to 5 p.m. Closed Christmas, New Year's Day, Independence Day and Thanksgiving.

Admission: Suggested donation is $4 per adult or $8 per family

This garden is located 1.5 miles north of I-10, between Indian Hill Boulevard and Mills Avenue and 2 blocks south of I-210 between Indian Hill Boulevard and Mills Avenue off of Foorthill Boulevard.

La Cañada
Descanso Gardens
1418 Descanso Drive, (818) 949-4200,
www.descansogardens.org

Descanso Gardens is a rare find—a woodland garden in the midst of California chaparral and Los Angeles urban sprawl. It includes a twenty-acre California live oak forest containing 39,000 camellias, the five-acre International Rosarium with more than 3,100 antique and modern roses, North America's largest clematis collection, and a one-acre lilac grove where lilacs for warm-winter climates originated.

Hours: Year round, daily, 9 a.m. to 5 p.m.; ticket sales end at 4:30. Closed Christmas Day.

Admission: $7 adults, $5 seniors/students, $2 children 5 to 10, children under 5 free.

From I-210, exit onto Angeles Crest Highway. Turn south. Turn right onto Foothill Boulevard, left onto Verdugo Boulevard, and left onto Descanso Drive.

Los Angeles
Exposition Park Rose Garden
State Drive at Exposition Park,
(213) 763-0114, www.laparks.org/
exporosgarden/rosegarden.htm

This rose showcase is a beautiful place to experience nature and a respite from urban activities. Opened in 1928, it is considered the first municipally operated public rose garden in the United States. Designated as a Los Angeles County Point of Historic Interest in 1987, the seven-acre garden contains approximately 10,000 rosebushes of more than a hundred varieties. All-American Rose Selections, Inc., donates its new, award-winning rose cultivars each year.

Hours: April 9 through December 31, daily, 10 a.m. to dusk; closed January 1 to April 8 for maintenance.

Admission: Free

From I-110, exit at Exposition Boulevard. Exposition Park is west of I-110 between Exposition Boulevard and University of Southern California on the north, Figueroa Street on the east, Martin Luther King Boulevard on the south, and Vermont Avenue on the west. The Rose Garden faces Exposition Boulevard. A decorative brick wall and trees screen the garden from the street. Parking is available inside Exposition Park or on the street.

The Getty Center
1200 Getty Center Drive,
(310) 440-7300, www.getty.edu

The Getty Center offers tranquil gardens and water features amid dramatic architecture, breathtaking hillside views, and outdoor spaces. Lush plantings and trees provide color, texture, and shade in counterpoint to the architecture of Richard Meier. The central garden is conceived by Robert Irwin as a "sculpture in the form of a garden aspiring to be art."

Hours: Year round, Tuesday, Wednesday, Thursday, and Sunday, 10 a.m. to 6 p.m., Friday and Saturday, 10 a.m. to 9 p.m.; closed Monday and major holidays.

Admission: Free. Parking is $8 per car

From I-405, exit at Getty Center Drive. Take Sepulveda to Getty Center Drive.

Palos Verdes
South Coast Botanic Garden
26300 Crenshaw Boulevard,
(310) 544-1847,
www.southcoastbotanicgarden.org

California's first major successful reclamation project, this eighty-seven acre garden includes the Waterwise Garden, as well as rose, cactus, fuchsia, and palm gardens. There are also pine, ficus, flowering areas, and a garden for the senses.

Hours: Year round, daily, 9 a.m. to 4 p.m., closed Christmas Day.

Admission: $7 adults, $5 seniors, $2.50 children 5 to 12

Located about 5 miles west of I-405 on Crenshaw Boulevard, just past Pacific Coast Highway.

PASADENA

The Huntington Library, Art Collection, & Botanical Gardens

1151 Oxford Road, (626) 405-2100, www.huntington.org

The former estate of railroad magnate Henry Huntington showcases more than 14,000 plant species in 150 acres of gardens. Highlights include a twelve-acre desert garden, rose garden, Japanese garden, jungle garden, and ten acres of camellias. English tea is served in the Rose Garden Tea Room.

Hours: September through May, Tuesday through Friday, 12 p.m. to 4:30 p.m., weekends, 10:30 a.m. to 4:30 p.m.; June through August, Tuesday through Sunday, 10:30 a.m. to 4:30 p.m.

Admission: $15 adults, $12 seniors, $10 students, $6 children, children under 5 and members free.

Located near Pasadena, about 12 miles northeast of downtown Los Angeles. From downtown, take I-110 until it becomes Arroyo Parkway. Continue north 2 blocks and turn right onto California Boulevard. Go 2 miles, turn right onto Allen Avenue, and go 2 short blocks to Huntington gates. For recorded directions from other freeways, call.

La Casita del Arroyo Garden

177 South Arroyo Boulevard, (626) 449-9505

Situated on the east bank of the Arroyo Seco, La Casita del Arroyo Garden surrounds a small community meeting house designed by Myron Hunt in the early 1930s. In the late 1980s Isabelle Greene designed a water demonstration garden divided into sections with the purpose of illustrating plants suitable for different water requirements. In 1999 a butterfly sanctuary was dedicated on a slope leading down to the arroyo.

Hours: Start your tour here for the April 29 Open Day between 9:30 a.m. and 3:30 p.m. Tickets, Open Days Directories, maps and Garden Conservancy membership information will be available in the parking lot. Otherwise, year round, daily, dawn to dusk.

Admission: Free

From I-210 in Pasadena, exit south onto Orange Grove Boulevard. Turn right onto Arbor Street to Arroyo Boulevard. Turn right and #177 is on left.

From I-110, continue from end of freeway north on Arroyo Parkway. Turn left onto California Boulevard which dead ends at Arroyo Boulevard. Turn right and continue to #177.

From Highway 101 east, exit at Orange Grove Boulevard, just before the I-210 junction. Turn right onto California Boulevard which dead ends at Arroyo Boulevard. Turn right and continue to #177.

Norton Simon Museum Sculpture Garden

411 West Colorado Boulevard, (626) 449-6840, www.nortonsimon.org

The Norton Simon Museum Garden, redesigned by Nancy Goslee Power & Associates, was unveiled in 1999 in conjunction with the reopening of the museum galleries concurrently renovated by Frank O. Gehry & Associates. Highlighting the Giverny-inspired garden is a large natural pond filled with water lilies and other aquatic plant life, with several works by important twentieth-century sculptors greatly enhancing the artistic excursion. Pathways and colorful vegetation encircle the pond and a small café overlooks the garden.

Hours: Year round, daily except Tuesday, 12 p.m. to 6 p.m.; Friday, 12 p.m. to 9 p.m. Closed Thanksgiving, Christmas, and New Year's Day. Garden is closed on rainy days.

Admission: $8 adults, $4 seniors, free for students and children under 18.

Located on corner of Orange Grove and Colorado Boulevard. Entrance is on Colorado.

SAN MARINO

The Old Mill "El Molino Viejo"

1120 Old Mill Road, (626) 449-5458, www.old-mill.org

El Molino Viejo was built during the Mission days, about 1816. The local Indians built the gristmill for the Mission San Gabriel. The

Diggers Garden Club maintains the drought-tolerant gardens appropriate to the period. The grounds have native oaks, citrus orchards, sycamore, bay, and olive trees. Pomegranate trees surround a patio area. There are ceanothus, heuchera, many sages, calla lilies, ribes, rosemary, and Douglas iris. Lady Banks' roses grow on the side of the building as well as over the pergola.

Hours: Year round, Tuesday through Saturday, 1 p.m. to 4 p.m.

Take Lake Avenue South until it curves and turns into Oak Knoll Road. Go past Ritz Carlton at bottom of hill. Turn left at Old Mill Road. Garden is located about 1 block east of intersection of Old Mill and Oak Knoll Roads.

Santa Monica
Merrihew's Sunset Gardens
1526 Ocean Park Boulevard,
(310) 452-1051

Merrihew's Sunset Gardens has been a Santa Monica institution since 1947. It is one of the few privately owned nurseries left in the West Los Angeles area and has long been a source of expertise and advice for gardeners on the Westside. The nursery is now under the ownership of Santa Monica native Dick Lahey who has been involved in a wide variety of aspects of the nursery and plant world for more than thirty-five years, ranging from twenty years brokering and escorting thousands of trees for many Saudi royal family projects throughout the Middle East, to his lifetime fascination with the world of exotic plants. Custom redwood benches and gravel-filled beds at Merrihew are home to a wide variety of plants including exotics specially selected by the owner. In addition to trees, herbs, and vegetables, the nursery carries seeds from American and Italian suppliers and features an ever-changing collection of succulents and tropicals.

Hours: Start your tour here for the May 12 Open Day between 9:30 a.m. to 3:30 p.m. Tickets, Open Days Directories, maps, and Garden Conservancy information will be available.

From the 10 West, exit at Lincoln Boulevard South. Turn left onto Ocean Park Boulevard and then right onto 16th Street. The nursery is located on the southwest corner of 16th Street and Ocean Park Boulevard in Santa Monica.

Sun Valley
Theodore Payne Foundation California Native Plant Nursery, Seed, and Bookstore
10459 Tuxford Street, (818) 768-1802,
www.theodorepayne.org

This twenty-one-acre site includes hiking trails, a picnic area, demonstration garden of native plants, and more than 700 species of California native plants and seeds saved from extinction. The non-profit foundation was established in 1961 to propogate and make available native plants and seeds, to educate the public through classes and promote habitat restoration. The nursery carries more than 400 species of native plants. The Wildflower Hotline runs March through May, (818) 768-3533.

Hours: July through September, Tuesday through Saturday, 8:30 a.m. to 4:30 p.m. Call for summer hours.

Admission: Free

From I-210, exit at La Tuna Canyon. Go west for 4 miles, turn right onto Wheatland. Turn right onto Tuxford Street. Nursery is half block on left.

MARIN COUNTY

Ross
Marin Art & Garden Center
30 Sir Francis Drake Boulevard,
(415) 455-5260, www.maagc.org

A community center in more ways than one, these gardens are now certified as a Habitat Sanctuary by the National Wildlife Federation. We are "green" gardeners, using organic, sustainable practices. The emphasis is on California native plants and other Mediterranean species that are deer resistant and attract local species of birds and butterflies.

Hours: Year round, daily, dawn to dusk.

Admission: Gardens are free, $5 for Garden Education Programs.

Take Highway 101 to Sir Francis Drake Boulevard exit. Head west about 2.5 miles to main entry at intersection and traffic light at Lagunitas Road.

ORANGE COUNTY

LAGUNA BEACH

The Hortense Miller Garden
(949) 497-3311 ext.426,
www.hortensemillergarden.org

The Hortense Miller Garden, established in 1959, covers two and one-half acres. More than 1,500 species of plants are represented, including exotics from around the world, old-fashioned favorites, and native coastal sage scrub. In her well-designed, sustainable garden, Mrs. Miller uses little fertilizer, almost no pesticides, and a minimum of irrigation. Plants are available for purchase.

Hours: Year round, Tuesday through Saturday. Closed on major holidays. Visits booked in advance by Laguna Beach Recreation Department at (949) 497-3311, ext. 426.

Admission: Free

Garden is located at a private residence in a gated community. Guests are met by docents at Riddle Field on Hillcrest Drive and escorted to garden. Call for reservations.

SAN FRANCISCO COUNTY

SAN FRANCISCO

Gardens of Alcatraz
Alcatraz Island, (415) 561-4900,
www.nps.gov/alcatraz/

 A PROJECT OF THE GARDEN CONSERVANCY

Nearly every bit of soil and plant life found on Alcatraz are the result of 150 years of tenacious gardening. Superintendents, officers' families, and inmates have all had a role in coaxing plants to survive in this harsh environment. More than 140 types of plants have survived long periods of neglect, many have successfully naturalized into the thin soil. The Garden Conservancy has formed partnership with the Golden Gate

National Recreation Area (National Park Service) and the Golden Gate National Parks Conservancy to restore, preserve, and maintain the gardens created by the inmates, officers, and the families who lived and gardened on Alcatraz over its long history as s military fortification and prison.

Hours: Year round, daily. Closed Christmas and New Year's Day.

Admission: There is no entrance fee to visit Alcatraz Island. However there is a charge for the ferry service to and from the island which is supplied by a private company under contract with the National Park Service. For additional information on schedules, prices, and to purchase tickets in advance (tickets are made available about 30 days in advance) please visit the www.alcatrazcruises.com or call (415) 981-7625. The Alcatraz ferry departs from Pier 33, located on The Embarcadero near the intersection of Bay Street.

San Francisco Botanical Garden at Strybing Arboretum
Ninth Avenue at Lincoln Way in
Golden Gate Park, (415) 661-1316,
www.sfbotanicalgarden.org

San Francisco's unique botanical garden inspires visitors with the extraordinary diversity of rare and unusual plants that can be grown in coastal California. Through its programs and displays, the garden celebrates the bond between people and plants, and instills a deeper understanding of the necessity to conserve Earth's biological diversity. The garden's plant collections now include more than 7,500 different kinds of plants, presented in geographic groupings as well as in themed specialty gardens. Signs throughout the garden document and interpret plant species from the world's Mediterranean, mid-temperate, and tropical cloud forest climatic regions. A wide variety of activities are available, including docent-led walks, classes, tours, and plant sales.

Hours: Year round, weekdays, 8 a.m. to 4:30 p.m.; weekends and holidays, 10 a.m. to 5 p.m.

Admission: Free, donations welcome.

Located in Golden Gate Park, at corner of Ninth Avenue and Lincoln Way.

The Japanese Tea Garden
Hagiwara Drive (415) 831-2700

The oldest public Japanese garden in the United States, dating from 1894, it was created for the California Mid-Winter Exposition to represent a Japanese village. The five-acre stroll garden includes a drum bridge, teahouse, pagoda, two gates built for the 1915 Panama Pacific Exposition, and Temple Belfry Gate. It also has a large bronze Buddha cast in 1790.

Hours: October through February, daily, 9 a.m. to 5 p.m.; March through September, daily, 9 a.m. to 6 p.m.

Admission: $4 adults, $1.50 seniors, $1.50 children 6 to 12, children under 6 free

Located in center of Golden Gate Park near DeYoung Museum and Academy of Sciences on Hagiwara Drive.

SAN MATEO COUNTY

MENLO PARK
The Gardens of *Sunset* Magazine
80 Willow Road, (650) 321-3600,
www.sunset.com

Sunset sits upon land that was originally part of a grant to Don José Arguello, governor of Spanish California in 1815. In every aspect of our home—from our landscaping to the architecture and furnishings of our early-California ranch-style buildings—you'll sense our relationship with the history of California and the West. The original Sunset display garden, designed in 1951 by Thomas Church, included a border that followed the contours of San Francisquito Creek, with distinct areas representing the major climate zones of the West, from the deserts of Arizona to the cold, wet areas of the Northwest. In early spring 2000, Chris Jacobson and Beverly Sarjeant of Garden Art brought a fresh new look to the garden while retaining much of the regional flavor. Trees, shrubs, vines, groundcovers, perennials, and ornamental grasses now show how foliage textures and colors can combine for beautiful effects. Flower color comes from blooming shrubs and perennials, making this a garden for all seasons.

Hours: Open for self-guided walking tours Monday through Friday from 9 a.m. to 4:30 p.m., except holidays. Gardens are closed in mid-May each year for Celebration Weekend.

Admission: Free

From Highway 101 in Menlo Park, take the Willow Road exit west and continue on Willow Road 1 mile to the intersection of Willow and Middlefield Roads. Sunset is across the intersection on the left. Parking is available in front of the building.

WOODSIDE
Filoli
86 Canada Road, (650) 364-8300,
www.filoli.org

Surrounded by 654 acres of oak and madrone forests at the edge of the foothills of the Santa Cruz Mountain Range, Filoli is the only remaining example of an early twenti-

🕭 indicates parts of garden are handicapped accessible

eth-century country estate in California. Its modified Georgian-style house is now filled with seventeenth-and eighteenth-century furnishings. The sixteen-acre garden contains a series of formal rooms and a complete working garden with a cutting garden, two knot gardens, a 300-foot-long perennial border, and extensive plantings of period fruit trees. Filoli is a registered State Historic Landmark and a site of the National Trust for Historic Preservation.

Hours: Mid-February through October, Tuesday through Saturday, 10 a.m. to 3:30 p.m. Sundays, 11 a.m. to 3:30 p.m. (last admission at 2:30 p.m.) Self-guided and docent-led tours every Tuesday through Saturday. Please call for information or email tours@filoli.org.

Admission: $12 adults, $5 students, $5 children 5 to 17, children under 5 free

From I-280, take Edgewood Road exit and follow signs.

SANTA CLARA COUNTY

PALO ALTO
The Elizabeth F. Gamble Garden
1431 Waverley Street, (650) 329-1356,
www.gamblegarden.org

This two-and-one-half-acre urban garden, located forty miles south of San Francisco, surrounds a turn-of-the-century house and carriage house. The formal gardens have been restored from the original plans. The working gardens include experimental demonstrations and displays. The formal gardens and buildings may be rented to private parties on weekends.

Hours: Year round, daily, dawn to dusk; access to certain areas may be restricted on weekends

Admission: Free

From Highway 101, exit onto Embarcadero west. Turn left onto Waverley Street. Parking lot is on left.

From I-280, exit onto Page Mill Road east, cross El Camino, and continue on Oregon Expressway. Turn left onto Waverley Street.

House is on corner of Waverley and Churchill. Parking lot is north of house.

Emma Prusch Farm Park
647 South King Road, (408) 926-5555,
www.sjparks.org

Emma Prusch Farm Park offers visitors opportunities to learn about San Jose's agricultural past. Its forty-seven acres features San Jose's largest barn, more than 100 community and school garden plots, a rare fruit orchard featuring a strawberry tree, wild pear tree, and a raisin tree, a grove of international trees, and various farm animals.

Hours: Year round, daily, 8:30 a.m. to dusk, closed Thanksgiving, Christmas, and New Year's Day

Admission: Free

From Highway 101, take Story Road east exit. Turn left at King Road and left at next traffic light into the driveway.

From I-680, take King Road exit and turn left. Turn right at second light into driveway.

From I-280, take King Road exit and turn right. Proceed to next light and turn right into driveway.

SONOMA COUNTY

OCCIDENTAL
Western Hills Nursery
16250 Coleman Valley Road,
(707) 874-3731,
www.westernhillsnursery.com

The three gently rolling acres of Western Hills Nursery have, over a period of forty years, been developed into a complete landscape incorporating many hundreds of varieties of perennials, ground covers, vines, shrubs, and trees, most of which are highly unusual or difficult to procure and many seen nowhere else in cultivation. Western Hills is a rare botanical gem and enjoys local and international attention. The adjoining nursery propagates and sells many of the plants seen in the garden.

The Garden Conservancy is happy to announce the re-opening of Western Hills Nursery and Gardens in Occidental and to introduce Robert Stansel and Joseph Gatta as the new proprietors. Through their stewardship, and the interestand support of many long-time garden friends, this forty-year-old garden and its wonderful nursery will continue to be one of the most remarkable garden and horticultural resources in California. We hope that you will plan your Open Days garden visits to include a stop at Western Hills to congratulate its owners and support their endeavor.

Hours: Special Garden Conservancy Open Day May 13, 10 a.m. to 5 p.m.; otherwise year round Thursday through Monday, 10 a.m. to 5 p.m.

Admission: Free

The Western Hills Nursery is located on right side of Coleman Valley Road, just before Willow Creek Road. Parking is limited.

SEBASTOPOL

A Mother's Day Rose Garden
3003 Pleasant Hill Road,
www.vintagegardens.com

The private rose garden of Phillip Robinson and Gregg Lowery, owners of Vintage Gardens, a nursery of antique and extraordinary roses, has traditionally opened its gates to clients and guests on Mothers' Day. As a participant in The Garden Conservancy's Open Days Program, you are invited to visit their garden on May 13 as their guest.

Hours: Special Garden Conservancy Open Day, May 13; 10 a.m. to 3 p.m.

Admission: Free

From Highway 101 take the Rohnert Park/Sebastopol exit at Cotati and travel west on Highway 116/Gravenstein Highway. At approximately 5.5 miles, turn left at traffic light onto Bloomfield Road and continue about 1 mile to garden. At 3-way intersection of Bloomfield and Pleasant Hill Roads, look for parking along the road adjacent to orchard on southeast corner of intersection. Walk about 2 minutes along Pleasant Hill Road to garden entrance on right.

COLORADO
Denver Open Day
Saturday, June 30

DENVER COUNTY

DENVER
Cynthia's Urban Garden
355 Albion Street

Cynthia's garden is located in an urban setting eight miles from downtown Denver. The curving tree-lined street is full of houses built in the mid to late 1930s and 1940s. Cynthia's garden was inspired by the drought now affecting the Southwest and was created in memory of one of the owners' mother, Cynthia Spinner. There is not a blade of conventional grass to be found, rather there is a mixture of xeriscape grasses, plants, and flowers amid flagstone pathways and patios. Composting done on the premises by the owners provides homegrown fertilizer. Constant tender love and care makes for a glorious garden May through the first frost. **NEW**

Hours: 10 a.m. to 4 p.m.

From Colorado Boulevard and Third Avenue, go east on Third Avenue. Turn left onto Albion Street. The garden is on west side of Albion.

From I-25, exit Colorado Boulevard north. Proceed as directed above.

From I-70, exit Colorado Boulevard south. Proceed as directed above.

Proceeds shared with Jewish Family Services of Colorado

Gedrose Family Garden
4400 East 6th Avenue

Welcome to our little oasis in Hilltop. Our garden has been in an ongoing transition since 1998. It is situated beautifully under the watch of seventy-five-year-old American and Siberian elm trees. The front perennial gardens are anchored perfectly with a tiered flagstone wall. The back garden is privately nestled inside an old-world charm brick wall. The hardscape in the backyard was cleverly designed by Ivy Street Design to maintain the integrity of the original sunken garden. The pergola is an exact replica of the original. It is truly a one-of-a-kind creation. The backyard also includes a small potager full of culinary and medicinal herbs, in addition to a relaxing water feature. The secret garden and the xeric garden were added last year. The secluded secret garden was designed to have something in bloom during every part of the growing season. The xeric garden has an abundance of drought-tolerant native plants along with a beautiful weeping white spruce. **NEW**

Hours: 10 a.m. to 4 p.m.

The garden is located on the southeast corner of Sixth Avenue Parkway and Birch Street; 4 blocks east of Colorado Boulevard. Sixth Avenue and Colorado Boulevard are the closest major intersections. We can be accessed from I-70 or I-25.

From I-70, go south on Colorado Boulevard to Sixth Avenue. From I-25, go north on Colorado Boulevard to Sixth Avenue. Please do not park in alley.

El Puesto de Paz—
Jon Snyder & Becca Robinson
550 Clayton Street

The inspiration for our garden is old Mexico. We wanted to create a space that is full of surprises and delights. We think of our garden as our outdoor living room and kitchen that is a welcoming place for family and friends. The gardens surround the patio as well as define the separate spaces. The plants and flowers are chosen to create drama, color, and uniqueness. Our favorite is the weeping pussy willow tree. If you peek around a corner you will find a French flower stand with cascading herbs. The décor is a kitschy blend of old doors, windows, iron accents, and clay pots. Bulldogs and bulls can also be found. Our shared vision was created by Xavier McBride and it continues to grow and evolve. **NEW** ♿

Hours: 10 a.m. to 4 p.m.

From I-25, take Colorado Boulevard north to First Avenue. Turn left and continue to

Clayton Lane. Turn right onto Clayton Lane which becomes Clayton Street. Go to #550. Parking allowed on east side of street only (across from house).

From I-70, go south on Colorado Boulevard to First Avenue. Proceed as directed above.

Susan Mathews Garden
455 Westwood Drive

Newly landscaped, this 1939 renovated French Tudor-style house in Denver's Country Club neighborhood, boasts multiple woodland perennial beds surrounding the house and large lawn. Several patios are filled with potted plants containing an assortment of deciduous trees, perennial grasses, and planters. A free-standing fireplace with sitting area is used for outside entertaining eight months of the year. In one area, a multi-tiered fountain surrounded by flowering plants, adds to the enchanting atmosphere and calmness of the backyard retreat. **NEW** ♿

Hours: 10 a.m. to 4 p.m.

The garden is 5 blocks northwest of First Avenue and University Boulevard, just off Fifth Avenue between Race Street and Vine Street. From I-25, go north on University to Fourth Avenue and turn west. Turn right onto Westwood Drive to #455.

From Colorado Boulevard, go west on First Avenue to University Boulevard. Turn north to Fourth Avenue. Turn west, and take first right onto Westwood Drive. Please park on street.

Scharfenaker Garden
650 Saint Paul Street

Sure, the green of a lawn is restful, but we considered ours wasteful. So, we removed the lawn—all of it—a somewhat unusual sight in urban Denver. The front garden is a four-season splash of bulbs, perennials, trees, and shrubs. Our favorite is the lime green ninebark with its exfoliating bark. Enter into the side yard through a rose-and-clematis-covered arch into a shade garden enclosed by the entangled branches of an eastern redbud and purple sand cherry. A path takes you through a natural garden of multi-stemmed serviceberries, tree lilac, annuals, and perennials. Watch out for

the angelica! The far portion of the yard is more eastern—a red wall, Buddha, pergola and Indonesian daybed. An adjoining flagstone area circled by aspen, a dogwood, and a redbud complete the picture. **NEW**

Hours: 10 a.m. to 4 p.m.

From I-25, take Colorado Boulevard north to Seventh Avenue Parkway. Turn left (west) and continue to St. Paul Street. Turn left (south) and continue to #650.

From I-70, take Colorado Boulevard south to Seventh Avenue Parkway. Turn right and proceed as directed above.

From Sixth Avenue and Broadway, go east on Sixth Avenue to St. Paul Street and turn left.

White Garden
1322 East Bayaud Avenue

During the 2003 renovation of our 1909 Mission-style house in the heart of Denver, we added a European-style perennial courtyard. Reflecting the casual, family-centered, design of southern France, our courtyard is adjacent to the kitchen and opens into the lawn. A multi-stemmed redbud anchors the courtyard, and is surrounded by lavender, shrub roses, and a fountain. Our lawn, dominated by a 100-year-old red oak, is surrounded by stucco walls with wooden gates. Inside the walls are shade gardens filled with English cottage-style perennials, mature shrubs, and flagstone paths. The garden serves as a serene haven for family and friends. **NEW** ♿

Hours: 10 a.m. to 4 p.m.

Located at the corner of Bayaud Avenue and Lafayette Street, 2 blocks north of Alameda Avenue and 2 blocks east of Downing Street.

From I-25 and Downing Street, go north to Bayaud Avenue and turn right. Take an immediate left and follow to Bayaud.

♿ indicates parts of garden are handicapped accessible

Public Gardens

DENVER COUNTY

Denver

Denver Botanic Gardens

*1005 York Street, (720) 865-3500,
www.botanicgardens.org*

Denver Botanic Gardens is an urban oasis. Stroll through the world-renowned Rock Alpine Garden or visit the Japanese, Herb, or Water-Smart Gardens, to name a few. The gift shop offers books, gifts, gardening tools, and more. The Helen Fowler Library has an extensive collection of horticultural books and catalogs. Special events and plant shows are planned throughout the year.

Hours: September 16 through April 30, daily, 9 a.m. to 5 p.m.; May 1 through September 15, Saturday through Tuesday, 9 a.m. to 8 p.m., Wednesday through Friday, 9 a.m. to 5 p.m.

Admission: May through September: $8.50 adults, $5.50 seniors, $5 students & children 4 to 15; September through April: $7.50 adults, $4.50 seniors, $4 students and children ages 4 to 15

Located 5 minutes east of downtown area and accessible by major RTD bus routes. From I-25, exit east onto Sixth Avenue. Proceed east to Josephine Street and turn north. The parking lot is on left side of Josephine Street, between Ninth and 11th Avenues.

LITTLETON

Denver Botanic Gardens at Chatfield

*8500 Deer Creek Canyon Road,
(303) 973-3705*

Chatfield Nature Preserve's 750 acres wind along Deer Creek, encompassing several distinct High Plains habitats. Nature trails thread around wetland and prairie ecosystems. Educational stops along the trails explain surrounding vegetation and encourage wildlife watching. A nineteenth-century farmstead has been restored to present an authentic view of pioneer life on the Colorado High Plains.

Hours: Year round, daily, 9 a.m. to 5 p.m.

Admission: $5 per vehicle. Members are free.

Located just southwest of the Wadsworth Boulevard and CO-470 intersection. Proceed south on Wadsworth Boulevard from this intersection to the second traffic light and turn right onto Deer Creek Canyon Road. Chatfield's entrance gate is 0.4 mile on left.

Hudson Gardens

*6115 South Santa Fe Drive,
(303) 797-8565*

This is a thirty-acre regional display garden accenting sixteen individual gardens, including a historic rose garden, rock garden canyon, water gardens, demonstration gardens, and a railroad garden. There are excellent perennial and shrub collections for Zones 4 and 5. Gardens are labeled and individual handouts are available. There are also large summer sculpture displays, educational programs, space rentals, and a gift shop.

Hours: April 1 through October 31, daily, 9 a.m. to 5 p.m.; reduced winter hours

Admission: $4 adults, $3 seniors, $2 children 3 to 12

From CO-470 go north on South Santa Fe Drive 3 miles, on left, across street from Arapahoe Community College; or 0.5 mile south on South Santa Fe Drive from the Bowles Avenue/Littleton Boulevard junction to South Santa Fe Drive on right.

CONNECTICUT
Fairfield County Open Day
Sunday, April 22

FAIRFIELD COUNTY

WESTON

Toscairn
25 Hillside Road South

At the end of a narrow, dead-end road, lies a compound of small buildings that harkens back to a simpler time. Passing a meadow you will enter the section of the property that has been fenced for protection from deer. On this rugged, two-acre site, a daffodil collection, started by the previous owner in the 1920s, now includes thirty different cultivars that reach their peak in late April. A work in progress, this difficult and rocky hillside is being tamed by the use of stone walls and a collection of antique stone used throughout the gardens. Ferns, specimen trees, and shrubs, as well as vegetable, rock, and perennial gardens, provide flowers and plants of interest year round. **2006**

Hours: Guided tours at 10 a.m. and 12 p.m.

From Merritt Parkway/Route 15, take Exit 42 north on Route 57. At blinking traffic light past Weston Center, turn left, cross river and continue for 0.25 mile. Hillside Road South is on right.

From I-84, take Route 7 south. Turn left at Shell gas station onto Route 107, then right onto Route 57/Georgetown Road. Hillside Road South is 4 miles on left. Because of the challenge of reaching this site, parking will be on other side of Route 57 on Calvin Road, requiring a 0.25-mile walk to garden. Please park as directed. Sorry, no exceptions.

New Haven County Open Days
Saturday & Sunday
May 12 & 13

NEW HAVEN COUNTY

MIDDLEBURY

John N. Spain
69 Bayberry Road

Garden areas include a rock garden, woodland garden with paths, an outdoor (winter-hardy) cactus garden, planted walls, and troughs. The rock garden combines dwarf conifers with hardy cacti and many unique rock garden plants. There is also a thirty-two-foot-long landscaped greenhouse of cacti and succulents. **2006**

Hours: 10 a.m. to 4 p.m.

From I-84 west, take Exit 17. Go straight on Route 64 to second traffic light. Turn right onto Memorial Drive. At end, turn left onto Kelly Road. Go 0.25 mile and turn onto second street on right, Three Mile Hill Road. Continue to third street on right, Bayberry Road. Number 69, is second on right. Please park along road.

From I-84 east, take Exit 17. At bottom of ramp turn left, go under I-84 and go to second light. Turn left onto Route 64 and go to first light. Then turn right onto Memorial Drive and proceed as directed above.

Fairfield County Open Day
Saturday, June 2

FAIRFIELD COUNTY

FAIRFIELD

Nancy & Tom Grant
4014 Redding Road

Our garden is an extension of an eighteenth-century reproduction Fairfield, Connecticut, Georgian-style house we built in 1972. Despite the fact that the house is new, it is listed in the historic and architectural survey of Fairfield by the Connecticut Historical Commission. We have tried to create an eighteenth-century feel to our garden to complement the house. What was once a vegetable garden has been taken over by more than 100 roses and peonies, perennials, shrubs, herbs, and annuals. We start many plants from seed and continually divide and change. Recently we have installed a deer fence around our property, which we have partially concealed with hedges. **2004**

Hours: 10 a.m. to 4 p.m.

From Merritt Parkway/Route 15, take Exit 44/Fairfield from New York. Turn left off exit ramp, then left at traffic light onto Route 58/Black Rock Turnpike. From New Haven, turn left off exit ramp and right at light onto Route 58/Black Rock Turnpike. Go north towards town of Redding for 1.9 miles to North Street/Division Street, turn left, and go west past 2 stop signs for 1.5 miles. At third stop sign, turn right onto Redding Road. Go north 0.3 mile to #4014. Garden is on southeast corner of Redding Road and Mile Common Roads. Please park on Mile Common Road.

GREENWICH
Stonybrooke— Sandra Fales Hillman
29 Taconic Road

About thirty years ago, we fell in love with this rambling old property of waterfalls, rock outcroppings, and open space. It was the site of Caleb Meade's sawmill, which in the eighteenth and nineteenth centuries, provided lumber and fine paneling for this and many other houses in Greenwich. During the Depression, the house was restored and enlarged by architect Richard Henry Dana for the Carleton Granberrys. Many gardens, plantings, and trees enhance the natural Connecticut landscape. There is a wildflower meadow beside the ponds, which were restored in 2001. The ponds are fed by two brooks, which are slowed in their descent by six dams. The property was designated the first historic property in Greenwich in September 2004. This means the three houses can never be demolished, nor built over. A conservation easement held by the Greenwich Land Trust

preserves the property for all to enjoy the views from the road. **2006** ♿

Hours: 10 a.m. to 4 p.m.

From Merritt Parkway/Route 15, take Exit 31/North Street south towards town. Take third road on left, Taconic Road. Go down hill to Byfield Lane on right and park. Stonybrooke begins just past Byfield. There are a few spaces to park farther on by mailbox. Those who have difficulty walking may go up drive to park on level.

Proceeds shared with the Green Fingers Garden Club/Garden History Design

RIDGEFIELD
Garden of Ideas
647 North Salem Road

Twenty years ago, this spot was covered with Kentucky bluegrass and poison ivy-infested woods. Today a fine collection of both woody and herbaceous ornamental plants grow here, along a stunning natural marsh. A large raised-bed vegetable garden produces a bounty of delicious edibles from April through November. Stroll through shade and sun, ponder poetic verse displayed along the way, and relax in one of many secluded nooks. Other points of interest include hand-built cedar structures, whimsical statuary, water features, unusual annuals, and lots of birds and bugs. A plank way across the marsh allows visitors a close-up look at a lovely crop of wild rice, *Zizania aquatica*. **2003**

Hours: 10 a.m. to 4 p.m.

From Route 35 in Ridgefield, take Route 116 for 2.9 miles. Garden is on left.

From Route 121 in North Salem, take Route 116 into Connecticut. Garden is on right, 1.3 miles from New York border. Please look for driveway with Garden of Ideas sign.

RIVERSIDE
Susan & Bruce Cohen
7 Perkely Lane

Overlooking a tidal inlet, this small, sloping property has been shaped over the past twenty years by its current owners, who first removed overgrown shrubs and vines to create a garden

in harmony with its waterfront setting. Susan Cohen, a landscape architect, created a fountain grotto from the old foundation walls of a derelict boathouse, regraded parts of the land, and designed flowering borders to surround the house. The new stone terrace contains a small lily pond and provides a sitting area overlooking the garden. **NEW**

Hours: 12 p.m. to 4 p.m.

From I-95, take Exit 5. Turn right onto Post Road/Route 1. Turn right again at first intersection onto Sound Beach Avenue. Continue into Old Greenwich. Turn right at traffic light onto West End Avenue. A Mobil gas station will be on right. At traffic circle, go left onto Riverside Avenue; there is a boatyard on left. Turn left onto Marks Road, then take first left onto Perkely Lane. The house, #7, is second on left. Please park on Marks Road, beyond Perkely Lane.

WESTON
Toscairn
25 Hillside Road South

At the end of a narrow, dead-end road, lies a compound of small buildings that harkens back to a simpler time. Passing a meadow you will enter the section of the property that has been fenced for protection from deer. On this rugged, two-acre site, a daffodil collection, started by the previous owner in the 1920s, now includes thirty different cultivars that reach their peak in late April. A work in progress, this difficult and rocky hillside is being tamed by the use of stone walls and a collection of antique stone used throughout the gardens. Ferns, specimen trees, and shrubs, as well as vegetable, rock, and perennial gardens, provide flowers and plants of interest year round. **2006**

Hours: Guided tours at 10 a.m. and 12 p.m.

From Merritt Parkway/Route 15, take Exit 42 north on Route 57. At blinking traffic light past Weston Center, turn left, cross river and continue for 0.25 mile. Hillside Road South is on right.

From I-84, take Route 7 south. Turn left at Shell gas station onto Route 107, then right

onto Route 57/Georgetown Road. Hillside Road South is 4 miles on left. Because of the challenge of reaching this site, parking will be on other side of Route 57 on Calvin Road, requiring a 0.25-mile walk to garden. Please park as directed. Sorry, no exceptions.

WESTPORT
Susan Lloyd
59 Center Street

A stone outcropping along the early nineteenth-century house hides the garden beyond. The long, narrow property ends at a brook with astilbe and hosta beds. This is a family garden with a tree house and playground. The large perennial bed is a collection of purple, yellow, white, and some pink and illustrates a love of different foliage shapes and textures. **2006**

Hours: 10 a.m. to 4 p.m.

From I-95, take Exit 18. If northbound, turn left at end of exit ramp; if southbound, turn right. Turn right at second traffic light onto Greens Farms Road. First left is Center Street. Number 59 is third house on right, with a white picket fence.

From Merritt Parkway/Route 15, take Exit 42. If southbound, turn left at end of exit ramp; if northbound, turn right onto Weston Road; turn left at second stop sign onto Cross Highway. Make first right onto Roseville Road and cross Post Road/Route 1. Take first left onto Hillandale. Turn right at stop sign onto West Parish and turn right at "T" onto Center Street. Number 59 is on left. Please park on house side of street.

WILTON
"Seven Gardens, Three Frogs"
80 Chestnut Hill Road

A diverse array of gardens surround our Frazier Peters Tudor revival-style stone house perched on top of a rugged, terraced rock outcropping. The unique topography of the land on this three-acre site provides opportunities for different garden rooms where specimen Japanese maples and perennials thrive. The gardens include a dwarf conifer garden, large woodland gardens, a daylily garden of seventy varieties, a terrace garden lined with troughs, a perennial cutting garden, a wildflower garden, and a raised-bed parterre vegetable garden. Three human-size copper frogs protect and provide whimsy to the gardens. The gardens were featured in *Garden Design* magazine, April 2002. **NEW**

Hours: 10 a.m. to 4 p.m.

From I-95, take Exit 17/Route 33 west. Follow Route 33 for 4.5 miles to Route 53/Chestnut Hill Road. Turn right. The garden, #80, is first driveway on right.

From the Merritt Parkway, take Exit 41/Route 33 West toward Wilton. Follow Route 33 for 1.2 miles to Route 53/Chestnut Hill Road. Proceed as directed above.

From Route 7, take Route 33 for 1.3 miles to Route 53/Chestnut Hill Road. Turn left. The garden, #80, is first driveway on right. Park on Chestnut Hill Road only.

Hartford County Open Day
Sunday, June 3

HARTFORD COUNTY

BURLINGTON
The Salsedo Family Garden
15 Half King Drive

Our gardens have been created on a unique location, a hilltop with a magnificent view 1,000 feet above sea level bordering on 4,000 acres of watershed and state forest. Begun in 1977, this site has undergone various physical transformations, resulting in stone-walled terraces that render this acre-plus location usable. The last big change in 1995 added an expanded backyard terrace with a pool, post-and-beam gardener's tool shed, dwarf conifer collection, vegetable garden, and a collection of hardy chrysanthemums. The front yard features low-maintenance lawns punctuated by beds of native and exotic trees, shrubs, and perennials. The emphasis of this landscape is sustainability with a focus on low maintenance and minimal water requirements. **2006** ♿

Hours: 10 a.m. to 4 p.m.

Take I-84 to Exit 39 and go west on Route 4 towards Farmington. Go through Farmington about 3 miles to Unionville Center to traffic light; pass Friendly's on left. Bear right onto Route 4 (Old Masonic Hall on right, church on left). Go 1 mile along Farmington River. At light, turn left onto Route 4 and go up hill towards Burlington. Go about 1 mile and turn left onto Belden Road (fish hatchery sign is on left). Go to stop sign. Turn right onto George Washington Turnpike, and then take next left onto Cornwall. Go up hill and turn right onto Nassahegan, then make second left onto Half King Drive. Go to bottom of cul-de-sac to middle gravel drive with granite mailbox post labeled #15. Please park in cul-de-sac.

Proceeds shared with Connecticut 4-H Development Fund, Inc./Sustainable Landscaping

CANTON
Premiager Garden
1 Dry Bridge Road

This unique property was built and landscaped in 1937 by Dorothy and Alan Morris. Ms. Morris was a member of the American Society of Landscape Architects, at a time when female landscape architects were uncommon. The design of the house and grounds was influenced by the architecture of Williamsburg, Virginia. The four-plus acres include a walking trail on the original Hartford-to-Albany railroad bed, a babbling brook, charming outdoor "garden house," and a Williamsburg-inspired storehouse. The old bones of this formal garden have aged gracefully over the years as is evident by the mature plantings. **NEW**

Hours: 12 p.m. to 4 p.m.

From I-84, take Exit 39/Farmington/Route 4. Go about 5 miles to center of Unionville and turn right onto Route 177 North/Lovely Street. Go about 4.5 miles and cross over Route 44 (Lovely Street becomes Lawton Road). Bear left at fork and continue on Lawton Road to end. Turn right onto Dry Bridge Road to first house on right.

Proceeds shared with North Central Hospice & Palliative Care

♿ indicates parts of garden are handicapped accessible

EAST WINDSOR HILL
Patricia Porter
1533 Main Street

Surrounding an early nineteenth-century historic house in an historic district and on a scenic road, our gardens are both formal and English country. There are formal English-style rose beds, an herb garden, moon gardens, and perennial borders backed with yew or hemlock hedges. Plants and ferns swing on long hooks from old maple trees. A spectacular wall of climbing hydrangea backs a border of old roses that faces an espaliered apple tree allée. This leads to horse barns, an English glasshouse, a grape-covered pergola, swimming pool, ornamental grasses, and a rugosa rose border, all overlooking the Connecticut River meadows. In the south yard, a golden hops-covered pergola is surrounded by azaleas and rhododendrons. **2006** ♿

Hours: 10 a.m. to 4 p.m.

From I-91, take I-291 east. Cross Connecticut River. Take Exit 4. Stay in left lane. Turn left onto Route 5 north. Go 3 miles. Turn left at traffic light onto Sullivan Avenue. Turn left again onto Main Street and go 1 mile south. Number 1533 is on right.

From I-84, take I-291 west. Turn right onto South Windsor exit. Turn left onto Route 5 north and proceed as directed above. Please park on street.

PLANTSVILLE
The Kaminski Garden
513 Marion Avenue

"Wow" is usually the first word spoken as visitors pass through the gates and enter the garden. Mature trees anchor the sweeping curves of the oversized garden beds to the earth. Interesting foliage and a succession of bloom keep this garden looking great year round. Shade predominates throughout the space, as does an ever-growing collection of shade-tolerant perennials, shrubs, and Japanese maples. A soothing sense of softness is provided by the use of tumbled bluestone for the patio, the raised garden beds surrounding the deck, and the curved pathways to the freeform pool. Years of

organic gardening have resulted in an environment that supports vigorous plant growth and provides a safe haven for the wildlife that live here. For the past two seasons we have been working at improving the "curb appeal" of the front yard. We added a granite obelisk and garden courtyard; ripped up the tar that ran up to the house and replaced it with pea stone and granite pavers; added a boulder garden; and installed another shade garden at the front of the house. **2006** ♿

Hours: 10 a.m. to 4 p.m.

From I-84, take Exit 30/Marion Avenue. From Hartford (I-84 west), turn right at the light onto Marion. From Waterbury (I-84 east), turn left at the stop sign at the end of exit. At the light turn left onto Marion Avenue. Once on Marion, travel about 1 mile, passing Frost Street. Next driveway on right is our house, #513. House is slate blue with detached two-car garage. Please park in driveway.

Proceeds shared with Dana Farber Cancer Institute/Women's Cancer Research

New Haven County Open Day
Saturday, June 9

NEW HAVEN COUNTY

MERIDEN
Jardin des Brabant
131 Corrigan Avenue

Since 1972, this has been one woman's enclosed garden retreat on three quarters of an acre. The upper lawn features a large beech and a perimeter of flowering shrubs, dwarf conifers, shade and sun perennials, kousa and Florida dogwoods, and annuals. A seventy-five-foot dawn redwood dominates the lower gardens of perennials, roses, annuals, and vines. Grass paths lead toward, and past, a stone-and-stucco storage house with hayrack planters. A small potager, an ancient apple tree shading hostas and ferns, a side border with miniature lilac standards and lilies, and a *Viburnum plicatum* hedge complete the secluded rear garden which dissolves into open lawn. **2006** ♿

Hours: 12 p.m. to 5 p.m.

From I-84, take I-691 east to Exit 5/Chamberlain Highway. Turn right at end of exit ramp and take an immediate right onto Steuben Street. Steuben becomes Corrigan at top of hill. Go around bend to beginning of cemetery on right. Garden is directly across street.

From I-91, take I-691 west to Exit 6/Lewis Avenue. Turn left at end of exit ramp. Turn left at end of Lewis onto Kensington Avenue. Turn left onto Chamberlain Highway. Pass Target store on right and look for Steuben Street immediately after 7-Eleven on left and highway exit on right. Proceed as directed above. Please park on either side of street. Watch for children in area.

Sabbatical Garden

490 Gracey Avenue

An extended drive from the road leads to a serene get-away created and designed by Joseph S. LaRosa. His residence overlooks two large excavated ponds, one with a bridge and pond house, and the other with a replica of Meriden's own Castle Craig. Several fish species and many waterfowl call this home too. Bluebirds sail around this sunny expanse with stone walkways and bridges leading to interconnected stone pools with boulder fountains. Surrounding the pools are compositions of dwarf conifers, shrubs, Japanese maples, perennials, and roses. A stone bridge reaches across a wide swale to a hilltop gazebo. Island beds of annuals and mixed perennials are located throughout the garden's new additions every year. The tranquility of this beautiful garden is a wonderful "sabbatical". **2006** ♿

Hours: 12 p.m. to 5 p.m.

Take Exit I-91 west to Exit 6/Lewis Avenue. Turn left at end of exit ramp. At end of Lewis, turn right onto Kensington Avenue. Go about 0.5 mile to Gracey Avenue and turn left (Gracey is last left off Kensington before Colony Street). Continue, bearing right going under overpass, and look for #490 on left, about 1.25 miles after turning off Kensington.

From I-84, take I-691 east to Exit 5/Chamberlain Highway. Turn left and then right at third traffic light onto Kensington Avenue.

Proceed as directed above. Please park on drive as marked.

Proceeds shared with Our Lady of Mt. Carmel School

Litchfield County
Open Day
Saturday, June 23

Hollister House—The Garden of George Schoellkopf in Washington, Connecticut is also open on this date. See their listing on page 115. You may read more about the Garden Conservancy's preservation work at Hollister House on our website, www.gardenconservancy.org.

LITCHFIELD COUNTY

FALLS VILLAGE
Nancy McCabe
163 Dublin Road

This garden was begun in 1980. A small kitchen garden features paths and antique tile edging enclosed by espaliered apple trees. You will see a collection of old pots, rhubarb forcers, and French cloches. A rustic trellis leads to the main garden past the potting shed. A sunken garden is enclosed with a fence and buttressed with boxwood. Divided sections contain shrubs and perennials, a quince tree, and a medlar tree. A chicken house and woodland walk with naturalized bulbs, ferns, and hellebores completes the garden. **2006**

Hours: 10 a.m. to 4 p.m.

Take Route 7 into Falls Village. Go west at blinking traffic light onto Main Street/Route 126. Bear right staying on Route 126. Turn right onto Point of Rocks Road. Make first left onto Dublin Road. The house, #163, is stucco with dark green trim; near end and close to canal. Please park along road.

Bunny Williams
Point of Rocks Road

Interior designer and garden book author Bunny Williams' intensively planted fifteen-acre estate has a sunken garden with twin

♿ indicates parts of garden are handicapped accessible

perennial borders surrounding a fishpond, parterre garden, year-round conservatory filled with tender plants, large vegetable garden with flowers and herbs, and woodland garden with meandering paths and a pond with a waterfall. There are also a working greenhouse and an aviary with unusual chickens and fantail doves. Recent additions include an apple orchard with mature trees, a rustic Greek Revival-style pool house folly, and a swimming pool with eighteenth-century French coping. **2006**

Hours: 10 a.m. to 4 p.m.

From Route 7 north, go to Falls Village. Turn left at blinking traffic light onto Main Street/Route 126. Bear right (still on Route 126). Go to stop sign at Point of Rocks Road. Driveway is directly ahead. Please park in field adjacent to house.

SHARON
Lee Link
99 White Hollow Road

Three stone walls cascade down a sunny hillside. The space between each is planted with perennial borders, which bloom with the flowering seasons of spring and summer. One level is set off by a water garden, which reflects a winter conservatory on the hill behind it. **2006**

Hours: 10 a.m. to 4 p.m.

From junction of Routes 7 & 112, turn onto Route 112. Go about 2 miles to "Entrance to Lime Rock Race Track" sign. Turn left onto White Hollow Road and travel 2.5 miles. Garden, #99, is on right, opposite a white fence.

From Route 41 in Sharon, turn right onto Calkinstown Road. Take second left onto White Hollow Road. Driveway is on left opposite a white fence.

Sally Pettus
2 Main Street

These gardens were designed to unify the grounds of a small townhouse/cottage complex. Discrete spaces have been planted with an exuberant variety of perennials leaning decidedly towards large. The collection, including many tall grasses and shrubs, succeeds in making the property seem much more spacious than it is. There is a parterre, a pond with a fountain, a tiny sleeping house, a spring stream garden, a rock garden, and a wild frontyard garden screening the road. **2006** &

Hours: 10 a.m. to 4 p.m.

From Cornwall Bridge, take Route 4 to four-way stop sign at clock tower in Sharon. Turn left onto Route 41 and house is first on right.

From Amenia, take Route 343 to four-way stop sign at clock tower in Sharon. Turn left onto Route 41 and house is first on right. Please park on green.

WASHINGTON
Linda Allard
156 Wykeham Road

High on a hillside, with a panoramic view of the Litchfield Hills, this garden has Old-World charm. Surrounded by stone walls covered with espaliered fruit trees and climbing roses and hydrangeas, the garden is partly formal and partly potager. A lush rose arbor filled with pale pink and white roses interwoven with clematis separates the two. Boxwood hedges define the white formal garden enhanced by a variety of green textures. Geometric beds overflowing with fruits, vegetables, herbs, and flowers are a true depiction of potager. This part of the garden changes yearly; plantings are worked by color and color combination. **2006**

Hours: 10 a.m. to 4 p.m.

From Washington Green, at Gunn Memorial Library, turn onto Wykeham Road. Follow for about 1.5 miles until Old Litchfield Road forks left. Stay right on Wykeham for about 0.25 mile. Go up a small hill to a red barn on right. The entrance to garden is opposite barn. Number 156 is on stone wall; proceed through gate to garden.

Charles Raskob Robinson & Barbara Paul Robinson
88 Clark Road

Brush Hill includes a series of gardens on varied topography around an eighteenth-century Connecticut farmhouse and barn amidst old stone walls. The garden includes a rose walk featuring old roses and climbers, a fountain garden planted in yellows and purples, herbaceous borders, and a terraced garden planted in hot colors leading up to a garden folly and through an arch to a woodland walk with a series of cascading pools. Many colorful garden structures have been designed and built by Charles including inventive disguises for the irrigation system and deer fence. There is an old Lord & Burnham greenhouse and a turquoise bridge over a half-acre pond with grass borders. The gardens have been featured on HGTV, "A Gardener's Diary," Rosemary Verey's book *The Secret Garden*, and in *House & Garden* and numerous other magazines. Be sure to visit www. brushhillgardens.com. **2006** ♿

Hours: 2 p.m. to 6 p.m.

From I-84, take Exit 15/Southbury. Take Route 6 north to Route 47 and turn left. Go 4 miles, passing Woodbury Ski Area on left, and turn right onto Nettleton Hollow Road. Go 4.1 miles, past intersection of Wykeman and Carmel Hill Roads, and watch for sign to enter parking field on left.

WEST CORNWALL
Michael Trapp
7 River Road

This Old World-style garden is intimate, with cobbled paths, terraced gardens, raised perennial beds, and reflecting pools. Overlooking the Housatonic River, the property has a distinct French/Italian flavor. **2006** ♿

Hours: 10 a.m. to 4 p.m.

From Route 7, take Route 128 east through covered bridge into West Cornwall. Continue on Route 128, taking second left onto River Road. House is yellow with gray trim, first on left. Please park in front or in town.

♿ indicates parts of garden are handicapped accessible

Hartford County
Open Day
Sunday, June 24

HARTFORD COUNTY

GLASTONBURY

The Murray Gardens

576 Thompson Street

This is a colorful collection of gardens created for new construction, utilizing mature plantings of perennials divided and moved from our previous property and unusual native trees. The property features three perennial borders and a daylily bed planted along old stone walls and fences, a carpet rose bank and herb garden, and woodland paths with a wide variety of shade plants and garden art in a naturalized front yard setting. Our backyard includes sun and shade plantings built into the pool deck and an inviting sunken Japanese garden accessed by a footbridge over a small stream connecting two ponds. **2006** ♿

Hours: 10 a.m. to 4 p.m.

From Hartford, take Route 2 east to Exit 10. Turn left off exit ramp onto Route 83. Take first right onto Chimney Sweep Hill. Go up hill 1.5 miles to end. Turn left onto Thompson Street. House is about 0.25 mile on right, across from farm.

From east, take Route 2 west to Exit 11. Go left off exit ramp, then take second right onto Thompson Street. Our house, #576, is 1.5 miles on right. Please park on street.

HARWINTON

Archer-Chiarmonte Garden

131 Burlington Road

The Catlin House, an eighteenth-century farmhouse in Harwinton, Connecticut, is blessed to sit atop a south-facing hill with views to the south and west. The garden is entered through a rustic grape arbor paved with natural fieldstone. At the top of the garden near the house there is a granite terrace with herb garden, period trellises, French antique wire plant stands, and a granite farm sink that has been used to display plants. The property is surrounded by ancient stone walls with granite steps leading down into the gardens. About seven years ago we worked with garden designer Rob Camp Fuoco to add several new Colonial revival-style gardens. A happy froggy (a Longwood gardens reproduction) presides over the blue and lime green water garden. Close by is a pink, red, and white garden, featuring a French cider millstone which appears to float on English chimney pots (a tricky engineering achievement!). Rustic French seats add to the charm of this garden. The garden picture ends with the View Garden, early nineteenth-century hay barn, and the dahlia garden which sit at the lower end of the property. **NEW** ♿

Hours: 10 a.m. to 4 p.m.

From Litchfield, take Route 118 east through Harwinton center, 0.5 mile to Locust Road.

From the east, take Route 84 to Farmington Exit/Route 4 west 16 miles to Locust Road, turn left. Locust Road is right after gas station in Harwinton historic district. Please park on street.

SIMSBURY

Skyflower—Ingram Garden

20 Stafford Road

This hilltop garden delivers all season long. Big sky, sunshine, and forest trees reflect on the elongated pond in the front yard. Drawn in by splashing sounds and open space, you will see specimen trees, shrubs, countless perennials, annuals, ornamental grasses, and more. What's up behind that massive stone foundation? The English sunken garden awaits you with thick rock walls, brick floors, a reflecting pool, and water fountain guarded by weeping pear trees and perennial beds. Up through the rose-covered arbor along an avenue of flowers, you arrive at the overlook terrace encased by curved stone walls, bluestone floors, blooming planters, and the house as a backdrop. Take a few steps down to check out the vegetable garden with its brick-lined pathways if you must, but everything can be viewed from the terrace, driveway, and street. **2006** ▸

Hours: 10 a.m. to 4 p.m.

From Route 44, take Nod Road north at Avon Old Farms Restaurant & Hotel. Turn right onto Route 185. At very top of hill at a blinking yellow traffic light, turn right onto Stafford Road. The garden is at second house on left.

From Route 91 north take Exit 35A towards Bloomfield. Turn left off exit onto Route 218. From Route 91 south, take Exit 35B and turn right at end of ramp. Go through about 3 traffic lights, stay straight on Route 218/Cottage Grove Road. Stay straight, pass 4 traffic lights and a shopping center. Continue to traffic light at Route 185, turn right and go about 3 miles. Pass Tumblebrook Country Club, Route 178, and Wade's vegetable stand on right. At traffic light at top of hill, turn left onto Stafford Road. The garden is at second house on left.

From Route 84 west take Exit 61/Route 291 west over Connecticut River. Take Exit 1/Route 218 to Bloomfield. At end of exit ramp turn left onto Route 218 and go to Route 185. Turn right and go towards Simsbury, passing Wade's vegetable stand. Proceed as directed above. Please park beyond driveway on both sides of street.

Litchfield County Open Day Sunday, June 24

LITCHFIELD COUNTY

BRIDGEWATER
Maywood Gardens
52 Cooper Road

This private estate features a sunken perennial garden protected by ten-foot stone walls, a gazebo garden planted with butterfly-and hummingbird-attracting flowers and shrubs, a rose garden arranged in a French pattern design surrounded by a circle of hemlocks, a woodland path populated by mature beech and cherry trees as well as viburnums and rhododendrons, a ledge garden on an exposed hillside, a heather bed, white garden, herb garden, ornamental

kitchen garden, and 4,000-square-foot greenhouse. **2005**

Hours: 10 a.m. to 2 p.m.

From I-84, take Exit 9 and travel north on Route 25 towards Brookfield Village. Turn right onto Route 133 east towards Bridgewater. Cross Lake Lillinonah Bridge and take first right onto Wewaka Brook Road. Go 0.75 mile and turn right onto Beach Hill Road to end. Turn right onto Skyline Ridge. Go 0.5 mile and turn right onto Cooper Road. Please park on right across from greenhouse complex.

NEW HARTFORD
Jillian Gardens
70 Town Line Road

Our gardens are nestled high on a hill in New Hartford surrounded by large red oaks and maple trees. We have various water features that are enhanced with annuals, perennials, and shrubs. We have a wisteria-covered pergola as well as several arbors, one that is covered with climbing hydrangea. A hand-carved eagle sculpture overlooks our gardens and small barns. Hanging baskets and ornamental posts are located on our patio and deck. More than 1,000 impatiens are planted in our pots and perennials beds, giving color throughout the growing season. We like to stroll under the natural canopy of the high bush blueberry and over a small bridge that straddles a dry stream bed. Our woodland garden is one of several outdoor rooms. We also have an outdoor potting shed and an organic vegetable garden bordered by ornamental grasses and sun-loving perennials. We love fragrance in our gardens, so we have planted gardenias, Confederate jasmine, oriental lilies, and butterfly bushes to make our gardens even more inviting. Come and walk the yellow brick path and enjoy a little nostalgia. Then stroll over to another bridge through a tropical garden and then over to a new formal garden we put in last year. **2006 ♿**

Hours: 10 a.m. to 4 p.m.

From Route 84 take Exit 39 to Farmington. Take Route 4 through Unionville and to traffic light at Routes 179 and 4. Turn left and go through Burlington Center, past Hogan's Cider

Mill on right. Continue to Woodchuck Lane (across from Route 72) and turn right. Go about 2 miles to a stop sign. Turn right onto Town Line Road. We are about 0.25 mile down road on left. Please park on side of road.

New London County Open Day Sunday, June 24

NEW LONDON COUNTY

STONINGTON

Mr. & Mrs. Juan O'Callahan
40 Salt Acres Road

The six-acre seaside garden consists of grass with trees and border gardens along stone walls, a pool, and tennis court. There are six large cutting beds with a variety of flowers and bulbs, and a vegetable garden enclosed in a yew hedge. A "secret garden" is built into the rock ledge next to the seawall. The greenhouse holds succulent plants in the summer. The view of Watch Hill, Sandy Point, and Fishers Island is spectacular. **2006** ♿

Hours: 10 a.m. to 2 p.m.

From I-95, take Exit 91/Stonington Borough Village. At the end of the exit ramp, if coming from the north, turn left; from the south, turn right. Go 0.25 mile, and turn left onto North Main Street. Continue for about 2 miles across Route 1 to a stop sign and turn left onto Trumbull Street. At the next stop sign, turn right over the bridge (railroad tracks) into the village. Follow Water Street to Church (Noah's Restaurant) and turn left. Go 2 blocks, then turn left onto Orchard Street. Turn right at the next block onto East Grand Street. Continue to the end of the causeway. Please park under the trees.

Mrs. Frederic C. Paffard, Jr.
389 North Main Street

A century-old boxwood hedge a quarter of a mile long, rose arbors, and a perennial cutting garden are highlights of this old-fashioned garden. There are interesting old outbuildings, a carriage house, grapery, greenhouse, annual cutting gardens, a ha ha, and a pond once used for ice—now home for the herons. **2006** ♿

Hours: 10 a.m. to 4 p.m.

From I-95, take Exit 91/Stonington Borough Village. Go south to North Main Street, then turn left toward Stonington Borough. Go about 1.5 miles to #389.

From Route 1, turn north onto North Main Street at traffic light. Number 389 is second driveway on right. Park anywhere.

New Haven County Open Day Sunday, July 8

NEW HAVEN COUNTY

GUILFORD

Angelwood— Mary Anne & Dale Athanas
66 Christopher Lane

This is a secret garden. From the front of this well-landscaped southern Colonial you would not realize that we have fifty-one gardens, garden rooms, and water features awaiting your enjoyment. Observe from the multi-level deck the amphitheater of plantings and streams surrounded by woodland. Highlights of the garden include a large circular garden with its nine-foot, four-tiered fountain embraced by seven mermaids with water cascading into a large reflecting pool. The formal garden beyond the fountain is in the style of a French parterre with a magnificent six-foot urn centerpiece flanked on each side by raised beds with two life-sized statues depicting Spring and Summer. The azalea walk includes many varieties of azaleas, boxwood, hostas, and coral bells and is highlighted by a two-tiered fountain within a raised bed surrounded by boxwood. A new addition is the garden of St. Fiacre, the patron saint of gardeners. This large garden expands the back of the twin ponds and contains many varieties of shade and bog plants. Also, many of the gardens in front of the house have been fine tuned to include many new and interesting plantings. The woodland path surrounded by two streams consists of ferns and many varieties of hosta, ferns, and other shade-loving plants—this is where the Angel of Angelwood can be found. Many visitors to our garden have described a feeling of peace and tranquility. We designed and planted all of the gardens over a period of ten years and we continue to plan and design more gardens each year. **2006** ♿

Hours: 10 a.m. to 4 p.m.

From I-91 south, take Exit 15/Route 68/Durham. At end of exit ramp, turn left onto Route 68 and follow until it ends in Durham. Turn right onto Route 17 and follow about 1.5 miles (past Route 79, which will be on left) to Route 77. Turn left and go several miles to a traffic light at a major intersection. Turn right onto Route 80 and travel 1 mile to light. Turn left onto Long Hill Road. Travel 1.3 miles and look for Christopher Lane on left (two stone entrance walls). Turn left and look for #66 on left just before a cul-de-sac. It is a large white Colonial with a formal front porch (columns) set back from road.

From I-95 north, take Exit 57. Turn right at end of exit ramp and go 1 mile (past Bishop's Orchards on left) to first light. Turn left onto Long Hill Road. Go about 3 miles to Christopher Lane, turn right, and look for #66 on left just before a cul-de-sac.

Proceeds shared with Yale Cancer Center Fund

MERIDEN
Jardin des Brabant
131 Corrigan Avenue

Since 1972, this has been one woman's enclosed garden retreat on three quarters of an acre. The upper lawn features a large beech and a perimeter of flowering shrubs, dwarf conifers, shade and sun perennials, kousa and Florida dogwoods, and annuals. A seventy-five-foot dawn redwood dominates the lower gardens of perennials, roses, annuals, and vines. Grass paths lead toward, and past, a stone-and-stucco storage house with hayrack planters. A small potager, an ancient apple tree shading hostas and ferns, a side border with miniature lilac standards and lilies, and a *Viburnum plicatum*

hedge complete the secluded rear garden which dissolves into open lawn. **2006** ♿

Hours: 12 p.m. to 5 p.m.

From I-84, take I-691 east to Exit 5/Chamberlain Highway. Turn right at end of exit ramp and take an immediate right onto Steuben Street. Steuben becomes Corrigan at top of hill. Go around bend to beginning of cemetery on right. Garden is directly across street.

From I-91, take I-691 west to Exit 6/Lewis Avenue. Turn left at end of exit ramp. Turn left at end of Lewis onto Kensington Avenue. Turn left onto Chamberlain Highway. Pass Target store on right and look for Steuben Street immediately after 7-Eleven on left and highway exit on right. Proceed as directed above. Please park on either side of street. Watch for children in area.

Sabbatical Garden
490 Gracey Avenue

An extended drive from the road leads to a serene getaway created and designed by Joseph S. LaRosa. His residence overlooks two large excavated ponds, one with a bridge and pond house, and the other with a replica of Meriden's own Castle Craig. Several fish species and many waterfowl call this home too. Bluebirds sail around this sunny expanse with stone walkways and bridges leading to interconnected stone pools with boulder fountains. Surrounding the pools are compositions of dwarf conifers, shrubs, Japanese maples, perennials, and roses. A stone bridge reaches across a wide swale to a hilltop gazebo. Island beds of annuals and mixed perennials are located throughout the garden's new additions every year. The tranquility of this beautiful garden is a wonderful "sabbatical." **2006** ♿

Hours: noon to 5 p.m.

Take Exit I-91 west to Exit 6/Lewis Avenue. Turn left at end of exit ramp. At end of Lewis, turn right onto Kensington Avenue. Go about 0.5 mile to Gracey Avenue and turn left (Gracey is last left off Kensington before Colony Street). Continue, bearing right going under overpass, and look for #490 on left, about 1.25 miles after turning off Kensington.

♿ indicates parts of garden are handicapped accessible

From I-84, take I-691 east to Exit 5/Chamberlain Highway. Turn left and then right at third traffic light onto Kensington Avenue. Proceed as directed above. Please park on drive as marked.

Proceeds shared with Our Lady of Mt. Carmel School

The Stankevich Garden
48 South Broad Terrace

Twenty years ago, we planted a threadleaf Japanese maple tree in our front yard and "garden fever" began. Now, the front garden is completely covered in perennials, a hydrangea and various ornamental trees and shrubs, grasses, and groundcovers. Past a bubbling fountain through the gate is a deep shade area with a variety of container plantings leading to several well-defined gardens. Along the back fence is a spring garden containing a variety of clematis, goat's beard, and lilies. A weeping cherry tree sits in the middle of a rose garden. A fountain splashes in the background surrounded by ornamental shrubs, perennials, daylilies and Oriental lilies. A large hardy hibiscus, crocosmia 'Lucifer", phlox 'David', and dahlias circle a stone patio. This garden space which features garden art and many annual containers is an example of a small area transformed into a serene and colorful space that changes every year. **2006** ♿

Hours: 12 p.m. to 4 p.m.

From Hartford, take I-91 south to Exit 18/Meriden/Waterbury. Turn left onto Broad Street/Route 5 south. Go about 2.5 miles and turn right onto South Broad Terrace (opposite Harte Chevrolet).

From New Haven, take I-91 north to Exit 15. Turn left onto Route 68. Take Meriden exit, turn right onto Route 5 about 1.75 miles, and turn left onto South Broad Terrace (across from Harte Chevrolet).

From Middletown, Route 66 west/Washington Street becomes I-691 west. Take Exit 8/Route 5/Broad Street. Turn left onto Broad Street and go about 2.5 miles to South Broad Terrace (across from Harte Chevrolet).

From Waterbury, take I-84 east to Exit 27/I-691 east. Take I-691 east to Exit 8/Route 5/Broad Street. Proceed as directed above. Please park on street, not in front of garden.

Proceeds shared with The American Heart Association

George Trecina
341 Spring Street

This landscape designer's garden, with its profusion of annuals and tender perennials, is best seen from mid- to late summer. Although we have maintained the property since the 1950s, the serious gardening efforts came during the 1970s with a series of hardscape and garden-building projects. The one-third-acre site is best described as mostly garden accented with ribbons of lawn connected by paths, stairs, and walls. This past fall we replaced the remaining front lawn with pea stone and brick edging and planted a seventy-foot-long boxwood hedge around the oval garden. A new "observation garden" overlooks the front yard. One guided tour is available at 1:00. Live music will be provided by After All from 2 p.m. to 4 p.m. **2006** ♿

Hours: 12 p.m. to 4 p.m.

From I-91 north, take Exit 18/I-691 west to Exit 6/Lewis Avenue. Turn right onto Lewis Avenue (which becomes Linsley Avenue) and go to end. Turn right onto Hanover Street to first traffic light. Turn left onto Columbus Avenue to second stop sign. Turn left onto Prospect Avenue and turn right onto Spring Street. Go to fourth house on right, #341.

From I-91 south, take Exit 15/Route 68. Turn left onto Route 68 and go about 2.75 miles. Turn right onto Route 150/Main Street. Turn left onto Route 71/Old Colony Road and about 2.25 miles to third traffic light. Turn onto Flower Street and go to end. Turn left onto New Hanover Avenue and then first right onto Prospect Avenue. Take first left onto Spring Street.

From I-84, take Exit 27/I-691 east to Exit 5/Route 71/Chamberlain Highway. Turn right onto Route 71 and go to end. Turn left onto West Main Street and go to first light. Turn right onto Bradley Avenue and go to stop sign. Turn left onto Winthrop Terrace and go to first light. Continue through intersection up Columbus Avenue to second stop sign. Turn left onto Prospect Avenue and then right onto Spring Street.

Please park along Spring Street. Persons with walking problems may drive up driveway.

Fairfield County Open Day Saturday, July 21

FAIRFIELD COUNTY

REDDING
Stone Orchard
116 Peaceable Street

Visitors to Stone Orchard describe this naturalistic setting as magical and transporting. The garden designed by distinguished landscape designer Douglas Maclise, surrounds the house on three acres of woodlands, brooks, stone walls, stone terraces, gravel paths, meadow, and lawn. Starting in 1990 with a master plan for the property, Maclise created a series of garden settings until his death in 2002. During this time Stone Orchard became his home. This is a collector's garden containing hundreds of unusual trees and shrubs including dwarf conifers and conifers, hydrangeas, boxwood, hollies, rhododendrons, magnolias, tree peonies, weeping katsura, Japanese maples, metasequoias, dogwoods, beeches, and a Korean lilac hedge. This collection of plants, with a succession of bloom from March to October, is incorporated into a finely orchestrated entrance garden leading to a gravel and stone woodland meditation garden in one direction and a rustic pergola room in another. Beyond is a beech ellipse, meadow, orchard, cutting garden, Japanese maple nursery, and peony border, all leading down to terraced hillside poolscape. From there a gravel path through the woods leads to the front of the property to an elevated stone terrace with stone slab railings hand-cut by Maclise himself. Everywhere

there is evidence that Maclise was a master of stonework. The garden is now lovingly cared for by master gardener and landscape designer Terry Karpen. **NEW** ♿

Hours: 10 a.m. to 4 p.m.

From I-84 take Route 7 south. From I-95 or the Merritt Parkway take Route 7 north. From Route 7, turn right onto Route 107. Go 1.6 miles to Peaceable Street. Turn left and go 0.3 mile. Garden is on left. Please park on street, do not enter drive.

WESTON
Birgit Rasmussen Diforio
7 Indian Valley Road

A steep and dramatic 100-foot-long granite ledge, uncovered and terraced by the owner, dominates this hilly site. It culminates at the rear of the property with a recirculating waterfall and pond. Large, undulating mixed borders emphasize contrasts in the color and texture. The garden includes open, sunny areas, a woodland walk, and a shady wetland.

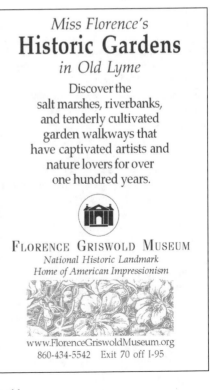

♿ indicates parts of garden are handicapped accessible

A variety of seating areas, containers, and ornaments accent this two-acre property which is surrounded by deer fencing. **2006**

Hours: 10 a.m. to 4 p.m.

From Merritt Parkway/Route 15, take Exit 42 and go north on Route 57. At blinking traffic light past Weston Center, turn left, cross river and continue on Route 57 for about 3 miles. Indian Valley Road is on right.

From I-84, take Route 7 south. Turn left at Exxon gas station at Route 107, then right onto Route 57/Georgetown Road. Indian Valley Road is less than 1 mile on left.

New London County
Open Day
Saturday, July 21

NEW LONDON COUNTY

NORTH STONINGTON

Blue Flag Farm
449 Pendleton Hill Road

Blue Flag Farm, named for the masses of *Iris versicolor* in the pastures, is an old New England farm. An eighteenth-century Cape Cod-style house next to the Pendleton Hill Brook overlooks stone walls, sheep pastures, and tall oaks. In the fields among glacial outcroppings are beds containing 600 daylily cultivars—large flowered, small, miniatures, and spiders. Some beds feature pink, purple, and red daylilies; others yellow, gold, and red. I take great pleasure in a seventy- by forty-foot perennial border where perennials, shrubs, and annuals accompany daylilies in pleasing combinations. Delphinium, annual poppies, roses, salvia, clematis, nasturtium, herbs, and coleus are included. **2006** ⅍

Hours: 10 a.m. to 4 p.m.

Take Route 95 to Exit 93/Clark Falls. At bottom of ramp, turn left if traveling north; right if traveling south. Go straight at stop sign onto Denison Hill Road/Route 216. Go 1.5 miles to stop sign in middle of a dairy farm. Turn left and continue on Route 216. Go 1 mile to stop sign at junction of Pendleton Hill Road/Route 49. Go straight 0.5 mile to Garden

Conservancy or Daylily Garden sign on left. Turn left onto farm road. Follow blue streamers to end. Please park in pasture on left.

Hartford County
Open Day
Sunday, July 22

HARTFORD COUNTY

AVON

Green Dreams—
Garden of Jan Nickel
71 Country Club Road

This established twenty-five-year-old garden of quiet timeless natural beauty, gives a sense of permanence upon entering the iron gates. There is a profusion of four-season color and texture woven in a tapestry of unusual perennials, shrubs, and trees. A distinctive use of architectural elements creates illusions and expand the boundaries of ample compositions, while seamlessly blending living and outdoor spaces. Unanticipated twists and turns in garden paths create vignettes; while hidden pots, packed with unusual annuals, come into view. This artful designer's garden has been featured in *Woman's Day: Garden and Deck Design* (Fall 2004), in Sydney Eddison's book *Gardens to Go*, and *The Welcoming Garden* by Gordon Hayward (2006). **2006** ⅍

Hours: 10 a.m. to 4 p.m.

From I-84, take Exit 39/Farmington/Route 4. From intersection of Routes 10 & 4, turn right onto Route 10 for 5.7 miles to Route 44. Turn left and follow 0.7 mile to intersection of Route 10 and Old Farms Road. Turn left and go 1.3 miles to Country Club Road. Turn right and go 0.3 mile to #71. Please park across street on Tamara Circle.

Proceeds shared with Animal Friends of Connecticut

BLOOMFIELD
Terrace Hill Farm
27 Duncaster Road

Informal, lush, and expansive mixed borders, island beds, and a terraced garden surround an 1870 farmhouse and outbuildings with a view of Talcott Ridge. Collections of daylilies, hosta, viburnum, hens and chicks, spirea, and dwarf conifers are interplanted with companion perennials, grasses, shrubs, and specimen trees. A pergola screens a brick patio laid in the foundation of an old carriage shed. A shaded garden room is perfect for afternoon parties. Gardens are edged with brownstone and "souvenir" rocks have become garden ornaments. A collector at heart, I have tried nevertheless to create gardens that are pleasing combinations of a variety of plants while still indulging my passion for particular ones. **NEW** ⅚

Hours: 10 a.m. to 4 p.m.

From I-91/Exit 35, take Route 218 west to Bloomfield. At about 4 miles, turn right onto Route 189 (Ruby Tuesdays at intersection). At 1 mile, turn left onto Route 178/Mountain Avenue. Pass cemetery on right to next traffic light. Continue straight. Take second right after light. You are still on Mountain Avenue. Take next right onto Duncaster Road (sawmill on left). Number 27 is 0.4 mile on left, look for fence. Please park in driveway or on grass in front of fence or along road.

Litchfield County Open Day Sunday, July 22
LITCHFIELD COUNTY

NEW HARTFORD
Jillian Gardens
70 Town Line Road

Our gardens are nestled high on a hill in New Hartford surrounded by large red oaks and maple trees. We have various water features that are enhanced with annuals, perennials, and shrubs. We have a wisteria-covered pergola as well as several arbors, one which is covered by a climb-

ing hydrangea. A hand-carved eagle sculpture overlooks our gardens and small barns. Hanging baskets and ornamental posts are located on our patio and deck. More than 1,000 impatiens are planted in our pots and perennials beds, giving color throughout the growing season. We like to stroll under the natural canopy of the high bush blueberry and over a small bridge that straddles a dry stream bed. Our woodland garden is one of several outdoor rooms. We also have an outdoor potting shed and an organic vegetable garden bordered by ornamental grasses and sun-loving perennials. We love fragrance in our gardens, so we have planted gardenias, confederate jasmine, oriental lilies, and butterfly bushes to make our gardens even more inviting. Come and walk the yellow brick path and enjoy a little nostalgia. Then stroll over to another bridge through a tropical garden and then over to a new formal garden we put in last year. **2006** ⅚

Hours: 10 a.m. to 4 p.m.

From Route 84 take Exit 39 to Farmington. Take Route 4 through Unionville and to traffic light at Routes 179 and 4. Turn left and go through Burlington Center, pass Hogan's Cider Mill on right. Continue to Woodchuck Lane (across from Route 72) and turn right. Go about 2 miles to a stop sign. Turn right onto Town Line Road. We are about 0.25 mile down road on left. Please park on side of road.

SHARON
Lynden Miller's Garden
1 Williams Road

This country garden features a large mixed border and a daylily walk under crabapples. In recent years we have expanded the woodland and have introduced several varieties of overwintered flowering pink and blue hydrangeas. Recently we have added a small pond and a recirculating stream. **2004** ⅚

Hours: 10 a.m. to 2 p.m.

From Route 41 north, go through Sharon, pass shopping center on left and Texaco gas station on right. Take first right onto Calkinstown Road. Go 0.7 mile and turn left onto Williams Road. The garden (#1) is on left corner. Please park off road or along the shoulder.

⅚ indicates parts of garden are handicapped accessible

WEST CORNWALL
Garden of Roxana &
Ledlie Laughlin
63 Ford Hill Road

Extensive stone walls accentuate the natural lines of the gardens near the house and the surrounding pasture and hills. A mixed border of shrubs, perennials, and inherited peony plants stretches in front of a long, high retaining wall of massive stones. Water beckons in the distance; frogs jump into the ponds as you approach. Plantings at the stream have gradually become established. An existing design plan from the 1930s provides the structure for the main garden. Together Tiziana Hardy and the owner designed the renovated border gardens which were planted in 2001. Tiziana designed the restful central garden with large foundation stones and gravel surrounded by two abundant species of boxwood. **2005** ♿

Hours: 12 p.m. to 4 p.m.

From the south, take Route 7 north to Cornwall Bridge, then bear right onto Route 4 east towards Goshen. Go about 5 miles to an intersection with a flashing traffic light. (Berkshire Country Store is on the right.) Go straight on Route 43 north towards Canaan. Go 3.5 miles to a monument on the left. Turn left onto Ford Hill Road. Go uphill, and bear right at the fork, the Laughlin house is on the right, # 63.

From the west or east, take Route 4 to Cornwall intersection with Route 128 and Route 43, where there is a flashing light. Take Route 43 north towards Canaan and proceed as directed above.

From the north, take Route 7 south to Canaan. Go about 5 miles, then bear left onto Route 63 south towards Goshen. Go about 5 miles on Route 63 south and turn right onto Route 43 south towards Cornwall. Go about 1 mile to a monument on the right. Just before the monument, turn right onto Ford Hill Road. Go uphill and bear right at the fork. The garden on right at #63. Please park on the road, handicapped in the driveway.

Litchfield County
Open Day
Sunday, August 5

There are gardens open on this date in nearby Berkshire County, Massachusetts.
See page 150 for details.

LITCHFIELD COUNTY

TACONIC
Rivendell
50 Channel Road

We live on the point of the Channel of the Twin Lakes with our house and garden surrounded by water on three sides. Twenty-five years ago the garden was a weedy hillside, but after stone steps were set in place, the hillside slowly evolved into a scent-filled garden set off by trellises wrapped in clematis, roses, and honeysuckle. A weeping Japanese maple filters sunlight over the koi pond. Down the path toward the dock is a shade garden of astilbes, hosta, and ferns. On the upper level is our secret garden, an enclosed garden where clematis, roses, and ferns mingle with pots of annuals. **NEW**

Hours: 10 a.m. to 4 p.m.

From the north, take Route 7 to Canaan and turn right at traffic light onto Route 44 West. Go 5 miles to blinking traffic light and turn right onto Taconic Road. Go 2.4 miles and turn right onto Channel Road (single lane dirt road) to last house at end of road. There is room for eight to ten cars. Volunteers will direct parking if none is available.

From the south, take Route 44 through Salisbury. Look for the White Hart Inn on left and continue on Route 44, 1.4 miles to blinking traffic light. Turn left onto Taconic Road and proceed as directed above.

Proceeds shared with Berkshire Botanical Gardens

Hartford
& New Haven County
Open Day
Sunday, August 12

HARTFORD COUNTY

PLANTSVILLE
The Kaminski Garden
513 Marion Avenue

"Wow" is usually the first word spoken as visitors pass through the gates and enter the garden. Mature trees anchor the sweeping curves of the oversized garden beds to the earth. Interesting foliage and a succession of bloom keep this garden looking great year round. Shade predominates throughout the space, as does an ever-growing collection of shade-tolerant perennials, shrubs, and Japanese maples. A soothing sense of softness is provided by the use of tumbled bluestone for the patio, the raised garden beds surrounding the deck, and the curved pathways to the freeform pool. Years of organic gardening have resulted in an environment that supports vigorous plant growth and provides a safe haven for the wildlife that live here. For the past 2 seasons we have been working at improving the "curb appeal" of the front yard. We added a granite obelisk and garden courtyard; ripped up the tar that ran up to the house and replaced it with pea stone and granite pavers; added a boulder garden; and installed another shade garden at the front of the house. **2006** ♿

Hours: 10 a.m. to 4 p.m.

From I-84, take Exit 30/Marion Avenue. From Hartford (I-84 west), turn right at the light onto Marion. From Waterbury (I-84 east), turn left at the stop sign at the end of exit. At the light turn left onto Marion Avenue. Once on Marion, travel about 1 mile, passing Frost Street. Next driveway on right is our house, #513. House is slate blue with detached two-car garage. Please park in driveway.

Proceeds shared with Dana Farber Cancer Institute/Women's Cancer Research

NEW HAVEN COUNTY

MERIDEN
George Trecina
341 Spring Street

This landscape designer's garden, with its profusion of annuals and tender perennials, is best seen from mid- to late summer. Although we have maintained the property since the 1950s, the serious gardening efforts came during the 1970s with a series of hardscape and garden-building projects. The one-third acre site is best described as mostly garden accented with ribbons of lawn connected by paths, stairs, and walls. This past fall we replaced the remaining front lawn with pea stone and brick edging and planted a seventy-foot-long boxwood hedge around the oval garden. A new "observation garden" overlooks the front yard. One guided tour is available at 1 p.m. Live music will be provided by After All from 2 p.m. to 4 p.m. **2006** ♿

Hours: 12 p.m. to 4 p.m.

From I-91 north, take Exit 18/I-691 west to Exit 6/Lewis Avenue. Turn right onto Lewis Avenue (which becomes Linsley Avenue) and go to end. Turn right onto Hanover Street to first traffic light. Turn left onto Columbus Avenue to second stop sign. Turn left onto Prospect Avenue and turn right onto Spring Street. Go to fourth house on right, #341.

From I-91 south, take Exit 15/Route 68. Turn left onto Route 68 and go about 2.75 miles. Turn right onto Route 150/Main Street. Turn left onto Route 71/Old Colony Road and about 2.25 miles to third traffic light. Turn onto Flower Street and go to end. Turn left onto New Hanover Avenue and then first right onto Prospect Avenue. Take first left onto Spring Street.

From I-84, take Exit 27/I-691 east to Exit 5/Route 71/Chamberlain Highway. Turn right onto Route 71 and go to end. Turn left onto West Main Street and go to first light. Turn right onto Bradley Avenue and go to stop sign. Turn left onto Winthrop Terrace and go to first light. Continue through intersection up Columbus Avenue to second stop sign. Turn left onto Prospect Avenue and then right onto Spring Street.

Please park along Spring Street. Persons with walking problems may drive up driveway.

Fairfield County Open Day Sunday, September 16

FAIRFIELD COUNTY

GREENWICH

Topiary Fancies— Garden of Lucy & Nat Day
Hillside Drive & North Maple Avenue

Jumbo the elephant welcomes you to sit in his elegant *howdah*. Made of boxwood with a steel frame, he is eleven feet long and five feet tall, with a fountain coming out of his trunk, and resides in a grove of winter-hardy palm and banana trees. Our garden, which is designed to amuse and amaze, has fifteen topiary forms in seven vignettes. They include two full-size lions flanking a stone staircase, three frogs cavorting by the swimming pool, a hunting dog and pheasant going up a hillside, and other surprises tucked in a secret garden near a Machin greenhouse. The house dates from 1901 and it is on less than an acre. It has a soaring addition behind it with contemporary art and sculpture. The greenhouse and the entry to the addition will also be open to visitors. **2006** ♿

Hours: 10 a.m. to 4 p.m.

From Merritt Parkway/Route 15, take Exit 31/North Street/Greenwich and turn towards North Street/Greenwich business district. Continue on North Street 4.2 miles to where it dead-ends. Turn right onto North Maple Avenue and take next right onto Hillside Drive.

From I-95, take Exit 4/Indian Field Road/Cos Cob and follow signs for Route 1. At traffic light, turn left onto Route 1. Go 0.8 mile and turn right onto Maple Avenue. Go 0.4 mile and turn right onto Hillside Drive. Please park on street.

Proceeds shared with the Breast Cancer Alliance

RIVERSIDE
172 Indian Head Road
172 Indian Head Road

This house was purchased by its current owner in 2002 and substantial renovations were completed over a two-year period. The owners asked landscape architects Peter Cummin and Chris Thorpe, of Cummin Associates, Inc., to develop a master plan with them for the terraces and gardens. Work on the gardens began in 2003 and included new layouts for the driveways and motor courts; construction of the rear terraces, staircases, retaining walls; spa; and design of the garden plantings. In the front garden area, large boxwood groups, a pair of mature European beech, and clusters of evergreen shrubs create a lush and private entrance. The oval boxwood parterre, which is centered on the front door, along with the domed boxwoods in large lead pots at the four corners of the stone and brick courtyard serve to frame the entrance to the house. The western views over the salt marshes and out to the bay are lovely and ever-changing, especially at sunset. Cummin Associates added a shaded terrace at the far end of the pool to take advantage of the lovely "framework" afforded by the large oak trees. The bench and seat swings offer a shady, cool spot for summer reading. Along the seawall, generous plantings of native switch grass, bayberries, and beach roses extend the garden out to the salt marsh and to the wonderful views beyond. **NEW** ♿

Hours: 10 a.m. to 4 p.m.

Take I-95 to Exit 5/Riverside/Old Greenwich. At the end of exit ramp, turn left onto Putnam Avenue/Route 1. Go to second traffic light and turn left onto Riverside Avenue. (St. Catherine of Siena, Balducci on corners). Go over I-95 and over railroad tracks. At end of railroad bridge, bear right to stay on Riverside. At stop sign (St. Paul's church on right), turn right onto Indian Head Road. Go about 1 mile; 172 is on right.

Hartford County
Open Day
Sunday, September 16

HARTFORD COUNTY

AVON

Green Dreams—
Garden of Jan Nickel
71 Country Club Road

This established twenty-five-year-old garden of quiet timeless natural beauty, gives a sense of permanence upon entering the iron gates. There is a profusion of four-season color and texture woven in a tapestry of unusual perennials, shrubs, and trees. A distinctive use of architectural elements creates illusions and expand the boundaries of ample compositions, while seamlessly blending living and outdoor spaces. Unanticipated twists and turns in garden paths create vignettes; while hidden pots, packed with unusual annuals, come into view. This artful designer's garden has been featured in *Woman's Day: Garden and Deck Design* (Fall 2004), in Sydney Eddison's book *Gardens to Go*, and *The Welcoming Garden* by Gordon Hayward (2006). **2006** ♿

Hours: 10 a.m. to 4 p.m.

From I-84, take Exit 39/Farmington/Route 4. From intersection of Routes 10 and 4, turn right onto Route 10 for 5.7 miles to Route 44. Turn left and follow 0.7 mile to intersection of Route 10 and Old Farms Road. Turn left and go 1.3 miles to Country Club Road. Turn right and go 0.3 mile to #71. Please park across street on Tamara Circle.

Proceeds shared with Animal Friends of Connecticut

FARMINGTON

Kate Emery & Steve Silk
74 Prattling Pond Road

Our evolving, ambitious one-acre garden in the woods reflects a fascination with using colorful foliage for season-long interest. It also includes elements of both formal and informal design, which are enhanced by our ongoing experiments with color. The garden peaks around tulip time and again late in the season, brightened by architectural annuals, tropicals, and a host of fall-flowering perennials. Many of the beds have been reworked in the past year to beef up their structure and to accommodate our increasing affinity for tropical plants and unusual annuals. **2006**

Hours: 12 p.m. to 4 p.m.

From I-84, take Exit 39. Move to right lane of exit ramp. At end, turn right toward UConn Health Center. Go about 100 yards, turn left onto Prattling Pond Road (across from entrance to commuter parking lot), and go straight to #74, last driveway on right. Please park in driveway or on road past driveway.

GLASTONBURY

The Murray Gardens
576 Thompson Street

This is a colorful collection of gardens created for new construction, utilizing mature plantings of perennials divided and moved from our

♿ indicates parts of garden are handicapped accessible

previous property, and unusual native trees. The property features three perennial borders and a daylily bed planted along old stone walls and fences, a carpet rose bank and herb garden, and woodland paths with a wide variety of shade plants and garden art in a naturalized front yard setting. Our backyard includes sun and shade plantings built into the pool deck and an inviting sunken Japanese garden accessed by a footbridge over a small stream connecting two ponds. **2006** ⅃

Hours: 10 a.m. to 4 p.m.

From Hartford, take Route 2 east to Exit 10. Turn left off exit ramp onto Route 83. Take first right onto Chimney Sweep Hill. Go up hill 1.5 miles to end. Turn left onto Thompson Street. House is about 0.25 mile on right, across from farm.

From east, take Route 2 west to Exit 11. Go left off exit ramp, and then take second right onto Thompson Street. Our house, #576, is 1.5 miles on right. Please park on street.

WETHERSFIELD
Idyll Haven—Sue & Tom Webel
49 Toll Gate Road

Our garden, located on a small suburban lot, began in 1996 with a ring of annuals around the lamp post. Since then we have developed a series of intensely planted meandering mixed borders and pathways that encompass all four sides of the house. Emphasis is on late-season interest and is accomplished with the use of rare and unusual woody plants, variegated and colored foliage, late blooming perennials, and an extensive use of tropicals and "temperennials". We've tried to identify microclimates and take advantage of them when possible. A remodeling of our house in 2004 included a large bluestone patio area and additional sunny garden space that allowed us to further explore our obsession with designing tender plant combinations in containers. It is here where we garden in a state of "zonal denial". **NEW**

Hours: 10 a.m. to 4 p.m.

From I-91 North, take Exit 24. Turn right off exit ramp onto the Silas Deane Highway/ Route 99. Go 1.5 miles and turn left onto Wells Road/Route 175. Go 1.3 miles and turn right onto Ridge Road. Go about 1 mile and turn left onto Toll Gate Road. Please park in cul-de-sac.

From I-91 South, take Exit 28 onto Route 5/15. Take first exit (Exit 85) onto Route 99 South. At first traffic light, turn right onto Jordan Lane. Go 1.2 miles and turn left at traffic light onto Ridge Road. Go 0.25 mile and turn right onto Toll Gate Road. Please park in cul-de-sac.

Fairfield County
Open Day
Saturday, September 22
FAIRFIELD COUNTY

WESTPORT
Judith & Charles Kiernan Garden
196 Long Lots Road

The driveway descends to the front garden. Along the drive grows an espaliered *Magnolia acuminata*, a weeping hornbeam, and a grove of native trees. Weeping katsura flank the house and columnar beeches frame the front entry. Maturing boxwoods moor the architecture. A group of weeping *nootkatensis* (Alaskan false cypress) grow at the edge of the front lawn. The back garden is enclosed by woodlands. Growing there are espaliered apple trees, a collection of standard wisteria (Cooke's purple), icy white birches (*Betula jacquemontii*), and pleached hornbeams. Weeping purpleleaf beeches play against gold threadleaf, false cypress. Narrow, vertical evergreens (deGroot's spire) rise over the terrace and swimming pool. Sun-loving perennials add midsummer and fall beauty to the center of the garden, while shade-loving perennials grow under nearby woodland trees. The garden design is by Mike Donnally. **2006** ⅃

Hours: 2 p.m. to 7 p.m.

From I-95, take Exit 18; from south turn left at end of ramp; from north turn right onto Sherwood Island Connector, which ends after 1 mile at Post Road. Turn left onto Post Road and make first right onto Long Lots Road. Go about 1.7 miles to #196. Please park on street, do not enter drive.

Proceeds shared with Project Inform

Public Gardens

FAIRFIELD COUNTY

DARIEN

Bates-Scofield House

45 Old King's Highway North,
(203) 655-9233,
www.historical.darien.org

The herb garden, adjacent to the Bates-Scofield House Museum, was planted and is maintained by the Garden Club of Darien. It contains many varieties of culinary, medical, and strewing herbs known to have been used in Connecticut in the eighteenth century.

Hours: Year round, daily, dawn to dusk

Admission: Free

From I-95, take Exit 13. Turn left onto Post Road. At second traffic light, turn left onto Brookside Road. Bear right at curve; house and parking lot are on left.

FAIRFIELD

Connecticut Audubon Society Birdcraft Museum

314 Unquowa Road, (203) 259-0416,
www.ctaudubon.org

This five-acre sanctuary, America's oldest private songbird sanctuary, was founded in 1914 and designed by Mabel Osgood Wright (1859-1934), a pioneering American conservationist, photographer, and author, to attract birds with trees and shrubs. Demonstration plantings and butterfly meadow restoration are in progress. This is a National Historic Landmark on the Connecticut Women's Heritage Trail. The site includes a museum with historic dioramas of local birds and wildlife in their natural environments at the turn of the century. New Visitor's Center and trails are handicapped accessible.

Hours: Year round, Tuesday through Friday, 10 a.m. to 5 p.m., weekends, 12 p.m. to 5 p.m.

Admission: $2 adults, $1 children

From I-95, take Exit 21/Mill Plain Road. Go north 0.5 mile to stop sign. Turn right onto Unquowa Road and proceed 0.5 mile to parking entrance immediately on left after I-95 overpass.

NEW CANAAN

Lee Memorial Garden/ Garden Center of New Canaan

89 Chichester Road,
www.gardencenterofnewcanaan.org

The Garden Center of New Canaan owns George Lee Memorial Garden. This garden is a four-season beautifully planted woodland offering visitors a splendid view of the many azaleas, rhododendrons, daffodils and wild flowers.

Hours: Year round, daily, dawn to dusk

Admission: Free

From Merritt Parkway/Route 15, take Exit 36. Go north on Route 106. Bear left at fork onto Weed Street. Go about 2.5 miles and turn left onto Wahackme Road. Turn right onto Chichester Road. Please park off road at entrance.

New Canaan Nature Center

144 Oenoke Ridge Road, (203) 966-9577,
www.newcanaannature.org

Two miles of trails crisscross natural areas of this forty-acre site, providing access to unusual habitat diversity—including wet and dry meadows, two ponds, wet and dry woodlands, dense thickets, and an old orchard and cattail marsh. Highlights include a bird and butterfly garden, a large herb garden, wildflower garden, naturalist's garden, small arboretum, and a 4,000-square-foot greenhouse.

Hours: Year round, Monday through Saturday, 9 a.m. to 4 p.m.

Admission: Free

From Merritt Parkway/Route 15, take Exit 37 and follow Route 124 through town. Located on Route 124, 1 mile north of New Canaan town center.

♿ indicates parts of garden are handicapped accessible

Waveny Walled Garden
677 South Avenue/Route 124,
(203) 594-3600

Waveny Walled Garden is located within New Canaan's Waveny Park. The property was designed for the Lapham Family by Frederick Law Olmsted's firm in 1917. In 1995, the New Canaan Garden Club restored the garden and tea houses and continues to maintain it. Inside its brick walls there are borders of roses, peonies, perennials, small trees, flowering shrubs, and annuals all overlooking a meadow and pond. Visitors enjoy the garden as a quiet contemplative space which frequently serves as a wedding garden.

Hours: Year round, daily, dawn to dusk
Admission: Free

Take the Merritt Parkway to Exit 37. Turn onto South Avenue. Take first left at Waveny Park. Follow signs to Power House. Garden and parking are on left.

REDDING
Redding "Parade Path"
Redding Town Green, (203) 938-2002,
www.townofreddingct.org

The Redding "Parade Path," on the historic town green, was created by volunteers and funded by donations. The design by Georgina Scholl provides a stroll along a native gravel and fieldstone path, past a nineteenth-century stone fire pit, to a Jens Jensen-inspired clearing with handsome rustic stone benches. The plantings are labeled and placed in chronological order from the twentieth century back to the seventeenth century, providing an educational resource to the community.

Hours: Year round, daily, dawn to dusk
Admission: Free

Take Merritt Parkway/Route 15 south to Route 58 north. At the first stop sign in Redding, turn left onto Cross Highway. Go to second stop sign and turn right. Town hall is on left.

From I-84 west, take Exit 11. Go to end of ramp and turn left. Follow to end. Turn right on Route 25, left on Route 302, left on Route 58, and right onto Route 107. Follow to center of town; town hall is on the left.

From I-84 east, take Route 7 south. Turn left onto Route 107. Follow Route 7 past Route 53 to town hall on right.

SHERMAN
The Sherman IGA Garden by Amy Ziffer
Route 39 North

Sherman IGA owner Mike Luzzi and local garden designer Amy Ziffer collaborated to create this unique garden in Sherman's small commercial zone. Ziffer planted for an English cottage-style garden feel and adaptability to the extremes of Connecticut's climate. Two large cedar pillars with climbing plants act as focal points. Many self-sowers give the garden a free-form, constantly changing aspect.

Hours: Year round, daily, dawn to dusk. This garden peaks during the first 10 days of July and is best viewed then.
Admission: Free

From the intersection of Routes 37 & 39 in center of Sherman at Sherman School and Rizzo's Garage, proceed north on Route 39 about 100 yards. Pass the Sherman Firehouse on left and take next left at sign for Sherman IGA. Park facing store, garden is on left. To right of store is a shady memorial garden maintained by Sherman Garden Club.

STAMFORD
Bartlett Arboretum & Gardens
151 Brookdale Road, (203) 322-6971,
www.bartlettarboretum.org

The arboretum is a ninety-acre living museum embracing natural woodlands, perennial borders, meadows, display gardens, and an educational greenhouse. The site includes a trail system and a raised boardwalk through a seven-acre wetland. The arboretum offers a wide variety of educational programs and courses for children, enthusiasts, and serious horticulturists, plant sales, a plant information service, and guided tours and walks.

Hours: Year round, daily, dawn to dusk
Admission: Free

From Merritt Parkway/Route 15, take Exit 35. Follow High Ridge Road/Route 137 north, (left off north or southbound ramps) for 1.5 miles to Brookdale Road on left.

Stamford Museum & Nature Center
39 Scofieldtown Road, (203) 322-1646, www.stamfordmuseum.org

The center's 118 acres include woodland trails and a 300-foot boardwalk along a stream for parents with strollers, the elderly, and people in wheelchairs. A garden with plants indigenous to Connecticut is at the boardwalk entrance. The setting for the property includes flowering trees, shrubs, and groundcovers, as well as a lake, waterfall, fountain, and sculpture.

Hours: Year round, Monday through Saturday and holidays, 9 a.m. to 5 p.m.; Sundays, 11 a.m. to 5 p.m.

Admission: $8 adults, $6 seniors, $4 children 4 to 14, children 3 and under free. Members free. Stamford residents free on Wednesday.

From I-95, take Exit 7 to Washington Boulevard/Route 137 north to Merritt Parkway/Route 15. Located 0.75 mile north of Exit 35 on Merritt Parkway at junction of High Ridge Road/Route 137 and Scofield Road.

STRATFORD
Boothe Memorial Park— Wedding Rose Garden
5774 Main Street, (203) 381-2046

A brick pathway lined with perennials, annuals, and shrubs leads to the exuberant Wedding Rose Garden. Separated into two garden rooms, the Wedding Garden has a restored fountain and displays 'Love,' 'Honor,' and 'Cherish' roses. The Rainbow Room features a colorful explosion of thirty-four varieties. Climbing roses on trellises and an arbor enclose the garden.

Hours: Year round, daily, dawn to dusk
Admission: Free

From I-95 south, take Exit 38/Merritt Parkway. Continue to Exit 53. Go south on Route 110 to Main Street in Putney, which forks to

right. Go south on Main Street 0.25 mile to park on left.

From I-95 north, take Exit 33. Follow Ferry Boulevard, bear left at fork, and go under thruway. Bear right onto East Main Street/Route 110 to its end (Main Street in Putney). Go 0.7 mile to park on right.

WESTPORT
The Bird & Butterfly Demonstration Garden and Native Plant Court at Earthplace
10 Woodside Lane, (203) 227-7253, www.earthplace.org

The Bird & Butterfly Demonstration Garden serves as an example of plants that do not threaten the Connecticut environment. Both native and well-behaved, non-native plants were selected for their function—to feed and protect birds and butterflies. The promise to promote the balance of nature has been kept. It is a pesticide-free garden. The Native Plant Court at Earthplace features native plants found in southern Fairfield County.

Hours: Year round, Monday through Saturday, 9 a.m. to 5 p.m.; Sunday, 1 p.m. to 4 p.m.

Admission: Please call

From I-95, take Exit 17; turn left at end of exit ramp onto Route 33 north. Go 1.5 miles and turn left onto Route 1. Go 0.5 mile and turn right at second traffic light onto King's Highway north. Take first left onto Woodside Avenue (becomes Woodside Lane). Go 0.9 mile to Earthplace.

WILTON
Weir Farm National Historic Site
735 Nod Hill Road, (203) 834-1896, www.nps.gov/wefa

From 1882 to 1919, Weir Farm was the summer home of the American Impressionist painter J. Alden Weir. Sixty acres have been preserved of the landscape that inspired Weir and his contemporaries. A Colonial Revival-style sunken garden, built by Weir's daughter in the 1930s, was rehabilitated in the spring of 1998.

❧ indicates parts of garden are handicapped accessible

Hours: Year round, daily, dawn to dusk. Visitor Center hours vary seasonally.

Admission: Free. There is a fee for house tours.

From I-84, take Exit 3/Route 7 south. Follow 10 miles into Branchville section of Ridgefield and turn right at traffic light onto Route 102 west. Take second left onto Old Branchville Road. Turn left at first stop sign onto Nod Hill Road. Follow 0.7 mile; garden is on right and parking on left.

HARTFORD COUNTY

FARMINGTON
Hill-Stead Museum's Sunken Garden
35 Mountain Road, (860) 677-4787, www.hillstead.org

A National Historic Landmark and a member of Connecticut's Historic Gardens, Hill-Stead is noted for its 1901 Colonial Revival-style house, one of the nation's few remaining representations of early-twentieth century Country Place Estates. Pioneering female architect Theodate Pope Riddle designed the 33,000-square-foot-house, set on 152 hilltop acres, to showcase the Impressionist masterpieces amassed by her father, Cleveland iron industrialist Alfred A. Pope. A centerpiece of the property is the circa-1920 Sunken Garden, designed by landscape architect Beatrix Farrand. This one-acre jewel is set within a natural depression and enclosed by a yew hedge. An octagonally shaped summer house forms a centerpiece, with brick walkways radiating outward toward the rustic stone walls defining the gardens perimeter. Ninety varieties of perennials, including peony, iris, platycodon, thalictrum, phlox, veronica, and anemone grace the beds.

Hours: Year round, daily, 7:30 a.m. to 5:30 p.m.

Admission: Free

From I-84, take Exit 39/Route 4 west. Go to second traffic light and turn left onto Route 10 south/Main Street. At next light, turn left onto Mountain Road. Museum entrance is 0.25 mile on left.

Stanley-Whitman House
37 High Street, (860) 677-9222, www.stanleywhitman.org

Period herb garden and apple orchard.

Hours: Year round, daily, dawn to dusk

Admission: Free

From I-84, take Exit 39. Go straight on Route 4 west 0.8 mile. Turn left at traffic light onto Route 10/Main Street, go about 0.2 mile to next light, turn left onto Mountain Road, and go 0.2 mile. Turn left onto High Street and go 0.1 mile. Look for museum sign on right.

HARTFORD
Butler-McCook House & Garden
396 Main Street, (860) 522-1806

The Butler-McCook Garden is an oasis in an urban setting. Designed by Jacob Weidenmann in 1865, who designed Hartford's Bushnell Park, the garden contains a formal rose garden and an informal lawn. The West Hartford Garden Club restored and maintains the garden.

Hours: Year round, Wednesday through Saturday, 10 a.m. to 4 p.m.; Sunday, 1 p.m. to 4 p.m. First Thursday of each month open until 8 p.m.

Admission: Free. Fee for house tours.

From I-91 south, take Exit 29A/Capitol Area and get off at second exit for Prospect Street. Turn left onto South Prospect Street. Look for Connecticut Historical Commission Building, a brick Colonial at 59 South Prospect Street. McCook House parking is inside gate on lot or grass.

From I-84 west, take Exit 54 to first left onto Columbus Boulevard. Take second right onto Arch Street to first left onto South Prospect. Proceed as directed above.

Elizabeth Park
Rose & Perennial Garden
Asylum Avenue, (860) 231-9443, www.elizabethpark.org

This 15,000-specimen rose garden is the oldest municipal rose garden in the country.

Also included are perennials, shade gardens, heritage roses, an herb garden, dahlias and iris, and annual displays. The Lord & Burnham greenhouses offer seasonal displays. The café is open year round.

Hours: Year round, daily, 6 a.m. to 10 p.m.; greenhouses only, weekdays, 8 a.m. to 3 p.m.

Admission: Free

From I-84, take Exit 44/Prospect Avenue. Go north on Prospect. Park is on corner of Prospect and Asylum Avenues.

Harriet Beecher Stowe Gardens
77 Forest Street, (860) 673-5782,
www.harrietbeecherstowecenter.org

A lovely example of overflowing, intimate cottage gardening on a domestic scale, the gardens were created by landscape designers Stevenson, Fuoco, and Canning. The main feature is the Blue Cottage Garden, ablaze in mid-June. July and beyond, the Pink and Red Garden, "High Victorian" Texture Garden, and Orange, Yellow, and White Garden take center stage. Enjoy many lovely historic roses in early June.

Hours: Year round, daily, dawn to dusk. Special tours offered May through October; Wednesdays and Saturdays, 10 a.m. to 1 p.m.

Admission: Free

From I-84, take Exit 46/Sisson Avenue. Turn right onto Sisson Avenue, then right onto Farmington Avenue. Turn right onto Forest Street. Parking lot is on right.

West Hartford
Noah Webster House
227 South Main Street, (203) 521-5362,
www.noahwebsterhouse.org

The Noah Webster House has a raised-bed teaching garden planted with herbs and other plants available to the Websters during the middle of the eighteenth century. A small demonstration plot of vegetables is also grown. Plants are labeled, so visitors may guide themselves through the garden.

Hours: Year round, daily, dawn to dusk
Admission: Free

Located 1 mile south of I-84 at Exit 41. Follow signs at end of exit ramp and travel for 1 mile. Museum is on left.

Wethersfield
Webb House Colonial Revival Garden at the Webb-Deane-Stevens Museum
211 Main Street, (860) 529-0612,
www.webb-deane-stevens.org

Designed by landscape architect Amy Cogswell and restored in 1999, the garden features a collection of "old-fashioned" perennials and annuals arranged in Colonial Revival-style borders framing garden rooms. Featured flowers in this summer-fall garden include eleven varieties of roses and traditional plants such as phlox, foxgloves, pinks, and hollyhocks. Member of the Connecticut Historic Garden Consortium.

Hours: May through October, Wednesday through Monday, 10 a.m. to 4 p.m.; November through April, weekends only, 10 a.m. to 4 p.m.

Admission: Free

From I-91, take Exit 26 and follow signs to Historic District and Webb House and Deane House.

LITCHFIELD COUNTY

Bethlehem
Bellamy-Ferriday House & Garden
9 Main Street North, (203) 266-7596,
www.hartnet.org/~als

The landscape boasts a circa 1915 formal parterre garden, collections of peonies, lilacs, and roses, as well as unusual specimen plants. An orchard, magnolia grove, terrace garden, landscape walks, and plant sales area are also available to enjoy at this property of the Antiquarian and Landmarks Society.

Hours: May through October, Wednesday, Friday, and weekends, 11 a.m. to 4 p.m.

Admission: $3 garden, $5 house and garden

🐾 indicates parts of garden are handicapped accessible

From I-84, take Exit 15/Southbury. At end of exit ramp, take Route 6 east 13 miles to Route 61 and turn left. At intersection with Route 132, stay on Route 61 and take first left into driveway.

BRIDGEWATER

Beatrix Farrand Garden at Three Rivers Farm

694 Skyline Ridge Road, (860) 354-1788, www.promisek.org

This stone-walled garden was rediscovered in 1993 and restored using the original 1921 Farrand design. Below the garden are a stone amphitheater, pergola, and pool. The garden is located on a beautiful 275-acre property where the Shepaug and Housatonic Rivers converge. Remnants of the Chinese garden and "arboretum of rare charm" described in a 1931 magazine article are scattered throughout the property.

Hours: May through September, last Sunday of the month, 12 p.m. to 4 p.m., or by appointment

Admission: $5

From I-84, take Exit 9 and travel north on Route 25 to Brookfield Center. Turn right onto Route 133 east towards Bridgewater. Cross Lake Lillinonah Bridge and take first right onto Wewaka Brook Road. Go 0.75 mile and turn right onto Beach Hill Road to end. Turn right onto Skyline Ridge Road. Go to very end of dead end road and take a sharp left. Please park along road between buildings.

LITCHFIELD

Laurel Ridge Foundation

164 Wigwam Road

The display of the genus *Narcissus* was planted over about ten acres in 1941. The original 10,000 daffodils have naturalized for the past sixty years. The current owners have maintained the display and encourage visitors to drive by and share its splendor.

Hours: April and May, daily, dawn to dusk

Admission: Free

Take Route 118 east from Litchfield, turn right onto Route 254, go 3.5 miles, and turn right onto Wigwam Road. The planting is about 1 mile on left.

White Flower Farm

Route 63, (860) 567-8789, www.whiteflowerfarm.com

White Flower Farm is best known as a mail-order nursery, but it's also a great place to visit. In addition to the working nursery, the grounds are home to an impressive collection of mature trees and shrubs. The Lloyd Border is a 280-foot mixed border of shrubs, perennials, annuals, and bulbs. Other display gardens feature perennials, tender perennials and annuals, and bulbs. Tour maps are available at the visitor center or the store.

Hours: April through October, daily, 9 a.m. to 5:30 p.m.

Admission: Free

Garden is located on Route 63; it is 0.7 mile north of Route 109 and 3.5 miles south of Route 118. Watch for sign, and please park in lot just north of store.

THOMASTON

Cricket Hill Garden

670 Walnut Hill Road, (860) 283-1042, www.treepeony.com

A visit to this garden/nursery has been likened to stepping into a scroll painting of Chinese tree peonies. See more than 300 named varieties of tree peonies in an array of color, flower forms, and fragrances.

Hours: May through mid-June, Thursday through Sunday, 10 a.m. to 4 p.m.; other times by appointment only

Admission: Free

From I-84, take Route 8 north. Take Exit 38/Thomaston, turning left at bottom of exit ramp onto Main Street. Turn left at third traffic light onto Route 254. Go 0.5 mile to a blinking yellow light. Turn left onto Walnut Hill Road. Go uphill 1 mile and see sign on right.

WASHINGTON
Hollister House—
The Garden of George Schoellkopf
300 Nettleton Hollow Road,
(860) 868-0163

A PROJECT OF
THE GARDEN
CONSERVANCY

This is an old-fashioned, but unusual, rambling formal garden informally planted with an exuberant abundance of both common and exotic plants in subtle, and sometimes surprising, color combinations. High walls and hedges divide separate rooms and open to create interesting vistas out towards the landscape. New areas are currently under construction.

Hours: Special Garden Conservancy Open Day, June 23, 3 p.m. to 6 p.m. Otherwise, May through September, Saturday, 8 a.m. to 10 a.m. and 3 p.m. to 6 p.m. Also open by appointment.

Admission: $5

From I-84, take Exit 15/Southbury. Take Route 6 north through Southbury and Woodbury. Turn left onto Route 47 north. Go 4 miles, past Woodbury Ski Area on left, and turn right onto Nettleton Hollow Road. Go 1.7 miles. Garden is on right. Please park along road.

WOODBURY
Gertrude Jekyll Garden
at the Glebe House Museum
Hollow Road, (203) 263-2855,
www.theglebehouse.org

In 1926, Gertrude Jekyll was commissioned to plan an "old-fashioned" garden to enhance a new museum dedicated to America's first Episcopal bishop. Although small in comparison to other designs she completed, the garden includes 600 feet of classic English-style mixed border and foundation plantings, with a small formal quadrant.

Hours: Year round, daily, dawn to dusk

Admission: $2 garden only, $5 house and garden

From I-84, take Exit 15/Southbury. Continue on Route 6 east for 10 minutes to Woodbury. Look for junction with Route 317. Take Route 317 to fork, bear left, and Glebe House Museum is 100 yards ahead.

MIDDLESEX COUNTY

MIDDLETOWN
Shoyoan Teien—
The Freeman Family Garden
343 Washington Terrace, (860) 685-2330,
www.wesleyan.edu/east

Shoyoan Teien is a Japanese-style viewing garden designed and built by Stephen Morrell in 1995. Inspired by the "dry landscape" aesthetic, the garden's raked gravel riverbed evokes the prominent bend in the Connecticut River as it flows through wooded hills near Middletown. Japanese tea ceremonies are periodically performed in the adjacent tatami room.

Hours: Tuesday through Sunday during academic year, 12 p.m. to 4 p.m. Please call for specific open dates.

Admission: Free

From the north, take I-91 South to Route 9 South. Take Exit 15. Follow Route 66 West. Turn left onto Veterans Way, and the right onto Washington Terrace.

From the south, take I-91 North to Exit 18/Route 66 East. Follow into Middletown. After the intersection of Routes 3 and 66, stay on Washington Street/Route 66 to the next traffic light. Turn right onto Veterans Way, and then right onto Washington Terrace.

From the east, take I-84 West to I-91 South. Follow I-91 to Route 9 South. Take Exit 15. Follow Route 66 West. Turn left onto Veterans Way, and then right onto Washington Terrace.

From the west, take I-84 East to I-691 East. Follow Route 66 into Middletown. After the intersection of Routes 3 and 66, stay on Washington Street/Route 66 to next traffic light. Turn right onto Veterans Way, and then right onto Washington Terrace.

OLD LYME
Florence Griswold Museum Historic Garden
*96 Lyme Street, (860) 434-5542,
www.florencegriswoldmuseum.org*

Using Miss Florence Griswold's records, paintings done on site, and historic photographs, landscape historian Sheila Wertheimer guided the Museum in the restoration of the garden to its appearance circa 1910, the height of the Lyme Art Colony. Miss Florence's garden can be characterized by what is referred to today as a "grandmother's garden" in which masses of flowers were informally arranged in bordered beds close to the home.

Hours: Year round, Tuesday through Saturday, 10 a.m. to 5 p.m.; Sunday, 1 p.m. to 5 p.m. Closed Monday

Admission: $8 adults, $7 seniors, $4 children 6 to 12.

From I-95 take Exit 70 in Old Lyme, Connecticut.

NEW HAVEN COUNTY

HAMDEN
The Connecticut Agricultural Experiment Station, Lockwood Farm Butterfly & Bird Garden
*890 Evergreen Avenue, (203) 974-8447,
www.caes.state.ct.us*

This one-acre site is comprised of three areas: the existing native shrub collection with a sand hill, a formal garden with butterfly plants connected by a water feature to a berry patch for birds, and a butterfly meadow.

Hours: Year round, weekdays, 8:30 a.m. to 4:30 p.m. Closed state holidays

Admission: Free

Take I-91 to Exit 10. Go north to second traffic light. Turn left onto Evergreen Avenue. Go about 400 feet and turn right onto Kenwood Avenue. Turn left after second barn, drive up hill to pair of barns and follow signs to garden.

Pardee Rose Gardens
180 Park Road, (203) 946-8142

The Pardee Rose Garden covers about three acres in East Rock Park. The rose beds are laid out geometrically, leading to a three-tiered central brick rose garden and are planted with 1,300 rose bushes. More than 125 named varieties are currently grown. There are four greenhouses, as well as annual and perennial flower plantings.

Hours: Year round, daily, dawn to dusk

Admission: Free

From I-95, take I-91 to New Haven. Take Exit 5 and continue north on State Street for 2 miles. Turn left onto Farm Road. Garden is 1 block up the hill.

NEW LONDON COUNTY

WATERFORD
Harkness Memorial State Park
*(860) 443-5725, www.dep.state.ct.us/
stateparks/parks/harkness.htm*

On the National Register of Historic Places, visitors can tour the forty-two-room Italianate-style mansion and Beatrix Farrand-designed formal gardens. Farrrand created a new plan for the West Garden and designed and installed the East Garden, the Boxwood Parterre and the Alpine Rock Garden.

Hours: Year round, 8 a.m. to sunset (park grounds). Mansion open Memorial Day Weekend through Labor Day Weekend, weekends and holidays, 10 a.m. to 2 p.m.

Admission: $7 residents, $10 non-residents. Parking fee.

From Hartford area, take Route 91 south onto Route 9 south. It will merge with Route 95 North. Take Exit 75. Bear right at end of exit onto Route 1. Go 3 miles to traffic light at Avery Lane/Route 213. Turn right onto Avery Lane. Avery Lane will become Great Neck Road. Park is on right.

From New York and New Haven, take Route 95 north to Exit 75. Bear right at end of exit onto Route 1. Go 3 miles to light at Avery Lane/Route 213. Turn right. Avery Lane will become Great Neck Road. Park is on right.

DELAWARE
Philadelphia Area
Open Day
Sunday, June 10

*There are also gardens open in nearby
Chester County and Delaware County,
Pennsylvania on this date.
See page 244 for details.*

NEW CASTLE COUNTY

WILMINGTON
Eve & Per Thyrum
19 Crestfield Road

This twenty-five-year-old garden has been lovingly designed, cultivated and maintained by the owners. They have landscaped the two and one quarter acres with choice "woodies" and shade-loving perennials, all meticulously groomed and labeled, and imaginatively arranged among whimsical ornaments and inviting sitting areas. This artist's/collector's retreat includes an unusual pavilion, a knot garden, dovecote (cover, *Fine Gardening*, 2000), gazebo, three-story conservatory, and a number of unique water features. The garden is a registered wildlife sanctuary visited by birds, fox, and raccoons as well as horticulturists, painters, and photographers. **NEW** ら

Hours: 11 a.m. to 5 p.m.

From Routes 1 and 202, go south on Route 202/Wilmington Pike. Turn left onto Naaman's Creek Road/Route 491. Turn right onto Foulk Road. Turn left onto Crestfield Road to #19 on right.

Public Gardens

NEW CASTLE COUNTY

GREENVILLE
Mt. Cuba Center
*3120 Barley Mill Road, (302) 239-4244,
www.mtcubacenter.org*

The woodland gardens of Mt. Cuba have been, for more than three decades, the focus of Mrs. Pamela Copeland's interest in native plants and conservation. Most of the plants in this internationally renowned, naturalistic garden are native to the Piedmont region of the eastern United States. Mt. Cuba is located on the gently rolling hillsides of the Piedmont countryside in northern Delaware. The gardens exemplify the beauty and integrity that are created when a single hand and mind, working over time, dictate the style and form of a landscape.

Hours: Guided tours mid-April through May and mid-September through October, Tuesday through Sunday by appointment

Admission: $5

From Route 141, turn west onto Barley Mill Road at traffic light at that intersection. Drive 3.9 miles on Barley Mill Road. Go past a four-way stop sign, over a bridge, and across railroad tracks, past Barley Mill Stables on right, past Mt. Cuba Road (Road #261), around a sharp corner and into a valley with a split-rail fence on right. Look for painted white rocks at main drive on right. Please proceed up drive without turning.

WILMINGTON
Gibraltar
*2501 Pennsylvania Avenue,
(302) 651-9617, www.preservationde.org*

Gilbraltar was designed by the landscape architect Marian Cruger Coffin between 1916 and 1925 for Isabella du Pont Sharp and Hugh Rodney Sharp, Sr. Coffin considered Gibraltar to be the best of her many commissions, and it is perhaps the most intact of her extant works today. Typical of the European-influenced design so prevalent during the early twentieth century in America, the estate has become one of Wilmington's few remaining urban open spaces. Formal elements like the Italian Garden, the Boxwood Walk, and the Bald Cypress Allée leading to a belvedere, are set within a dramatically sloping English parkscape. An extensive collection of statuary and garden ornaments is displayed throughout the site. Stone and extensive wrought iron work of the highest caliber completes the design. In 1998,

ら indicates parts of garden are handicapped accessible

Gibraltar was placed on the National Register for Historic Places, and is owned by Preservation Delaware, Inc.

Hours: Year round, daily, dawn to dusk

Admission: Free

From I-95 into Wilmington, take Route 52 north/Pennsylvania Avenue, approximately 1.2 miles. Turn right at Greenhill Avenue. Please enter the property through the stone gatepost and park according to directional signage.

Winterthur Museum & Country Estate
Route 52 (5105 Kennett Pike),
(302) 888-4600, www.winterthur.org

Winterthur's 1,000-acre country estate encompasses rolling hills, streams, meadows, and forests. Founder Henry Francis du Pont (1880-1969) developed an appreciation of nature as a boy that served as the basis for his life's work in the garden. He selected the choicest plants from around the world to enhance the natural setting, arranging them in lyrical color combinations and carefully orchestrating a succession of bloom from late January to November. Du Pont translated his love of the land into a unified work of art that embodies a romantic vision of nature's beauty.

Hours: Year round, Tuesday through Sunday, 10 a.m. to 5 p.m. Closed Mondays (except holidays and during Yuletide), Thanksgiving Day, and Christmas Day.

Admission: $15 adults, $13 studens/seniors, $5 children ages 2-11, members free

Located on Route 52, 6 miles northwest of Wilmington, 5 miles south of Route 1, and 30 miles southwest of Philadelphia, Pennsylvania.

FLORIDA
Vero Beach Open Day
Saturday, April 7

INDIAN RIVER COUNTY

VERO BEACH
Drea's Garden
2661 Victory Boulevard

Some people call my front yard eclectic or Thai. I spend more time watching my plants grow than I do maintaining them, creating interest with foliage, color, and texture without relying on flowers. The garden's backbone is native material used in such a fashion that it harmonizes with the tropical landscape. As a collector of palms and cycads and being fond of bromeliads and Florida native plants, I prefer a look of "organized intrigue" without being unkempt. The backyard mission was to be more "woodsy" leaving one with a feeling of quiet contentment and being in touch with nature. To keep from having too large a variety of plant material, I selected species with similar forms but am rewarded with diversity of species in a unified design. My garden includes more than sixty palm species, twenty cycads, forty native plants species, thirty different bromeliads, and nine bamboos. **NEW** &

Hours: 10 a.m. to 4 p.m.

Take Highway 60 to 27th Avenue. Go north to stop sign at Atlantic/26th Avenue. Turn right and then next right onto Victory Boulevard. The house is on right (south). Please park along street.

Proceeds shared with McKee Botanical Garden

Marion's Garden
637 Lake Drive

Arriving at my house you are greeted by an explosion of color. Bougainvillea covers the courtyard wall and is the dominant feature of my house's exterior. Now pass into my courtyard, a protected space in the winter months. The back garden is the heart of the home, with an orchid house and herb garden enhancing the house and cuisine respectively. The exterior of my house is as important as the interior. I want an exciting, yet calm and restful atmosphere, and above all, a fun place to gather as a family. **2006** &

Hours: 10 a.m. to 4 p.m.

Take 17th Street Bridge to barrier island. Turn left onto Route A1A and go 0.2 mile to entrance of Riomar Bay II on river side of road. At stop sign, turn right onto Lake Drive.

Proceeds shared with McKee Botanical Garden

The Tropical Garden
of Vero Beach Avenue
2339 Vero Beach Avenue

This 1940s Key West-style house has inspired me to create a garden that reflects that same tropical and relaxing atmosphere. The front of the house is an explosion of color in the winter and early spring. The glass porch is framed by winter-blooming purple fire spikes, gold mound duranta, and blueberry flax lily. A short meandering rock path invites you to the front door and the rest of the front yard is loaded with tropical flowering plants, bamboo, and palms. The back yard is entered through wooden gates. The back yard is landscaped with a blend of tropical flowering plants and trees. Some of the major highlights are: the African tulip tree that has survived three Hurricanes, silk floss tree with its unique trunk of thorns, and a wonderful spinach tree specimen. The garden in the back also has a plethora of tropical plants like Panama rose in bloom in the winter, lavender fire spikes, gold cestrum, black timber bamboo, orchids hanging on the fence and in the trees, and many species of heliconia. There are many more plants nestled in the landscape making up this tropical feeling that reminds me of the Keys. **NEW** &

Hours: 10 a.m. to 4 p.m.

Take Highway 60 to Atlantic Boulevard toward 41st Street. Turn right onto Vero Beach Avenue to #2339.

Proceeds shared with McKee Botanical Garden

& indicates parts of garden are handicapped accessible

Public Gardens

INDIAN RIVER COUNTY

VERO BEACH

McKee Botanical Garden
350 Highway 1 (772) 794-0601,
www.mckeegarden.org

The garden is eighteen acres of what was originally an eighty-acre tropical hammock designed by landscape architect William Lyman Phillips in the 1930s. McKee is on the National Register of Historic Places and received the Outstanding Achievement Award for Historic Landscape by Florida Trust for Historic Preservation.

Hours: Year round, Tuesday through Saturday, 10 a.m. to 5 p.m.; Sunday 12 p.m. to 5 p.m. Closed major holidays.

Admission: $6 adults, $5 seniors, $3.50 children

Garden is located at 350 Highway 1, at southern gateway to Vero Beach, on mainland. It is 2 hours southeast of Orlando and 1 hour north of West Palm Beach.

ILLINOIS
Barrington Hills Open Day
Sunday, June 24
COOK COUNTY

BARRINGTON HILLS
Peggy & Eric Olsen
237 Oak Knoll Road

Tucked away on fifteen acres graced with towering oaks and a natural pond is our 1922 country estate. Amid quaint arbors and fountains, our garden includes formal venues—a flagstone walled terrace, a cottage perennial pool garden, arborvitae hedges, a boxwood-defined English rose garden, and informal areas such as a two-acre woodland walk teeming with daffodil beds overplanted with shade perennials. Our garden has three peak color seasons. Throughout spring masses of bulbs put on a show, along with many azaleas, rhodies, magnolias, redbuds, dogwoods, and forsythias. Summer brings an explosion of roses, lilies, clematis, astilbes, phlox, spirea, hydrangeas, and hostas. At summer's end, cimicifuga, anemones, and sedum complement the turning colors of oaks, maples, and serviceberries. **2002**

Hours: 10 a.m. to 4 p.m.

From I-90, exit onto Barrington Road north (about 12 miles). In Barrington, turn left at the traffic light onto Main Street, also called County Line (1 mile). Go through the light on Hart Road and turn right onto Old Hart Road (0.3 mile). Turn left onto Oak Knoll Road (0.25 mile). Turn left into the fourth driveway on the left side (1 block). Please park as directed.

Chicago Area Open Day
Sunday, June 24
COOK COUNTY

EVANSTON
McKenna Garden
1015 Michigan Avenue

Taking its cue from a roofline of our house that seemed to us somewhat Asian, our garden has become an exploration of English Chippendale motifs and a chinoiserie fantasy. Be enticed into our front garden by a lacquer-red bench where you can sit and ponder our full-scale bonsai Scotch pine. Step down into our sunken Fu Dog allée where whimsical ceramic dogs are set along exuberant mixed perennial borders that end in a latticework tea house. Designed by Claire and Ryan Kettelkamp, our garden is a quiet oasis that we welcome you to visit. **NEW** ♿

Hours: 10 a.m. to 4 p.m.

Take Edens Expressway/I-94 to Exit 37/Dempster Street. Go east 4.6 miles to Forest Avenue. Turn right and go 3 blocks to Lee Street. Turn left and go 1 block to Michigan Avenue. Turn left and look for Open Days signs. The garden is located 1 block west of Sheridan Road and 1 block north of Main Street.

WINNETKA
Liz & Bob Crowe
1228 Westmoor Road

A vista from every window was the goal in the creation of our small garden. The bones consist of a latticework fence, an arbor, a pergola, terraces, and a small shed. These design elements are used in various parts of the garden for interest, variety, and focal points with resting places for enjoyment throughout. Our garden is a work in progress as we continue to select and refine choices of plant material, with foliage color and texture high on our list. Two yellowwood trees grace the front yard, whitebuds shield us from neighbors, a golden raintree shadows the terrace, and a red chestnut tree is gaining in scale. The garden was designed and is completely maintained by its owners. **2002**

Hours: 10 a.m. to 4 p.m.

From the north, take the Edens Expressway/I-94 south to the Tower Road exit. Go east on Tower Road (1.4 miles) to Hibbard Road (3-way stop). Turn right onto Hibbard Road. Take the second left onto Westmoor Road. The house is the third on the right.

From the south, take the Edens Expressway/I-94 to the Willow Road east exit. Continue east on Willow Road (0.75 mile) to Hibbard Road. Turn left onto Hibbard Road to Westmoor Road (0.8 mile). Turn right onto Westmoor Road. The house is the third on the right. Please park along Westmoor Road.

Mr. & Mrs. Edgar D. Jannotta
1175 & 1171 Whitebridge Hill

This distinguished residence, built in 1857 by Jared Gage, is on the highest point of land above the Hubbard Woods ravine. The property originally extended from Lake Michigan through the Hubbard Woods area to the Skokie swamp. The Gages had been in their home scarcely three years when the Lady Elgin collided with a lumber schooner about three miles off shore. A great bonfire was built on the beach to guide swimmers to safety, and the survivors were laid on the oak floors throughout the house and revived with hot coffee and a little food. Many residents have lived in the house since that time, and some have made architectural changes. On the lake side, a large travertine terrace, added in 1985, provides areas for entertaining while viewing the water. At the bottom of a grand staircase, a serpentine path leads you to a series of perennial gardens, newly landscaped by Janet Meakin Poor. An herb garden, defined by low boxwood, and a cutting garden filled with various hues of blue, pink, and white annuals border the south lawn. At the crest of the bluff stand four very old and lovely osage orange trees. Wildflowers cover the bluff and give way to a grass winding trail that leads to a wooden deck just above the sand beach. Adjoining this property to the south is a smaller house, a future residence. The recently planted grounds have

also been designed by Janet Meakin Poor and encompass specimen trees: Japanese stewartia (*Stewartia pseudocamelia*), paperbark maple (*Acer griseum*), white fringe tree (*Chionanthus virginicus*), and mountain silverbell (*Halesia monticola*). On the east side, a low brick wall provides a backdrop for a plethora of white roses, Rosa 'Seafoam,' and a charming fountain outside the master bedroom. A bluestone terrace offers a wonderful area to relax and enjoy the views of Lake Michigan. Colorful perennials, shrubs, and trees separate the south brick terrace which is enclosed by two large fastigiate European hornbeams (*Carpinus betulus*). An arbor enhanced with *Rosa* 'Eden' and *Clematis* 'Henryi' and 'Nelly Moser' provides privacy and defines an intimate space. **NEW**

Hours: 10 a.m. to 4 p.m.

From Chicago, take the Edens Expressway to Willow Road exit. Turn right onto Willow Road and go east to Hibbard Road. Turn left onto Hibbard and go to end. Turn right onto Tower Road to Sheridan Road (0.5 mile). Turn left and go about 1 mile to top of ravines. On the left, sign reads "Scott Street" and on right it reads "Whitebridge Hill". Turn right, cross over a white bridge, and look for tall yellow brick house.

From the north, take Edens Expressway south to Lake Cook Road. Turn left onto Lake Cook Road to Sheridan Road. Turn right and go to Whitebridge Hill. Turn left and look for tall yellow brick house.

LAKE COUNTY

HIGHLAND PARK
Markus Collection and Garden
484 Hillside Drive

The Markus Collection and Garden represents years of horticultural experimentation. Brent began landscaping his family's garden when he was just a teenager: at first it was dwarf conifers and Japanese maples in the mail, then entire truckloads of them! When space became scarce, plant material was upgraded and grass removed. The collection of 200 dwarf conifers and fifty Japanese maple cultivars provides an ever-changing collage of sometimes unpredictable colors. Large pendulous dwarf conifers provide height and structure and are paired with red and yellow maples. You will enter a well-planned oasis featuring a collection of large pines which provide a seemingly endless landscape. Bolstered by success in his own garden and a passion for plants, Brent continued to pursue his teenage hobby by earning a degree in Landscape Architecture at Cornell University. He is currently tackling a PhD in Horticulture at Cornell while operating Markus Specimen Trees, Inc., a landscape design, rare plant acquisition, and horticultural consulting company servicing the greater Chicagoland area. You are sure to enjoy this captivating garden! **2006** ⅊

Hours: 10 a.m. to 4 p.m.

From Chicago, take I-94 west towards Milwaukee. Continue on Route 41 north. Exit at Clavey Road and turn right to go east. One mile down, before driving up hill, turn left onto Hillside Drive. Continue straight, past road on left, and turn into cul-de-sac on left. Number 484 is white house with fire hydrant in front. Please park on street.

From northern suburbs, take Route 41 south towards Chicago. Exit at Clavey Road/Skokie Boulevard. Turn right onto Skokie and immediately turn right onto Clavey Road. Proceed as directed above.

From western suburbs, take I-294 toll road to Lake Cook Road. Turn to go east. After 4 miles, turn left onto Skokie Valley Road and go 0.5 mile. Turn right onto Clavey Road and proceed as directed above.

Proceeds shared with The Chicago Botanic Garden

Chicago Area Open Day
Saturday, July 14

COOK COUNTY

GLENCOE
Litowitz Garden
610 Longwood Avenue

A new manor house and grounds inspired by English arts and crafts design, this collaboration of architects/landscape architect/interior

⅊ indicates parts of garden are handicapped accessible

designer and owner produced an idyllic setting. Plants, containers, garden ornaments, and lighting were carefully integrated among handcrafted landscape masonry and carpentry. A texturally diverse pool garden is juxtaposed with a folly garden of spheres. A sunken palm court features exotic specimen begonias. The stone terrace surrounded by a stone entablature frames the view to the large lawn. **NEW** &

Hours: 10 a.m. to 4 p.m.

The garden is 1 block east of Sheridan Road and 1.5 blocks south of Park Avenue (main east/west entry in Glencoe). The closest highway is Route 41. Take Dundee exit east to Greenbay Road and travel south to Park Avenue. Go east over railroad tracks and through traffic light at Sheridan Road. Go south on Longwood for 1.5 blocks (0.5 block south of Hazel Street).

GLENVIEW
Windmill
2660 Pfingsten Road

Windmill, our eight-acre estate, was originally a farm. Since we moved here fifty years ago, we have created five gardens: the perennial border, cottage garden, circular rose garden (planned to be as low maintenance as possible), small conifer garden, and vegetable garden, which has expanded over the years to satisfy our culinary interests. We also have the hobby greenhouses, where plants are started for the flower and vegetable gardens. In 2000, a mini-tornado destroyed the windmill and severely damaged many beautiful old trees, two of which we now fondly refer to as our Picasso Trees, because of their contorted forms. **2004**

Hours: 10 a.m. to 4 p.m.

From I-294 or Edens Expressway, exit at Willow Road and go east from tollway; or west from Edens to Pfingsten Road. Travel south 100 yards to #2660 on right (west side of road; southwest corner of Pfingsten and Willow Roads).

WILMETTE
The Drucker Garden
714 Forest Avenue

A love of the British Isles and a need to replace an unsightly garage were the impetus for creating our small English-style walled garden. Today in the old garage's place stands a uniquely detailed Tudor outbuilding which serves as the focal point of a garden that has become our own personal oasis. Enter through our stone-and iron-fenced front garden where you can enjoy a broadleaf evergreen collection that surrounds a beautiful copper beech tree carpeted with a tapestry of woodland perennials and groundcovers. Open the heavy wooden gates and enter our sunny walled garden where you will discover handcrafted fountains and an exuberant water lily pool. Stroll the aged brick-and-bluestone walkways and pass under the English hand-forged iron rose arbors to the long perennial border that terminates in a replica of our favorite English seventeenth-century cistern. Designed by Doug Hoerr and Ryan Kettelkamp, our garden is a retreat for us and we will enjoy sharing it with you. **2006** &

Hours: 10 a.m. to 4 p.m.

From Edens Expressway/I-94, take Lake Avenue East exit if traveling north, or Skokie Road exit to Lake Avenue if traveling south. Continue east on Lake Avenue about 2.8 miles to Eighth Street. Turn left and then right onto Forest Avenue. Ours is fourth house on left.

WINNETKA
Nantucket Garden
777 Bryant Avenue

The cedar-shingled Nantucket-style house, built in 1916 by Edwin Clark, with its flower-filled window boxes, provides a beautiful background for this enchanting country garden. A perennial garden of various shades of pink, blue, and white flowers cascades down a hillside. This garden includes many old flower favorites, stone walls, and roses climbing on trellises near a rose garden. A shrub border of green and variegated plantings provides a background. The owners are in the process of creating a ravine garden in the most southern ravine on the North Shore. Featured at the rear of the lawn is a boxwood knot garden surrounded by an alpine currant hedge and cranberry viburnums. The gardens have been created over the last twenty-five years by the husband, who together with his wife, spend summer evenings on the screened porch overlooking the garden and woodland setting. **2006** ₺

Hours: 10 a.m. to 4 p.m.

From Edens Expressway/I-94 north, take Willow Road exit. Go to Hibbard Road and turn left. Go straight to dead-end at Tower Road and turn right. Go east to Sheridan Road and turn right. Go 2 blocks to Humboldt Avenue and turn right. Go 1 block to Bryant Avenue. Our house is on right.

From Edens Expressway/I-94 south, take Tower Road exit and proceed as directed above.

Taylor Garden
901 Hill Road

After living in England for several years, we returned to the Chicago area in 1980 and wanted to recreate an English country garden with color throughout the summer months. We raised and re-designed the perennial bed along the back of our property in 1995 due to flooding concerns. Many of the original plants such as alchemilla, peonies, phlox, lysimachia, lilies, Shasta daisies, and veronica still remain. There is a small shade garden planted last year on one end of the property and a small shed on the other which has been converted to a playhouse for grandchildren. **NEW** ₺

Hours: 10 a.m. to 4 p.m.

From the Edens Expressway/94 coming north, exit east on Willow Road to Hibbard Road. Turn right at traffic light onto Hibbard Road. Turn left onto Hill Road and go east to Locust Road for parking.

From I-94 south, take the Tower Road exit and go east to Hibbard Road. Turn right and go to the third light and turn left onto Hill Road. Please park on Locust Road just west of the house about 1 block.

LAKE COUNTY

HIGHLAND PARK
Magic Garden
2219 Egandale Road

Stroll through the enchanted grounds of our Tudor-style house. Along with extraordinary views of the lake, tranquility is reflected throughout three acres of trees, gardens, and terraces designed by Jens Jensen seventy-nine years ago, and updated by Douglas Hoerr in 2001. Meander through the West Garden and Woodland Garden, and then enjoy the Jens Jensen Sculpture Terrace, views of the lake, and the colorful container gardens on the East Rose Garden and Pool Terraces. Feel transported inside a Monet painting as you enter our magic garden. Using lush pink, lavender, and blue flowers within curvilinear boxwood parterres, rose-covered arbors, and inviting gravel paths, Mr. Hoerr has created a garden room that evokes peace and serenity. Anchored by two rare myrtle topiaries and an antique rippling fountain, our romantic garden has become a place for butterflies by day and a perfect spot for late night dining with family and friends. **2005**

Hours: 10 a.m. to 2 p.m.

From Route 41, exit at Central Avenue east in Highland Park and continue east to downtown Highland Park. Cross railroad tracks to stop sign (St. John's Avenue). Proceed for 1 short block and turn left onto Sheridan Road. Proceed 1 block to Park Avenue and turn right. Continue along Park Avenue (road narrows and becomes one way), down hill to stop sign; Lake Michigan is in view. Turn left and proceed to top of hill. First house on right is #2219. Parking is available on Egandale and Vine Avenue.

From north on Sheridan Road, travel south to Park Avenue in Highland Park. Turn left and proceed along Park Avenue (road narrows and becomes one-way), down hill to stop sign; Lake Michigan is in view. Turn left and proceed to top of hill. First house on right is #2219.

From south on Sheridan Road, travel north to Highland Park. Near railroad track underpass, turn right onto St. John's and proceed to Central Avenue. Turn right on Central to next intersection turn left onto Sheridan Road. Proceed 1 block to Park Avenue, and turn right. Continue along Park Avenue (road narrows and becomes one-way), down hill to stop sign; Lake Michigan is in view. Turn left and proceed to top of hill. First house on right is #2219. Parking is available on Egandale and Vine Avenue.

LAKE FOREST
Old Mill Farm
499 West Old Mill Road

Once a working dairy farm siring championship bulls, this property consisted of a 1929 English Tudor home and several outbuildings eventually demolished by the original owner when selling a large portion of the property. Jens Jensen designed the original master plan for the entire property. The current owners purchased the property from the original owner's estate for their family residence, dreaming of restoring the property and house. Collaborating with John Mariani, Sara Furlan, and Jim Osborne of Mariani Landscape, they've created a truly magical garden. The Old Mill Farm focuses on the potager garden of boxwood partitions filled spring to fall with bulbs and annuals for flower arranging and herbs and vegetables for cooking. Next to this garden is a berry patch and, unusual for this northern climate, a bed of Italian figs. Two perennial borders are adjacent to the potager garden. One border focuses on perennials with annuals added for seasonal color. The other border is a butterfly garden surrounded by yew hedges. Future gardens are in the beginning stages, including an orchard, a woodland garden, and prairie restoration. **2005** ⚘

Hours: 10 a.m. to 4 p.m.

From Route 41 north, take Route 22 West/Half Day Road. Turn right onto Route 43/Waukegan Road and go about 0.5 mile to first street on right, is Old Mill Road. Turn right and go east to end of street. House is last drive on right. Please park along north side street.

Chicago Area Open Day
Sunday, July 29
LAKE COUNTY

LAKE FOREST
Camp Rosemary
930 Rosemary Road

This garden was designed by Rose Standish Nichols in the 1920s and is made up of wonderful garden rooms partitioned by pines, yews, and boxwood hedges. A sweeping lawn and luscious container plantings at the front steps are the first hints of delightful discoveries inside: a charming box-edged parterre, a thyme garden, and an urn brimming with roses, perennials, and annuals set against an ancient yew hedge affectionately called "the couch." Other areas include a chapel-like white garden with two reflecting pools and a vine-and-rose entwined pergola garden with three exuberant borders surrounding a small pool. During the spring of 1998, work began in earnest on the walled garden, which now graces the area surrounding the pool house. Elegant wide grass steps, paired rose borders, a linden allée, intricately patterned knot gardens, and four well-planted perennial borders are all key elements of this new landscape. In contrast to the softer colors of the perennial beds near the pergola, these borders reflect a stronger palette of red, orange, violet, and blue. Some wonderful burgundy and silver foliage plants complement the whole scheme. Beyond the walled garden is a lush wooded ravine. A meandering path traces the ravine's edge beginning at the grass labyrinth and ending in the small glade, which overlooks the ravine. From this vantage point, a statue of Diana, the huntress, watches over the whole garden. **2006** ⚘

Hours: 10 a.m. to 4 p.m.

From Route 41, take Deerpath Road exit right. Proceed through town, over railroad tracks, to stop sign at Sheridan Road. Turn right. Go 0.5 mile, past Lake Forest College, past blinking yellow light, and past Rosemary Road on right. Go half block to Rosemary Road on left. Turn left. Number 930 is in middle of block on left. Please park in front driveway area and on south side of Rosemary Road.

Lake Forest
Country Gentleman's Farm
549 North King Muir Road

These historic and significant garden, house, and outbuildings began as the A.B. Dick Estate created during the beginning of the 1900s. After subdividing the property, the Gardener's Cottage and the Stable/Greenhouse Production Center were preserved to create a unique assembly of architecture and recreated to suit today's owner's needs. The long entrance drive recreates the approach one would have taken to gain access to these buildings. Original trees were preserved and new plantings added to accent the long sweeping vista. The guest parking area, once used as a staging area for carriages and horse, creates a quiet entrance to house and garden. Stone and brick walks lead you to the house's entrance and gardens, just beyond brick garden walls. Plantings create a setting for the historic buildings and entrance courtyard, creating a sense of "arrival" to what awaits you beyond the main house. A series of garden rooms, paths, and plantings unify the three historic buildings. A bluestone and old street paver terrace surrounded by boxwood hedges, cascading perennials, and specimen trees anchor the main house and offer an intimate formal retreat for reading, dining, or entertaining. Curvilinear pathways and sweeping lawn areas lead to the garage and guesthouse, new uses for the stable and greenhouse production center. A sunken garden was created within the foundations of the old greenhouses. Naturalistic sweeps of flowering shrubs, perennials, and specimen and ornamental trees create the backdrop for this garden. Wander this unique garden created by Scott Byron & Company Landscape Architects, which carefully adds new elements and uses while preserving the historic elements that once made this a classic garden from the era of country estate gardens.
NEW ♿

Hours: 10 a.m. to 4 p.m.

Take Skokie Highway/Route 41 to Deerpath Road west. Go 0.25 mile past Lake Forest Hos-

pital entrance to King Muir Road. Go north on King Muir Road to garden. Parking on street only, approval from City of Lake Forest.

METTAWA
Mettawa Manor
25779 St. Mary's Road

The house and grounds were built in 1927 as a family compound. Donna and Bill are only the second owner in the manor's rich history and have been working for the past fifteen years to refurbish some garden areas and create new ones. The centerpiece is a walled English-style garden with forty foot perennial borders on either side of a sunken lawn that leads to a spring walk and rose room centered on an old fountain. Outside the east gate is a golden garden and an orchard/meadow bordered by a fenced potager, cutting garden and circular herb garden. The sixty five-acre property has two ponds, a woodland tree house, a ten-acre prairie, a parkland of specimen trees, and is surrounded by a newly reclaimed oak-hickory forest. The most recent additions include an ornamental lily pool, aqua-theatre, a three-tiered mound and a grass labyrinth with central fire pit. This year's Open Day will be celebrated with activities and festivities throughout the grounds. **2006**

Hours: 10 a.m. to 4 p.m.

Take Edens Expressway/I-94 to Route 41. Exit at Route 60 west, follow 3 miles to St. Mary's Road, and turn left just past horse stables to Open Days signs on left side of St. Mary's Road marking driveway entrance.

Western Chicago Open Day
Sunday, August 5
DU PAGE COUNTY

WEST CHICAGO
The Gardens at Ball
622 Town Road

Guests will enjoy a unique opportunity to stroll the colorful seven-acre Gardens at Ball, usually reserved for the wholesale customers of the 101-year-old Ball Horticultural Company,

♿ indicates parts of garden are handicapped accessible

world leader in the breeding, production, distribution, and marketing of horticultural products. The Ball Gardens have been the site for the evaluation and display of the newest annuals and perennials since the early 1930s. This is the only opportunity in 2007 for the general public to see the thousands of annual and perennial varieties showcased in the Hillside Garden, the Windings, the Sky Frame Garden, the Container Trials, the annual All-America Selections evaluation trials, and many other gardens. Guides will be available throughout the day to discuss the Gardens at Ball and answer questions. Guests may also view wetland and woodland restoration projects on the Ball property. Allow up to two hours or more to visit these exceptional gardens. Portable restrooms and a drinking fountain are available. **2006** ♿

Hours: 10 a.m. to 4 p.m.

Entrance to parking is just off Roosevelt Road/Route 38 in West Chicago. Turn north onto Town Road from Roosevelt Road/Route 38. Turn left at the marked driveway which will be just south of the Ball building. Parking attendants will direct guests.

The main gardens are handicapped accessible, but the wetland/woodland restoration areas are not. Please notify attendants upon arrival so that alternative parking arrangements can be made.

Proceeds shared with University of Illinois Extension Master Gardener Program

Public Gardens

COOK COUNTY

CHICAGO

Garfield Park Conservatory

300 North Central Park Avenue,
(312) 746-5100

Opened in 1908, the conservatory is one of the largest gardens under glass in the world. It was the vision of landscape architect Jens Jensen, who based its form on the domed haystacks that dotted the Midwest. The conservatory's eight exhibit houses feature plants from around

the world, as well as an indoor Children's Garden.

Hours: Year round, daily, 9 a.m. to 5 p.m., Thursdays 9 a.m. to 8 p.m.

Admission: Free

From I-290, take Eisenhower Expressway exit at Exit 26A/Independence and go north. Turn right onto Washington Boulevard, go east to North Central Park Avenue, and turn left.

Grandmother's Garden

2400N Fullerton Avenue
& 50W Stockton Drive, (312) 747-0740

Wide, undulating island beds of annuals, perennials, and grasses are set off by broad expanses of lawn weaving the gardens together. These lovely, freeform beds are a fine counterpoint for the formal plantings at the Lincoln Park Conservatory across the street.

Hours: Year round, daily, dawn to dusk

Admission: Free

Take Fullerton Avenue to Stockton Drive. Garden is located on west side of Stockton Drive, south of Fullerton, near entrance to Lincoln Park Zoo.

The Lincoln Garden

1600 North Avenue, (312) 747-0698

Set amid a broad expanse of lawn in Lincoln Park adjacent to the Chicago Historical Society, these gardens are at the foot of a handsome sculpture of Abraham Lincoln (1897). The six raised beds, thirty by 360 feet, contain eighty varieties of perennials. Annuals are added to provide seasonal color and interest. The gardens remain standing in winter, with the perennials and ornamental grasses giving form and color to the landscape.

Hours: Year round, daily, dawn to dusk

Admission: Free

North State Parkway at North Avenue just east of Chicago Historical Society.

Lincoln Park Conservatory

2391 North Stockton Drive,
(312) 742-7736

Lincoln Park Conservatory has provided a botanical haven in the city for over a century.

It was designed by well-known Victorian-era architect Joseph L. Silsbee to showcase exotic plants and grow flowers for use in Chicago's parks. Today the conservatory houses palm, fern, and orchid collections, and produces four annual flower shows.

Hours: Year round, daily, 9 a.m. to 5 p.m.
Admission: Free
From Lake Shore Drive, take Fullerton Avenue exit and travel 2 blocks west.

From I-94, take Fullerton Avenue exit and travel 2 miles east. Conservatory is located on southeast corner of Fullerton Avenue and Stockton Drive.

Michigan Avenue Streetscape
Michigan Avenue

Stretching thirty city blocks, these island beds fill Michigan Avenue with big, bold, beautiful seasonal plantings. Tulips underplanted with grape hyacinth herald spring. Masses of annuals, perennials, and grasses celebrate summer. Kale, pansies, and chrysanthemums, added to the fall-blooming perennials and grasses, announce fall, creating a stunning effect.

Hours: Year round, daily, dawn to dusk
Admission: Free
From north, take Lake Shore Drive south to Michigan Avenue exit. Central median planters extend from Roosevelt Road north to Oak Street.

EVANSTON
The Shakespeare Garden
Northwestern University, Garrett Place at Sheridan Road

Designed by Jens Jensen in 1915 and surrounded by the original hawthorn hedges planted in 1920, the garden is romantic, secluded, and especially beautiful in June and July when its eight flower beds are filled with roses, lilies, pansies, artemisia, herbs, campanula, forget-me-nots, and daisies, all evocative of Shakespeare's poetry.

Hours: Year round, daily, dawn to dusk
Admission: Free
From the north or south, enter Evanston along Sheridan Road and proceed to Garrett

Place (2200 North). Park on Garrett Place (about mid-campus), east of Sheridan. Garden is reached by bluestone walk on east side of Howe Chapel (on north side of street). Enter along this walk; garden is not visible from either Sheridan or Garrett.

GLENCOE
Chicago Botanic Garden
1000 Lake Cook Road, (847) 835-5440, www.chicagobotanic.org

The Chicago Botanic Garden spans 385 acres and features twenty-three display gardens and three native habitat areas. The Regenstein Center offers indoor galleries, exhibition spaces, greenhouses, a library and more. The gardens include the gardens of the great basin, an English-style walled garden, a three-island Japanese garden, and an enabling garden which shows strategies that make gardening accessible to everyone. Nine islands on seventy-five acres of waterways and six miles of shoreline distinguish this "garden on the water."

🔥 indicates parts of garden are handicapped accessible

Hours: Year round, daily, 8 a.m. to dusk. Closed Christmas.

Admission: Free. Parking fees apply.

Located 0.5 mile east of Edens Expressway/Route 41 on Lake Cook Road.

LAKE FOREST
Lake Forest Open Lands Association
272 Deerpath, (847) 234-3880, www.lfola.org

Mellody Farm Nature Preserve, one of six Open Lands preserves, is a fifty-acre nature preserve with restored prairies, savanna, and wetlands. It is also the site of the Lockhart Family Nature Center, housed in a restored historic gate house of the J. Ogden Armour estate circa 1909. Vestiges of the original estate landscape designed by Ossian Simmonds and Jens Jensen are still evident today.

Hours: Year round, daily, dawn to dusk

Admission: Free

From Tri-State Tollway/I-294 and I-94, exit at Route 60 and proceed east to Waukegan Road north to Deerpath west into nature center parking lot. Located on southwest corner of Waukegan and Deerpath.

LISLE
The Morton Arboretum
4100 Illinois Route 53, (630) 968-0074, www.mortonarb.org

The Morton Arboretum is a 1,700-acre outdoor museum of trees and other woody plants from more than sixty countries. Highlights are a new four-acre Childrens Garden, a Maze Garden, education department courses and special events, all providing engaging, enriching experiences.

Hours: Year round, daily, 7 a.m. to 7 p.m. (OST); 7 a.m to 5 p.m. (CST). Tours offered daily, family activities on weekends.

Admission: $7 adults, $5 seniors, $4 children 3 to 12. Wednesday is discount day.

Located at I-88 and Route 53, 25 miles west of Chicago.

DU PAGE COUNTY

WHEATON
Cantigny
*1 South 151 Winfield Road
(630) 668-5161, www.cantignypark.com*

Cantigny is a 500-acre public park with fifteen acres of manicured gardens including numerous formal designs, a rose collection, and the Idea Garden, which demonstrates unique gardening projects for adults and children. The estate also includes the McCormick Museum, the First Division Museum, large shaded picnic grounds, and marked nature trails along the perimeter of the park.

Hours: March through December, Friday through Sunday, 9 a.m. to sunset; closed Thanksgiving and Friday after, Christmas Eve, Christmas, New Year's Eve, and New Year's Day.

Admission: Weekends $8 per car, weekdays $4, twilight $5; bus rates available.

Take I-88 west to Winfield Road exit. Go north about 2 miles. Entrance is on right before Roosevelt Road/Route 38.

LAKE COUNTY

VERNON HILLS
Cuneo Museum & Gardens
*1350 North Milwaukee Avenue,
(847) 362-3042, www.cuneomuseum.org*

A crushed red granite roadway leads the visitor across a fieldstone bridge and into the seventy-eight acres of gardens and grounds surrounding Cuneo Museum. The property includes formal gardens originally designed by Jens Jensen in 1915, a conservatory, and Deer Park. Plantings change with the seasons and feature antique fountains and statuary and three lakes.

Hours: Year round, Tuesdays through Sunday, 10 a.m. to 5 p.m.

Admission: $7 per car

Located 2 miles west of I-94 at Route 60. Museum and garden's entrance is on Milwaukee Avenue 0.5 mile north of Route 60 on west side of road.

MAINE
York Open Day
Saturday, June 23
YORK COUNTY

CAPE NEDDICK
413 Shore Road
413 Shore Road

The gardens at 413 Shore Road have, like the house itself, evolved. They include a large border a shade garden, rock and rose gardens, a Japanese garden by the sea, a goldfish pond, and a harvest garden of fruits and berries. The gardens are eclectic, even eccentric, all the work of two retirees. No professional landscaping, no over-arching design, just plants and ideas gathered here and there. Visit us at www. shorefront.com. **NEW** ♿

Hours: 10 a.m. to 4 p.m.

The garden at 413 Shore Road is 0.5 mile below The Cliff House on Shore Road in Cape Neddick. It is 1.5 miles north of intersection of Shore and River Roads on ocean side. Shore Road parallels Route 1 and I-95, which are to the west.

Cragmere
6 Cragmere Way

The Cragmere gardens were only planted after major renovations to the 1895 "Summer Cottage" were completed in 1999. The house, sitting on a knoll, is grounded by the addition of a stone patio, connecting the kitchen deck to the front entrance deck. The stone walls of the patios are softened by climbing hydrangeas and a garden on one side cascades down the slope in several tiers featuring roses, evergreens, and grasses. Various small gardens include a fern garden and a Japanese garden close to the house, which again serve to soften the severity of the stonework of the house. The Belvedere garden was begun as an English cottage-style garden, but the harsh coastal weather has not allowed all plants to flourish. However, there is lots of color throughout the season begin-

ning with the red poppies and ending with the autumnal sedum. **NEW** ♿

Hours: 10 a.m. to 4 p.m.

From I-95, take Exit 7 towards Route 1/Ogunquit/York. Turn left onto Route 1/Blue Star Memorial Highway. Go 3 miles and take a slight right onto Clark Road. Go 0.5 mile and turn right onto River Road. Go 0.5 mile and turn left onto Shore Road. Go 2 miles and turn right onto Cragmere Way.

Proceeds shared with Maine Coast Heritage Trust

Sealedges
Shore Road

Designed and planted by Christopher Keefe, the gardens at Sealedges are natural—largely shrub, tree, and hedge plantings of species that thrive by the sea. The sunken walled garden of roses, hedges, lavender, and a flowering hydrangea also provides winter views from the house. Look for a section of wild grasses, some of which stand all winter. There are also perimeter plantings of mugho pines, cotoneasters, rhododendrons, cherry trees, a courtyard garden of flowering magnolia, cherry and dogwood trees, and a frog pond with a central show of annuals. **NEW**

Hours: 10 a.m. to 4 p.m.

Please follow directions to Wind Acre at 427 Shore Road in Cape Neddick. Park here and follow signs to Sealedges, walking over a rough dirt road (about 150 yards). Parking is available at Wind Acre only.

Wind Acre
427 Shore Road

Once so choked by bittersweet and briar that the sea could only be heard, not seen from the long neglected house, these grounds reflect the vision of the owner who, when she first saw them, recognized Sleeping Beauty. The showplace garden, originally made for entertaining on a grand scale, was a study in traces: the croquet lawn, the reflecting pool, the orchard, and the terraced perennial and kitchen gardens surrounding the house were still discernable. The swimming pool, although boulder-filled, was

♿ indicates parts of garden are handicapped accessible

intact. The task was to restore, remove, and re-imagine. What you see is the fruit of her vision. The only license taken is with the four island beds by the sea which link the newly reordered landscape with its "wild period." The plantings are restricted only by the dictates of the sea, wind, salt, and winter snow cover. There is no longer any room for bittersweet, whose name says it all so eloquently. **NEW** ♿

Hours: 10 a.m. to 4 p.m.

Take I-95 north to York exit. Go north on Route 1 for 3 miles. Turn right onto River Road (see Pie in the Sky). Turn left onto Shore Road. Go about 2 miles (North Shore Road) and turn right into driveway at #427.

Proceeds shared with Maine Coast Heritage Trust

OGUNQUIT
Mayfair
19 Israel Head Road

Our 108-year-old garden is on a two-third-acre sloping site. Mature specimens and original plants flourish in a dry, shady, and sheltered environment. We have English country style perennial beds; an Asian tea garden with a small pond, tea house, and bridge; a thirty-year-old American chestnut tree; and a large climbing hydrangea. A potting shed shares space with the owners' flower arranging materials. My husband, the architect, and I have strived to integrate the house, decks, and garden into experiences of surprise and peace. **NEW**

Hours: 10 a.m. to 4 p.m.

From the south, take Route 1. Pass the Ogunquit Playhouse on the right just at the edge of Ogunquit. Go 0.1 mile and turn right onto Bourne Lane. Go 0.2 mile and turn left onto Shore Road. Go 0.1 mile and turn right onto Locust Grove Lane, a gravel road that parallels the cemetery. Please park in parking area.

From the north, take Route 1. At the center of Ogunquit, veer left onto Shore Road. Go 0.4 mile and turn left onto Locust Grove Lane. Look for assistant, parking is restricted.

Proceeds shared with Marginal Way Beautification Fund

Mid Coast Open Day
Friday, July 13
KNOX COUNTY

ROCKLAND
Nina Scott-Hansen
235 Rankin Street

When we purchased our house twenty years ago, my first comment was "I will not have a garden." This turned into meandering beds of perennials. Twenty years of making steel sculptures and creating a half acre of perennial beds has evolved into a colorful and whimsical environment. Now a multitude of welded steel sculpture, chairs, gates, fences, and birds complement the perennial beds, escaped seeds, and structural trees to make this a truly creative garden. **2006** ♿

Hours: 12 p.m. to 4 p.m.

Follow signs to North Haven, Vinalhaven Ferry Terminal, located on Main Street. Go north on Route 1/North Main Street toward Granite Street. Turn slight left onto Route 1 south/Rankin Street. Go to #235 on right after 0.9 mile. Please park on street.

ROCKPORT
Nonesuch Farm
220 Mill Street

Our gardens were first created twenty years ago when we built a house on top of one of the Camden Hills. It was a wind-swept, treeless, rocky sixty-plus acres that posed many challenges. To use the land wisely, we immediately planted more than 10,000 pine trees. Over the years we have added gardens for cutting and color—using hardy plants—and a Texas-sized fire pit for the grandchildren who love to roast marshmallows and sing around it. There is a rock wall for young climbers and a play yard for children and dogs. The latest addition is a wisteria-covered pergola for outdoor dining. **NEW** ♿

Hours: 1 p.m. to 4 p.m.

Maine Gardens | *Nature and Design*
July 12—15, 2007

Presented by: The Garden Conservancy / The Farnsworth Art Museum / The Maine Olmsted Alliance for Parks and Landscapes

In Maine the wild and the designed intertwine. Maine's wooded lakeshores and rocky beaches, its blueberry barrens and hayfields, wide lawns and flowering gardens are symbols of an idea, an ideal of a cultivated wilderness, a place of abundance and harsh, transcendent beauty.

This symposium will explore the fruitful mingling of the natural and the carefully planned. We will discover the writers and artists who imagined this American Paradise, and we will hear from those who continue to do so; we will explore the work of the designers, ordinary people and eminent landscape architects who shaped and softened the wild terrain. We will celebrate Maine's rich and unparalleled legacy; its confluence of nature and design.

Speakers Include: Patrick Chassé, Page Dickey, Nancy Harmon Jenkins, Erica Hirschler, Leslie Land, Tovah Martin, Pauline Runkle

Contact Information:
Maine Gardens/MOAPL
P. O. Box 508, Lincolnville, Maine 04849
T: 207-230-0142
www.mainegardenssymposium.com

Additional Weekend Events:
+ Visit private gardens along Maine's mid-coast on Friday, Saturday & Sunday through the Garden Conservancy's Open Days Program.
+ Judged Flower Show.
+ Garden Fair, Art Exhibition, and Historical Garden Books Exhibition at Farnsworth Art Museum.
+ Gardening Photography Workshop in an Open Days Garden organized by Maine Photographic Workshop
+ Land Conservation Exhibit featuring Coastal Maine Gardens Trust, Georges River Land Trust, and Maine Coast Heritage Trust.
+ Flower-centered Art on display at various galleries in Camden and Rockland.
+ Exhibition at Maine Photographic Workshops.
+ Theatrical performance in The Fletcher Steele Amphitheater in Camden.

On Route 90, 1 mile south of intersection of Routes 17 and 90, turn left onto Mill Street and go 1 mile. Black mailbox has #220 painted on it; driveway is just across. Please park in field.

Oyster River Farm Garden
259 Mill Street

There are four gardens on the Oyster River Farm property: a sunken garden in an old barn foundation, a decorative vegetable garden, a large mixed border, and a moon garden. Each area features perennials, ornamental grasses, shrubs, annuals, and herbs. They are surrounded by masses of *Rosa rugosa*, meadows, and breathtaking mountain views. **NEW**

Hours: 1 p.m. to 4 p.m.

The garden is a 10-minute drive from Rockland and The Farmsworth Museum. Take Route 90 from Route 1 going north and turn right onto Mill Street in Rockport. Go about 2 miles. Oyster River Farm will be on the right.

Mid Coast Open Day
Saturday, July 14
WALDO COUNTY

BELFAST
133 Miller Street
133 Miller Street

When we moved into our house, the garden was a blank slate (a dream of a gardener). I am a weaver and am drawn to color and texture. The path in the front heads off the patio. From the patio the path was designed to keep disappearing—leading the eye and visitor on. I respond to curves as opposed to straight lines. The garden is quite simple—filled with my favorites. As with most perennial gardens, the intention is to have a year-round garden. The winter is beautiful with the structure of shrubs and the color in brick and rocks. Spring is a wonderful display of bulbs and flowering shrubs. One by one flowers appear; one color, shape, and texture at a time, as well as the birds, the orioles, the most prized. **NEW** ♿

Hours: 10 a.m. to 4 p.m.

From the south, turn right onto Route 52, (Hannaford is on the left). Turn right onto Miller Street, the town pond is on left. The garden, #133, is at the fourth house on left, a shingled Cape Cod-style with a trellis across front.

From the north, turn left off of Route 1 and proceed as directed above.

From Route 52 in Lincolnville and Camden; cross Route 1 and proceed as directed above.

From center of Belfast, turn east onto Miller Street at the library. The garden will be on right.

39 Battery Road
39 Battery Road

The owners of this one-acre property on Penobscot Bay are passionate gardeners, cooks, and sailors. All these loves are reflected in the gardens. A newly re-sited small kitchen garden contains a wide variety of culinary herbs, tomatoes for canning, and a number of short-season vegetables. A large shrub rose left from an earlier use of the area anchors the area. Several fruit trees produce at their whim. Stone walls, a small pond, and water and gravel streams address issues of slope and soil and create opportunities for a series of rooms with roses, water plants, and shade perennials mixed with sculpture. A grandchildren's secret garden is under development. Since sailors sail, much of the summer garden is relatively self-sustaining. A small greenhouse allows the owners to start interesting herbs, perennials, and annuals. **NEW** ♿

Hours: 1 p.m. to 5 p.m.

From the south, Battery Road is on right about 16 miles north of Camden Library on Route 1. From the north, Batter Road is on left, south of the intersection of Route 1 and Northport Avenue. A long row of mailboxes indicate the dirt road. Turn down Battery Road. At the fork, turn right. It is the first house on left. Please park on side of road.

ISLESBORO
Homan's Garden
110 Aldrich Road

My house and gardens are situated on eleven waterside acres facing southwest. The hillside garden is quite steep, and has many rock garden plants, evergreens—dwarf and larger—cornus in variety, and a beautiful *Cornus kousa* 'variegata' from the Arnold Arboretum. A stone wall near the house is home to about twenty trough gardens. The terraces around the house were designed by Thomas Church and the house was designed by my cousin, Boston architect, Nelson Aldrich. **NEW**

Hours: 12 p.m. to 4 p.m.

Take the ferry to Islesboro from Lincolnville beach (about 20 minutes). On arrival turn right, then right again at end of road. Go through Dark Harbor Village. Aldrich Road will be on right. Entrance to #110 is first on left.

LINCOLNVILLE
Shleppinghurst
98 Quarry Road

Originally forested, the gardens, now four acres, are lawns, ledge, granite quarry, a pond, stone walls, bridges and stepping stones, and many evergreens. The site is stunning and I have attempted to cooperate with the *genius loci*, exotics and natives are blended. Buildings are enhanced with decorative shingles, and a cedar swamp (*Chamaecyparis thyoides*) was just installed. A path ends at a landing where you may sit and enjoy the view. **NEW** ♿

Hours: 10 a.m. to 4 p.m.

From Route 1 in Camden, take Route 52. Go exactly 10 miles to Quarry Road on right. Go to end of driveway. There is limited parking.

Mid Coast Open Day
Sunday, July 15
KNOX COUNTY

NORTH HAVEN
The Anchorage
Ferry Landing Road

The Anchorage is located on the water in the town of North Haven. Less than an acre of steep stone and shale were converted twenty years ago into an intensive south-facing garden sheltered by steep cliffs. The resulting year-round warm climate supports varied plant collections. Among the trees (many of them weeping) are: larix, picea, *Fagus sylvatica* tortusa, parrotia, and *Cedrus Atlantica glauca*. There are collections of heaths, heathers, roses, and lilies. Rare plant collections of hardy cyclamen, Paris, alpines, and unusual sedums are planted in all of the walls and terraces, and in the gravel drive. All of this is intimately set about a century old classic coastal Maine shingled house with a colorful fey tree house. **NEW**

Hours: 10 a.m. to 12 p.m.

This garden is accessible only by foot from the ferry terminal. There is no parking. Turn left after the ferry terminal and walk up past the American Legion and post office following the water. As the road turns right and away from the water, take the first left and go to a dead end marked "The Anchorage" (approximately 0.3 mile total distance from the ferry terminal).

WALDO COUNTY

TREVETT
Frogs Leap/Elsie Freeman
123 Kimballtown Road

Nestled within a 100-acre tract of spruce forest on the Maine coast, the garden is an amalgam of mossy forest, rocky coast and cultivated landscape. Frogs Leap has evolved over thirty years. First came a tent and a series of forest paths, then the house, demanding that something be done to address a barren, sodden slope. Conversations with site work contractors, landscape designers, and more seasoned gardeners laid the groundwork for an ongoing passion for garden history and design. Later visits to gardens in Europe and Asia inspired specific garden rooms: a 150-foot perennial border in the English style, an Asian-style dry garden, a hillside stroll garden, and a chess lawn. Despite having developed without any master plan, the gardens are unified by the native woodland of spruce, fern, birch, and winterberry, and by the path that meanders throughout. Plantings have been chosen to withstand the rigors of cold, wind, and salt spray, with mostly native plants and hardy perennials represented. Happily some tender experiments have survived: Japanese maples, hydrangeas, rhododendrons, and roses. The garden has color from March to November with plants chosen to provide scent and food for the birds and butterflies. In the past, it also provided food for the deer, but they have now been banned by a seven-foot deer fence. Since the owner has moved to Maine full time, the house was recently remodeled, requiring a new entry garden, the most formal of the spaces, with stone terraces edged in box and standard lilacs. A field cleared for the new septic system has opened up new garden possibilities which will be planted after hosting a wedding in early July. The lawn will become a playing field and the entry to this space will be a potager, cutting garden, orchard, and holding garden. **NEW**

Hours: 12 p.m. to 4 p.m.

From intersection of Route 1 and Route 27 in Edgecomb, Maine. Turn south onto ME-27 toward Boothbay. Go approximately 6 miles to Boothbay Center. Pass a gas station on right and see the Town Green on left. In Boothbay Center, bear right, leaving the Civil War monument to left. Proceed straight on Corey Lane for 0.3 miles. Turn slight right onto Barter Island Road for 1.28 miles. Cross two bridges, a longer one and a short one at the Trevett store. After the second bridge you will be on Barters Island. Once on the island, bear left and stay on the West Side Drive for about 1 mile. At the church, turn left onto Kimballtown Road and go about 0.73 miles. At the end of Kimballtown Road, turn right into the last driveway. It says "Freeman, Frog's Leap". The house and barn is

0.5 mile down this drive, the only house on the drive. The house is at the bottom of a steep hill and will not be open for parking. Please park on top of hill where indicated on left and walk down to the gardens, or take the van provided by Coastal Maine Botanic Gardens.

SOUTHPORT
Rabbit Point Gardens
43 Moores Point

Broad sweeps of spring bulbs including tulips, narcissus, hyacinths, and minor bulbs in curvlinear beds emerge in the spring. Summer displays start after the second week in June and last through September with a wide selection of dahlias, begonias, roses, unusual annuals, and foliage plants integrated into color themed gardens around the homestead. The larger-than-life garden sculpture, "Mr. MacGregor's Garden" is the centerpiece of the garden surrounded by ornamental edibles. An observation deck overlooks the Atlantic Ocean. **NEW**

Hours: 1 p.m. to 3 p.m.

From Route 1 in Edgecomb, Maine, follow Route 27 south toward Boothbay. Pass Boothbay Railway Village on left and a reservoir on right. After the Boothbay Baptist Church (on right), bear right and stop next to the Civil War monument (4 corners). Go straight through the intersection onto Lakeside Drive. There will be opportunities to bear right or left but follow the yellow lines; pass lake on left. Follow Lakeside Drive to a stop sign at 4 corners. Bear right at the stop (again Route 27) and continue over the Southport Island bridge. Follow Route 27 for about 4 miles. Pass town hall, school, and store. Look for a white fence with oval finials with "Cowan" on the listed names. This is also Moores Point Road. Bear right onto Moores Point Road and follow for about 100 feet; look for "Cowan Parking". Please park and walk down the paved driveway to access the gardens and do not use the woodland paths. Wheelchair access on asphalt driveway only.

Mt. Desert Open Day
Sunday, August 5

Garland Farm—The Last Garden of Beatrix Farrand on Mt. Desert Island is also open on this date. See their listing on page 137.

HANCOCK COUNTY

MT. DESERT ISLAND
Judith S. Goldstein
76 & 78 Oak Hill Road

Somes Pond and wetlands border this eight-acre landscape, recently designated as a center for the study of landscape history on Mt. Desert Island. It has views of the Western Mountains and contains a number of large erratic stones. Landscape architect Dennis Bracale edited and revealed this extraordinary and varied landscape through linking and highlighting its natural features and creating distilled garden spaces that resonate with the larger inclusive garden. Highlights are the paths and trails, two large moss gardens, an East Asian-inspired garden surrounding one house, a camp cantilevered over the pond, and a number of minimalist, symbolic steel and granite objects that accentuate the landscape. **2006**

Hours: 10 a.m. to 4 p.m.

Proceed to Somesville. At traffic light, continue towards Southwest Harbor. After about 0.25 mile, pass Port in a Storm bookstore on left. Turn right onto Oak Hill Road. Go 0.7 mile to sign for 76 & 78 Oak Hill Road. Please park on Oak Hill Road and walk down driveway.

NORTHEAST HARBOR
Westward Way
30 South Shore Road

The Westward Way garden was originally designed by Beatrix Farrand. She envisioned a pointed vista narrowed by spruce trees on either side of a lawn sloping to the ocean with flower gardens on both sides. The left flower garden remains. The current owner has opened up the right side for more expansive views of Greenings Island. The property includes the champion larch of Maine, a *Rosa rugosa* hedge on the beach, two metasequoias, Japanese maples, and other specimen trees and conifers. **NEW** ♿

Hours: 10 a.m. to 4 p.m.

Follow Route 198 through the village of Northeast Harbor, bearing left at the end and continue to the road's end at South Shore Road. Turn right and #30 will be fourth house on left.

SOUTHWEST HARBOR
Alexandra's Cottage
73 Seawall Road

This fourteen-year-old garden surrounds a Victorian-style shingled cottage. Patrick Chassé planned the bones of the garden, and the garage is designed to resemble a period carriage house. The entry court has an extensive collection of alpine troughs, bonsai, succulents, and dwarf conifers. A sloping lawn leads to a sunken terrace of native granite blocks. Below are perennial and vegetable beds divided by a fence. A path to the water begins behind the grafted apple trees. The southeast woods contain a carpet of moss. **NEW** ♿

Hours: 10 a.m. to 4 p.m.

Travel south through Southwest Harbor on Route 102, pass the head of the harbor with a fine view. Turn left immediately onto Seawall Road. Number 73 is the tenth driveway on the left.

Public Gardens
HANCOCK COUNTY

BAR HARBOR
Garland Farm—The Last Garden of Beatrix Farrand
1029 Route 3, (207) 288-0347, www.beatrixfarrand.org

This is the last home and garden of renowned American landscape architect Beatrix Farrand (1872-1959). It was purchased and is currently being restored by the Beatrix Farrand Society, and was listed on the National Register of Historic Places in 2005. It is perhaps the

♿ indicates parts of garden are handicapped accessible

most intimate, complex, and personal of all of Farrand's designs and marks the end of a long distinguished life in design. A design and horticultural education center is being established at Garland Farm.

Hours: Special Garden Conservancy Open Day August 5, 10 a.m. to 4 p.m. Not yet open for regular visitation, Garland Farm may be visited by specially arranged Wednesday tours and by private visits. E-mail visit@beatrixfarrand. org to make arrangements or call (207) 288-0347.

Admission: $5 suggested donation

From island bridge, go east toward Bar Harbor on Route 3 about 2 miles. Bayview Drive is near top of a long hill on left. From Bar Harbor, go north on Route 3, passing through Hulls Cove and Salisbury Cove. Look for Bayview Drive on right. There are two ends to this road, and second end is the destination! Visitor parking is just off Bayview Drive in a mowed field with a path leading to house and garden. Maps to the other Open Days gardens will be available here.

LINCOLN COUNTY

BOOTHBAY

Coastal Maine Botanical Gardens
Barters Island Road, (207) 633-4333,
www.mainegardens.org

Experience 248 stunning waterfront acres; the rose, hillside, meditation, kitchen, and other gardens surrounding the visitor center with gift shop, café, and meeting space; the Rhododendron and Perennial Garden; Shoreland Garden of Native Plants; Fairy House Village; miles of trails; magnificent stonework and water features; birch allée; and sculpture. Special events, programs, and exhibits for all ages year-round.

Hours: Year round, weekdays, 9 a.m. to 5 p.m. (open until 8 p.m. on Wednesdays in July and August); weekends, 9 a.m. to 6 p.m. Closed Thanksgiving and Christmas days. Café open May 1 through October 15, 10 a.m. to 3 p.m.

Admission: Members free, $10 adults, $8 seniors 65 and over, $5 children 5 to 17. Group rates available. The gardens participate in the American Horticultural Society's reciprocal program.

The gardens are in mid-coast Maine, just over an hour northeast of Portland. From Route 1 in Edgecomb (just northeast of Wiscasset), take Route 27 south 9.3 miles. Bear right of the Boothbay monument (across from the town common), and at the stop sign immediately ahead go straight. After 0.25 mile, turn right onto Barters Island Road. The main entrance is about 1 mile ahead on the left. Follow the entry drive to visitor parking.

OXFORD COUNTY

SOUTH PARIS

The McLaughlin Garden & Horticultural Center
97 Main Street, (207) 743-8820,
www.mclaughlingarden.org

For sixty years, gardeners and garden lovers have been welcome to enter the gate of the McLaughlin Garden. Bernard McLaughlin began the garden in 1936, gardening in his spare time until retiring in 1967. From that point until his recent death, he devoted his full energies to the garden, collecting plant material from everywhere. Bernard was a quiet mentor to countless gardeners, sharing his wisdom and promoting gardening at every opportunity. Since 1997, the garden has been stewarded by the McLaughlin Foundation.

Hours: May through October, daily, 8 a.m. to 7 p.m.

Admission: Free

Located at junction of Western Avenue and Route 26 in South Paris, 0.8 mile north of Oxford Hills Comprehensive High School. Parking available along Western Avenue.

MASSACHUSETTS

Berkshires Open Day
Sunday, May 20
BERKSHIRE COUNTY

HOUSATONIC
Under the Hemlocks
258 Great Barrington Road

Our bowl-shaped garden in the foothills of Tom Ball Mountain came with many natural gifts: boulders, hemlocks, black birch, and pines. Added shrubs, bulbs and perennials rich in textures and color, Goshen stone paths, and various sculptures completed it. We were lucky to uncover a perfect place within the given ledge for water to gracefully fall into a small lily and fish-filled pond. This is a major focal point in the garden. It's the flow of these gardens that seems to please: from our sunken "fairy woodland," with a succession of bluebells, foxgloves, then echinacea, to our over-scale rock garden, topped out by plume poppies. Look for the secretive, mossy "Othello Boudoir" engulfed by ligularias, next to the outdoor living room. Going behind the huge rhodies up the secretive path to the "upstairs" hosta path garden and around back to view the water garden will complete your tour. **2006** ♿

Hours: 10 a.m. to 4 p.m.

From Route 7/Main Street in Great Barrington, follow Route 41 toward West Stockbridge, going under the Housatonic Bridge. Go straight. From blinking light at Division Street, (past the Williamsville Inn on left), go 3.6 miles to #258.

From West Stockbridge, follow Route 41 South to Great Barrington. Go exactly 4 miles to #258. The driveway is on right just over the top of hill. Look for Under the Hemlocks sign hanging from a tree.

Proceeds shared with Berkshire Botanical Garden

LENOX
Foothill Farm
119 Under Mountain Road

Lovely Goshen stone walls define the three tiers of our major garden area at the foot of the hill. It has extensive perennial plantings in beds and parterres, plus beautiful old trees, shrubs, and ornamental grasses. A highlight is a massive iris collection. The garden continues around the house with two graceful rock gardens, a mini apple orchard, and a 1920s pheasant run. Our pool, sited near the road, is densely planted with evergreens and grasses for privacy, and summer blooming flowers for pleasure. There is even a waterfall down the mountain, emptying into a stream running along the edge of the property. **NEW** ♿

Hours: 10 a.m. to 4 p.m.

From all directions follow signs to Tanglewood. Under Mountain Road begins directly across from the Tanglewood Main Gate on Route 183/West Street. Follow Under Mountain Road north for 0.3 mile. On right is a black and white sign for "Foothill Farm," and on left a large white house. Park in field behind sign and walk up driveway across Under Mountain Road toward big white house.

Proceeds shared with Berkshire Botanical Garden

RICHMOND
Black Barn Farm
937 Summit Road

After being greeted by a pair of fantastical topiary birds, a relatively new garden unfolds behind an old Greek Revival-style farmhouse. Entering the privet-hedged bulb garden with *Fritillaria meleagris*, muscari, and thalia, a stroll down an allée of blooming Wyman crabapples leads you to the pool garden and shade pavilion. Proceeding west through a newly planted taxus colonnade, enjoy the sixty-odd-specimen topiary. A pergola of *Robinia pseudoacacia* leads

♿ indicates parts of garden are handicapped accessible

past the boxwood topiary garden and into the formal potager, with its beech hedge and rustic growing frames. The garden encompasses approximately three acres. **2006** ♿

Hours: 10 a.m. to 4 p.m.

From Taconic State Parkway, take Chatham/East Chatham exit onto Route 295 east. Go about 15 minutes, crossing Route 22, and follow to end at Route 41. Turn left and go about 100 feet. Turn right onto Summit Road. Go about 1 mile to #937 on left, a white Greek Revival-style house with black barn behind.

From I-90/Massachusetts Turnpike west, take Exit 1/West Stockbridge. Turn right off exit, then left at intersection of Routes 102 & 41. Go through West Stockbridge and stay on Route 41 north, as Route 102 veers left at flashing yellow traffic light. Go about 5 miles to a sign for Route 295 on left. Pass Route 295 and go about 100 feet to Summit Road on right. Turn right and go about 1 mile, #937 is on left. Please park on mowed areas off road.

Proceeds shared with Berkshire Botanical Garden

Williamstown Open Day
Saturday, June 23

BERKSHIRE COUNTY

WILLIAMSTOWN
260 Northwest Hill Road
260 Northwest Hill Road

This lovely house features a harmonious landscape of interweaving meadow, lawn, stone terrace, gardens, pools, and house. Elegant, yet informal, the outdoor spaces vary in character from a dramatic woodland ravine, to an intimate bedroom shade garden, to an expansive lawn with views of Mount Greylock and Dome Mountain. Guests are immediately welcomed by an arrival garden with a terraced front entrance. They will visit a rhododendron and hosta shade garden, a rock garden with fishpond, and a lower grove with a sitting garden. Each is unique in character, yet intimately connected with the house and the surrounding multi-level terrain. **NEW** ♿

Hours: 10 a.m. to 4 p.m.

Take Route 7 North into Williamstown. Stay on Route 7 North around the rotary. After 0.25 mile turn left onto Bulkley Street. Proceed to end of "T" intersection and turn right onto Northwest Hill Road. Driveway is on right. Please park along edge of road, not in driveway as gardens begin in driveway.

Ilona Bell's Garden
152 Ide Road

My garden, surrounding an old carriage barn, is divided into rooms to resemble the English gardens I grew to love as an English professor. A walled garden leads to a formal pool, with an island waterfall and the divine lotus that blooms in mid-July. The entrance, a rustic pergola, borders a trellised, ornamental kitchen garden. A white garden, surrounding clumps of native birch, pays homage to Sissinghurst. A folly, with broken stones and a dripping column, evokes ancient ruins, while an arched window on an old marble base, framing the folly, the long hot border, or the distant landscape, looks into the past and future. **2006** ♿

Hours: 10 a.m. to 4 p.m.

From Route 43 about 1 mile south of Williamstown, take Ide Road to right. Park along Ide Road at second access road on right. Number 152 is on mailbox with marker.

Proceeds shared with the Berkshire Botanical Garden

The Weber Garden
156 Ide Road

The Weber house is a Japanese-inspired courtyard house designed by Maya Lin. Two gardens embrace the property, a Japanese-style Zen garden designed by Shin Abe of Zen Associates and a restored English "secret garden." The Zen garden incorporates a principle in Japanese landscape architecture known as *shakkei* or "borrowed scenery." The concept relates to incorporating nature into a man-created garden offering of rocks, water, and plants in a still-life setting. The Zen garden includes a pond with colorful koi fish. Stone steps lead visitors into a two-tiered circular stone walled garden, which was part of the original estate, built in the 1920s. In the center of the garden is a raised fountain draped with creeping eponymous and surrounded by flowers. Along the outer edge of the sunken fountain area is a cutting garden of zinnias. The upper section of the English-style garden consists of roses, black-eyed Susan, foxglove, peonies, poppies, lupine, astilbe, iris, lilies, bleeding heart, and assorted perennials. The garden paths have been restored with the original stone and design. There are beautiful views from the entrance to the "Secret Garden." **NEW** ♿

Hours: 10 a.m. to 4 p.m.

Take Route 43/Water Street about 1 mile south of Williamstown Route 2. Ide Road is on right. Number 156 is second access road on right. Mailbox is black. Please park on Ide Road and walk down gravel lane to gray house on left. Handicapped parking only allowed on gravel lane in front of house.

Proceeds shared with The Williamstown Garden Club

Nantucket Open Day
Thursday, June 28

Open Day in the historic village of 'Sconset is a self guided walking or biking tour. The lead garden is at "Hedged About," 10 Sankaty Road. A good map can be found online. Tickets will be sold after June 1 at the English Trunk Show Company, 8 Washington Street. Brochures will be available at all garden centers and greenhouses. Taxis and a public bus run to the village from town; we encourage you to leave your car at home. The Gardens at Nantucket Wildflower Farm and the Siasconset Union Chapel are also open to visitors today. See their listings on page 155.

NANTUCKET COUNTY

SIASCONSET

"Barnagain"
6 Coffin Street

This unusual Siasconset house is an early 1800s oak barn moved to the island from New Jersey, then converted into an architecturally interesting house tucked into a deep lot. The subtle design of the garden surrounding the house is a calm, small shady area featuring painted ferns, groundcovers, and stepping stones that lead to the open porch at the rear of the house. The trees and shrubs are typical for Nantucket: tupelo, juniper, winterberry, and hydrangea—used with restraint. In season, a barn door covering an oversized window slides open at the side of the house to reveal a carefully planned view of three mature tupelos surrounding an intriguing old garden ornament. **NEW**

Hours: 10 a.m. to 4 p.m.

This is a walking tour. Tickets and maps available on the day of the event at "Hedged About," 10 Sankaty Road in Siasconset.

Proceeds shared with Hospice Care of Nantucket

♿ indicates parts of garden are handicapped accessible

Hedged About—
Charlotte & Macdonald Mathey
Polpis Road

Hedged About is a thirty-year-old garden, and in that time has been developed and maintained by its present owners. As its name suggests, it is surrounded and divided into garden rooms by privet hedges totaling almost one-half mile in length. The different spaces created by the hedges contain a very large perennial flower garden in the English style, a recent planting of more than thirty trees, an herb garden, wisteria arbor, a fenced area containing blueberry bushes, and finally, a secret garden the full width of the property which features flowering shrubs and trees with winding paths, a gazebo, decorative garden shed, and a fountain. **2003** ♿

Hours: 10 a.m. to 4 p.m.

From Siasconset, 6 miles from Nantucket Rotary on Milestone Road, go towards Sankaty Head on Polpis Road/Sankaty Road about 0.25 mile. Hedged About is on left. Flower garden is easily seen from hedge at end of driveway. House has green trim and upper enclosed porch. Please park along road by front hedge.

Linda & George Kelly—
"Up All Night"
23 Morey Lane

The garden, approached through a privet arch, nestles into the bend in the veranda surrounding two sides of the house. The narrow stone terrace, with its pleasing curved lines and clumps of thyme interspersed at intervals, widens to form a large circular terrace behind the house. Indigenous stone is used to elevate the terrace. A pleasing mix of inkberry and hydrangea provide height in the back of the perennial garden. On the veranda, seating areas are an invitation to enjoy views of the lawn and garden. Striking oversized pots of shade plants mark the many doorways from the house to the porch. **NEW**

Hours: 10 a.m. to 4 p.m.

This is a walking tour. Tickets and maps available on the day of the event at "Hedged About," 10 Sankaty Road in Siasconset.

Alan & Janet Morell
27 Bank Street, Codfish Park

There are no clues indicating the sophisticated, small, beautifully designed garden behind this typical 'Sconset beach house. Classic shingles, white trim, and tidy hedges form the street façade. Gravel and stone walkways along the house lead to the diminutive boxwood garden and terrace that serves as an outdoor space for relaxing; a pergola linking the guesthouse and main house provides shade for a dining table. Attention to detail is the secret to the appeal of this garden. Trellises have details copied from gardens in France as well as other subtleties picked up by the well-traveled owners. **NEW**

Hours: 10 a.m. to 4 p.m.

This is a walking tour. Tickets and maps available on the day of the event at "Hedged About," 10 Sankaty Road in Siasconset.

"None Too Big"
24 Broadway (entrance on Center Street)

This small garden (twenty-two feet by forty feet) is in the historic section of Siasconset and the house it lies beside was once the lightkeeper's cottage from Sankaty Light, as well as an 1800 country market. The garden was designed in 1984 by the owners when there was only the 300-year-old sycamore maple in the space. The idea was to create a garden similar to the Cotswold gardens in England, with seaside touches such as the stone steps with shells. Boxwoods thrive in the garden due to our mild climate and cranesbill geraniums, roses, ferns, clematis, Solomon's seal, and hostas support the annuals we plant every spring in soft pastels. The garden has won a gold medal from the Massachusetts Horticultural Society in 1991, and was featured on the "Victory Garden." **NEW**

Hours: 10 a.m. to 4 p.m.

In village of Siasconset, start from country store and stroll up Center Street past town pump and just before end of street (2 from end on right). Sign on house reads "None Too Big." Enter through garden door.

The Powerhouse
25 Morey Lane

When we bought "The Powerhouse" in the mid-eighties there was no garden. The house stood in the top right corner of a long green rectangle, like a postage stamp on an envelope. We enlisted the help of Susan Child and Douglas Reed of Cambridge, Massachusetts to design a garden for us. Because of the length of the garden, they decided to create rooms divided by differing heights of privet hedges. Along the long front of the cottage is a bed with hollyhocks, buddleia, hydrangea, and tall annuals. The idea is to peek in over the privet growing in front of it. Then one enters near an apple tree into the cottage gardens of perennials, herbs, cutting flowers, roses, and flowering bushes. Every year we make changes; adding and deleting. We use no chemicals, it is a completely organic garden. It is very pleasant and reflects the simplicity of our life in 'Sconset, filled with children, grandchildren, and friends. **NEW** &

Hours: 10 a.m. to 4 p.m.

Morey Lane is the first right as you enter 'Sconset off of Milestone Road. Go to the second fireplug and turn right down the shell lane to the bottom to "The Powerhouse". Please park along Morey Lane as we have room for only three cars and a small turn-around.

The Sheiling
41 Ocean Avenue

The gardens are on an open sweep of lawn on the south bluff in 'Sconset overlooking a private beach. A charming arbor, covered in roses and clematis, frames the sea and sky. The main property welcomes you with an antique ship weathervane set in a sea of native grasses, and a long perennial garden carries your eye across the lawn to the guest house. Around the property are numerous perennial beds, a small orchard, a tiny rose-covered cottage, and a unique water feature hidden behind tall circular walls of privet. **NEW** &

Hours: 10 a.m. to 4 p.m.

Take Milestone Road to 'Sconset. As you enter 'Sconset, turn right onto Morey Lane. Go

& indicates parts of garden are handicapped accessible

to the end and turn left onto Ocean Avenue. The Sheiling will be the third house on left. There is no parking on ocean side of road.

Summer Salt
25 Coffin Street

A woodland of overhanging juniper trees, a glimpse of a crushed shell drive, and a white picket fence provide a sense of mystery and surprise as you enter the first set of gates to Summer Salt. The gardens in front of the house are designed to be more structured and dramatic than the back. The juxtaposition of three small white-trimmed buildings facing one another creates the sense of a small village. They define their own space in such a way that one can enjoy each of them individually as well as in their entirety. There is a balance between foundation plants and herbaceous perennials with spots of annuals which are designed to connect the whole. Behind the main house, lawns slope toward a deep stand of junipers that extends through to the next street. The generous porch, tall grasses, and wildflower beds create serene sunny and shady spaces for dogs and children. **NEW**

Hours: 10 a.m. to 4 p.m.

This is a walking tour. Tickets and maps available on the day of the event at "Hedged About," 10 Sankaty Road in Siasconset.

Berkshire Open Day
Sunday, July 22

There is also a garden open in nearby Columbia County, New York on this date. See page 205 for details.

BERKSHIRE COUNTY

RICHMOND
Chelsea Woods
85 Cone Hill Road

A short walk along a wooded drive opens up to the 1765 farmhouse and expanse of lawn and perennial beds featuring lilies, geranium and allium species, grasses, hydrangea, roses, lavender, a peony allée, and heirloom asparagus bed. Stone walls define hillside gardens planted with rhododendron; azalea; many varieties of daffodils, hyacinth, and other spring-flowering bulbs; lilies; hosta; and other hardy perennials. At the top of the hillside is a small cabin for relaxation, picnicking, and viewing Lenox Mountain to the east. Trees of interest include a spectacular Kousa dogwood, weeping hemlock, very large white pine, a young weeping copper beech and several black walnuts planted twenty years ago. Finally, there is a path through 100 acres of woodland leading to Cone Brook and pond that plays host to a beaver family and blue heron every few years. **NEW**

Hours: 10 a.m. to 4 p.m.

From the Massachusetts Turnpike/I-90 Westbound, take Exit 1/West Stockbridge, turn right at stop sign. At next stop sign, turn left and take Routes 41 North & 102 West through West Stockbridge until they separate at a yellow blinking traffic light. Continue 2.9 miles north on Route 41 to hairpin right turn onto Cone Hill Road. Take the second driveway on left and park in the mowed field on left.

From the Massachusetts Turnpike/I-90 Eastbound, take Exit B3 onto Route 22 South for 1 mile. Take Route 102 to the stop sign where Route 41 joins Route 102 West. Turn left at that stop sign and proceed as directed above.

Proceeds shared with Berkshire Botanical Garden

Thomas Gardner
2171 State Road

This is a rustic vegetable and flower garden set in the side yard of an eighteenth-century farmhouse in the Berkshires. The farm currently raises Cotswold sheep and mixed poultry. Rustic picket fences, grass paths, and grapevine trellises are features of the rough and tumble site. The owner raises Australian shepherds and Italian Maremma sheepdogs. An open living porch and stone terrace face the garden. **2006** ♿

Hours: 10 a.m. to 4 p.m.

From I-90/Massachusetts Turnpike, take West Stockbridge exit to Route 41 north into Richmond and to corner of Route 41 and Lenox Road.

From New York State Thruway, exit at Routes 22 and 203. Take Route 203 east into West Stockbridge, then north on Route 41 to Richmond and corner of Lenox Road. The garden is at the yellow farmhouse surrounded by gray picket fence and with red barn behind. Parking will be marked.

STOCKBRIDGE
Fitzpatrick's Hillhome
9 Prospect Hill Road

Hillhome, a historic and distinguished Stockbridge estate, was designed in 1918 by a protégé of Charles F. McKim who was known for the design of private country houses and U.S. diplomatic offices abroad. Its gardens, created from 1933 to 1935 by the well-known landscape architect, Prentiss French, the nephew of the sculptor Daniel Chester French, set off an impressive view of the Berkshire Hills. Leading to a long stone-paved and grass terrace is a heavy wooden garden door. At the northern end of the terrace stands a three-sided stone architectural structure resembling an arched ruin and created by moving an old mill, stone by stone, from West Stockbridge. This folly continues to provide a quiet and secluded space from which to enjoy the expansive views beyond. French made extensive use of massive stone retaining walls, thereby creating dramatic terraces in the steep hillside. Today, the walls contain charming alpine plants. Not to compete however with the view, the *genius loci* of the property, are the generally more restrained plantings and perennial borders. Be sure to visit the twenty-foot waterfall which splashes through serpentine paths leading down to an iris-bordered lily pond. You will reach it through a small secret garden at the southern end of the main terrace. In 1949, Hillhome was awarded the prestigious Gold Medal by the Massachusetts Horticultural Society. Today, French's original design remains largely intact. **2006**

Hours: 11 a.m. to 3 p.m.

At fountain in Stockbridge where Route 7 and Route 102 intersect near Red Lion Inn, go up hill past town tennis courts on Prospect Hill Road. Hillhome is on left before Naumkeag, a Trustees of Reservations property.

Proceeds shared with Berkshire Botanical Garden

Mid-Cape Open Day
Saturday, July 28
BARNSTABLE COUNTY

BREWSTER
Gardens at the McLoud House
2095 Main Street

The garden is a series of rooms. The front gardens are formal with a rose garden as a focal point from the entrance path. Very extensive perennial gardens have containers, sculptures, and vessels as accessories. There is a small sunken garden with a water feature—behind which is a sculpture in a niche—from there you are led into the secret contemplative garden. **NEW** ⚒

Hours: 10 a.m. to 4 p.m.

From Route 6, take Exit 137. Turn right. Follow until dead end and turn right onto 6A/Main Street. Pass the General Store on left, then Breakwater Road and Crocker Lane. After Crocker Lane, 2095 is 4th house on left.

From Orleans on 6A, the garden is located between Chillingsworth Restaurant and Bramble Inn on right.

CHATHAM
Behind the Hedges— Peggy & Bob Black
441 Old Harbor Road

Barely visible from the road, this cottage garden consists of a heath and heather garden overlooking Pleasant Bay and a perennial garden featuring roses, lilies, phlox, and coneflowers. Other planted areas include a shade garden surrounded by hydrangeas, a vegetable garden, and a patio garden containing hostas, hellebores, and skimmia under the shade of redbud 'Forest Pansy'. Tall pines create a green backdrop for specimens of *Cornus kousa*, cryptomeria, stewartia, Franklinia, Davidia, and chionanthus. **NEW** ⚒

Hours: 10 a.m. to 4 p.m.

⚒ indicates parts of garden are handicapped accessible

If driving east from Harwich on Route 28 to Chatham, take Old Harbor Road from Chatham rotary to traffic light at Shore Road. Proceed straight through light to first lane on left (Menekish Lane).

From Orleans, turn left at traffic light onto Old Harbor Road and look for first lane on left. Park along Old Harbor Road and enter garden through opening in tall hedge.

The Cotnam Garden
54 Colonial Drive

Stone walls, weathered shingles, and white fences form the quintessential structure for our Chatham, Cape Cod garden. My passion for trees is evident in this naturalistic setting where mature native oaks, pitch pines, and curved lawns set the stage for paper bark maple, *Cornus kousa* 'Gold Star' and 'Wolfeye', *Stewartia pseudocamellia*, *Hepticodium microniodies*, and *Jacquemontii birch*. But the prize specimen tree is my twenty-five-foot *Syringa pekinensis*. This rare beauty takes center stage at the bottom of a hillside garden. Blooming twice with fragrant cream colored blossoms once in July and again in late fall, it is a must-see rarity. Viburnums and hydrangea are located throughout the gardens. Hemerocallis, hosta, heuchera, and hellebore perennials are featured. All told, an inviting garden to be shared with plant lovers. **NEW**

Hours: 10 a.m. to 4 p.m.

Take the Mid-Cape Highway/Route 6 to Exit 11. Turn left onto Route 137. Follow to end at Route 28 and turn left. Go about 1 mile to a big white fence and blue sign that reads "Colonial Drive". Turn right and go to #54 on right. Please park on street along Colonial Drive.

The Gnomerie—
Sarah & Prescott Dunbar Garden
78 Cedar Street

Designed in the spirit of an English garden, this four-and-one-half-acre seaside garden contains rare specimen trees (beeches especially), as well as many ornamental small trees, such as *Cornus kousa*, magnolia cultivars, maple cultivars,

and Davidia. There is a purple border, a red and black perennial garden, a gravel garden for Mediterranean sun-loving, sharp drainage plants, an extensive decorative potager with vegetables and flowers, hot-colored borders, a pond, rose garden, woodland walk, and a gnomerie with thirty-two clipped topiary gnomes formed out of 'Boulevard' cypress. **2004** ♿

Hours: 10 a.m. to 4 p.m.

Follow signs into Chatham on Route 28. At Chatham Rotary, turn right onto Stage Harbor Road. Go downhill, past Oyster Pond Beach. Turn right onto Cedar Street and go down to a tall clipped privet hedge with turrets and a green mailbox on right that reads "Dunbar." Turn right onto white shell driveway. Please park in meadow by front hedge.

HARWICHPORT
Pillar to Post—
Don & Cele Milbier
29 Wequasset Road

Many luscious choices await you when entering Pillar to Post. Because of a true passion for plants and creating spaces that bathe the senses, this unique site is a masterpiece of "vision becomes reality." Our son Kyle's passion for landscaping has become an integral part of these gardens. Graceful steel arches by Don Cosavant span a twelve-foot-wide rose and clematis laden promenade that beckons visitors from the seaside entrance. A look back provides a fragrantly framed view of Oyster Creek. Or, you may enter through a brown-stone-and-steel archway to the volleyball and croquet course in the lawn area. Wait! You may chose to enter via the key-stoned archway built into the twelve-foot-tall fieldstone wall giving way to a water sculpture display; a wrought-iron window creates an unforgettable vista of the gardens. Once inside, sit by the hand-dug sunken garden with its reflective pond that presents a delicate balance of aesthetics and water table. This four-season one-acre oasis also features an original copper fountain, vegetable gardens, a berry cage, bird baths and feeders, and spectacular plantings including snake bark maple, redbuds, Davidia, Franklinia, tricolor beech, stewartia, aralia, yellowwood, paperbark maples, and styrax. Among this permanent display of foliage is a special exhibit of sculptures by Roger DiTarando, Richard Hatfield, Steve Lynch, Tobias, Lyman Whitaker, Whitmore Boogaerts, Nathaniel B. Smith, Joe Danella, and stone sculptures from Zimbabwe from the Kingsley Gallery of Chatham. There are also stunning garden pieces by Australian master potter, Ted Secombe. This inspiring garden reflects harmony, balance, and an unmistakable heartfelt spirit. **2004** ♿

Hours: 10 a.m. to 4 p.m.

Take Route 6 east to Exit 9/Route 134. Go right at end of ramp. Go 0.75 mile and turn left onto Upper County Road/West Harwich/Harwichport. Go to Route 28 and turn left. Go 1.5 miles, and turn right onto Brooks Road (A&W Root Beer on corner). At stop sign, turn left onto Lower County, then take second right onto Wequasset Road. Garden is at the third driveway on left. Please park on street.

Proceeds shared with The Family Pantry

North Chatham
Amanda's Garden
31 Thayer Lane

A laboratory for horticultural experiments and a canvas for artistic expression, Amanda's informal seaside garden continues to develop and evolve. The challenge to this dedicated plantswoman is to create a soul-satisfying landscape in a sometimes harsh environment of northeast winds and salt spray, in earth more sand than soil. No pesticides or herbicides are used in an effort to nurture a healthy habitat hospitable to birds and insects (as well as nibbling rodents, kept partially in check by Archie, the cat). **NEW** ♿

Hours: 10 a.m. to 4 p.m.

From the Chatham Rotary, go east on Route 28/Old Harbor Road to traffic light (just under 1 mile). Continue straight on Old Harbor Road. Thayer Lane is 0.1 mile on right. Please park on Old Harbor Road and walk down to # 31, the first house.

Proceeds shared with Wellfleet Bay Wildlife Sanctuary

Mid-Cape Open Day
Sunday, July 29
BARNSTABLE COUNTY

East Orleans
Clairvue
32 Pochet Road

Our Cape Cod woodland garden is tucked in away from the street. A small lawn surrounds the house with many paths into the woodland. When we started the garden in 1985, we had to clear the poison ivy, briars, and pitch pine. We kept the oaks and planted many more trees and evergreens. There are an abundance of rhododendrons and azaleas, some pruned into tree form, as well as other shrubs, roses, vines, ornamental grasses, perennials, and groundcovers. The garden also includes a vegetable garden, Oriental garden, small fish pond, tea house, and shed with glass on the south side. We have a large brick patio and many rest areas throughout the garden. **NEW** ♿

Hours: 10 a.m. to 4 p.m.

From Cape Cod canal take Route 6 to Exit 12/Orleans and turn right onto Route 6A. Turn right at second traffic light (gas station on right) onto Main Street. Go straight through two lights and pass Windmill Shopping and post office on left. Road quickly splits in front of Barley Neck Inn. Stay right onto Barley Neck Road. Shortly, road splits again. Stay straight on Pochet Road. Third left from this point is Brickhill Road extension, a wide entrance dirt road. Look for sign on right with names Gaskill and LeClair. Go up paved driveway to house on right. Please park at house and at end of driveway.

Harwichport
Pillar to Post—
Don & Cele Milbier
29 Wequasset Road

Many luscious choices await you when entering Pillar to Post. Because of a true passion for plants and creating spaces that bathe the senses, this unique site is a masterpiece of "vision becomes reality." Our son Kyle's passion for landscaping has become an integral part of these gardens. Graceful steel arches by Don Cosavant span a twelve-foot-wide rose and clematis laden promenade that beckons visitors from the seaside entrance. A look back provides a fragrantly framed view of Oyster Creek. Or, you may enter through a brownstone-and-steel archway to the volleyball and croquet course in the lawn area. Wait! You may chose to enter via the key-stoned archway built into the twelve-foot-tall fieldstone wall giving way to a water sculpture display; a wrought-iron window creates an unforgettable vista of the gardens. Once inside, sit by the hand-dug sunken garden with its reflective pond that presents a delicate balance of aesthetics and water table. This four-season one-acre oasis also features an original copper fountain, vegetable gardens, a berry cage, bird baths and feeders, and spectacular plantings including snake bark maple, redbuds, Davidia, Franklinia, tricolor beech, stewartia, aralia, yellowwood, paperbark maples, and styrax. Among this permanent display of foliage is a special exhibit of sculptures by Roger DiTarando, Richard Hatfield, Steve Lynch, Tobias, Lyman Whitaker, Whitmore Boogaerts, Nathaniel B. Smith, Joe Danella, and stone sculptures from Zimbabwe from the Kingsley Gallery of Chatham. There are also stunning garden pieces by Australian master potter, Ted Secombe. This inspiring garden reflects harmony, balance, and an unmistakable heartfelt spirit. **2004** ♿

Hours: 10 a.m. to 4 p.m.

Take Route 6 east to Exit 9/Route 134. Go right at end of exit ramp. Travel 0.75 mile and turn left onto Upper County Road/West Harwich/Harwichport. Go to Route 28 and turn left. Go 1.5 miles, and turn right onto Brooks Road (A&W Root Beer on corner). At stop sign, turn left onto Lower County, then take second right onto Wequasset Road. Garden is at the third driveway on left. Please park on street.

Proceeds shared with The Family Pantry

Berkshire Open Day
Sunday, July 29
BERKSHIRE COUNTY

ALFORD
RavenTree
112 Green River Valley Road

A perennial gardener's delight, RavenTree offers almost every kind of planting condition from dry sun to wet bog. The variety of unusual plants that thrive here is one of its charms and makes this garden a rich experience in every season. Find ornamental grass beds, fern alcoves, cottage gardens, perennial borders, and more than 200 varieties of trees and shrubs. Woodland trails and rustic bridges lead to forest destinations, with plenty of places to sit along the way. **NEW** ♿

Hours: 10 a.m. to 4 p.m.

From New York State, take Route 22 north through Hillsdale. Take Route 71 south towards Great Barrington, 2.8 miles. Route 71 is also called Green River Valley Road. The house is on left; a beige house with a circular drive.

From Great Barrington, take Route 7 to Route 23. Go 1.6 miles to Route 71. Take Route 71 past Great Barrington airport 5.2 miles. The house is on right; a beige house with a circular drive. Parking is on adjacent property.

Proceeds shared with Berkshire Botanical Garden

GREAT BARRINGTON
Aston Magna
30 Berkshire Heights Road

Commissioned by Charles Freer, industrialist and well-known patron of oriental art, the main residence at Aston Magna was designed by Charles A. Platt, a prominent architect of private country houses. The gardens, designed during the 1930s, were laid out by Albert Spalding, the second owner of the property, and a distinguished violinist of international stature, who named the estate "Aston Magna" after an ancient village in Gloucester, England. The property is known for its extraordinary views to the south and west which are framed by carefully pruned majestic Eastern pines. The principal garden is a woodland glade between the main house and the original pool, created in 1935. Planted with perennial bushes and flowers so that there is continuous color for five months, the garden is dominated by a path which slowly cascades toward a secret opening in a hedge, revealing the splendid pool. Other perennials adorn another "room" with gardens surrounding the pool. At the main residence, other smaller woodland gardens have been created around an ancient fountain. A cutting garden is situated in the west pasture, above a producing vineyard, and groundcovers and wildflowers appear throughout the wooded areas. **NEW** ♿

Hours: 10 a.m. to 4 p.m.

From the north, take Route 7 from Stockbridge to Great Barrington (approximately 7 miles). Go 3 blocks through town on Main Street. At traffic light at St. James Church, turn right onto Taconic Avenue. Go under railroad trestle; continue two blocks until Taconic Avenue veers to right. Do not follow road to right, but go straight uphill onto Barrington Place.

Go up hill; turn left onto Berkshire Heights Road and go two blocks. At two stone pillars continue on private driveway marked "Aston Magna" and follow to main house.

From the south, take Route 7 north from Canaan, Connecticut. At first traffic light in Great Barrington, turn left onto Route 23 and Route 41. Proceed to railroad crossing and turn right onto West Avenue; turn left onto Taconic Avenue. Proceed as directed above. Please park at top of hill where marked.

Proceeds shared with Berkshire Botanical Garden

Seekonk Farm— Honey Sharp's Garden
296 Division Street

Nestled amidst fieldstone walls, iron gates, handmade fences, and a bog bridge, the rustic, eighteenth-century Seekonk Farm features gardens within a regional context. Perennial beds include heirloom *Hydrangea alternifolia*, viburnums, an *Acer griseum*—and last but not least, an 1831 "Cling not to Earth" marble tombstone. More contemporary pool gardens await in the meadow. Here, the texture and

♿ indicates parts of garden are handicapped accessible

foliage of Japanese maples, smoke bushes, conifers, sedums, and grasses predominate within a silver, chartreuse, and burgundy palette. An old stone well-cover, aged with lichen, offers a focal point. In the woodlands, a trail will lead you to where Honey Sharp continues to toil over re-introducing native species. **2006** ♿

Hours: 10 a.m. to 4 p.m.

From Main Street/Route 7 on south end of Great Barrington, turn left onto Taconic Avenue and go uphill towards Alford. Approximately 1 mile after Simon's Rock College turn right onto Division Street. Seekonk Farm is first on left.

From the north, follow Route 7 south from Stockbridge past Monument Mountain; turn right on road with sign: "To Rt.183". Make a sharp right onto Route 183, and soon a left onto Division Street at Taft Farms. Continue 1 mile to blinking light on Route 41; go straight uphill to next blinking light. Seekonk Farm (# 296) will be 1 mile on right.

Proceeds shared with Berkshire Botanical Garden

Berkshire Open Day
Sunday, August 5

There is also a garden open in nearby Litchfield County, Connecticut on this date. See page 104 for details.

BERKSHIRE COUNTY

SHEFFIELD
Good Dogs Farm
334 West Stahl Road

The gardens reflect our exuberance, whims, and an overarching philosophy that, like life, gardens are best when they are shared with friends, when simple pleasures are part of the plan, and when they aren't taken too seriously. Here, good dogs romp and friends linger. Garden paths lead to numerous garden rooms, secret sitting areas, an outdoor shower, and an outdoor sleeping pavilion. A handmade, rough-cedar "country Chippendale" fence surrounds our large vegetable/cutting garden where a very crowded bat house towers above. Further

out, meandering meadow paths wind through wildflowers and native self-sowers down to the river. Gone is the bocce court, replaced by an antique-marble & brick wood-burning bake oven surrounded by a young Nishiki willow hedge that defines a pea-stone cooking courtyard. Since being invited to last year's Open Days tour, our gardens have been featured in *Berkshire Living, The Litchfield Country Times,* and Oprah's *O at Home* magazine. The yuccas, roses, brugmansia, grasses, and cannas remind us of our roots in California and Texas. The hydrangeas, peonies, ligularia, flowering shrubs, and lobelia are classic New England. We picked early August for our Open Day in hopes that the heady fragrance of the 'Casablanca' lilies will be waiting to greet you. We look forward to seeing you. **2006** ♿

Hours: 10 a.m. to 4 p.m.

From south, follow Route 7 north into Massachusetts and about 3 miles from the state line, just past the sign for Ashley Falls, turn left onto small road called West Stahl Road (same road is called "Hewins" on east side of Route 7). Stay straight when road forks. Good Dogs Farm is less than 1 mile on right.

From north, follow Route 7 south past town of Sheffield and veer right onto Route 7A. Go 1 mile or so and cross over Housatonic River (old iron bridge) and immediately veer left onto West Stahl Road. Slow down; Good Dogs Farm is there on the left.

Proceeds shared with Berkshire Botanical Garden

Berkshire Open Day
Sunday, September 16

BERKSHIRE COUNTY

GREAT BARRINGTON
Seekonk Farm—
Honey Sharp's Garden
296 Division Street

Nestled amidst fieldstone walls, iron gates, handmade fences and a bog bridge, the rustic, 18th century Seekonk Farm features gardens within a regional context. Perennial beds include heirloom *Hydrangea alternifolia*, viburnums, an *Acer griseum*—and last but not least, an 1831 "Cling not to Earth" marble tombstone. More contemporary pool gardens await in the meadow. Here, the texture and foliage of Japanese maples, smoke bushes, conifers, sedums and grasses predominate within a silver, chartreuse and burgundy palette. An old stone well-cover, aged with lichen, offers a focal point. In the woodlands, a trail will lead you to where Honey Sharp continues to toil over re-introducing native species. **2006** ♿

Hours: 10 a.m. to 4 p.m.

From Main Street/Route 7 on south end of Great Barrington, turn left onto Taconic Avenue and go uphill towards Alford. Approximately 1 mile after Simon's Rock College turn right onto Division Street. Seekonk Farm is first on left.

From the north, follow Route 7 south from Stockbridge past Monument Mountain; turn right on road with sign: "To Rt.183". Make a sharp right onto Route 183, and soon a left onto Division Street at Taft Farms. Continue 1 mile to blinking light on Route 41; go straight uphill to next blinking light. Seekonk Farm (# 296) will be 1 mile on right.

Proceeds shared with Berkshire Botanical Garden

Wheelbarrow Hill Farm
Route 23

What captivated us about our house was its site, nestled in the trees on top of a hill with long views. With no flat ground for borders, we tried to use the trees and hill to frame the garden and the view. The tree line provided a place for woodland plants and shrubs. Flower beds terraced into the hill allow us to see the borders from above, below, and at eye level. Trees have been pruned and cut to frame the view. A cutting garden sits at the base of the hill. Wildflowers and groundcovers grow on trails through the woods. **2006**

Hours: 10 a.m. to 4 p.m.

From New York, take Taconic State Parkway to Claverack/Hillsdale/Route 23 exit. Follow Route 23 east through Hillsdale and South Egremont, Massachusetts, to our paved driveway on left with a sign for Wheelbarrow Hill Farm.

From I-90/Massachusetts Turnpike, take Exit 2 at Lee. Follow Route 102 west to Stockbridge. Go into center of Stockbridge. Turn left just past Red Lion Inn onto Route 7 south. Go through Great Barrington to traffic light south of town (church on right, police station on left). Turn right onto Route 23 (Route 7 goes straight). Go about 1.8 miles to our paved driveway on right just past Seekonk Crossroad. Please park in field next to cutting garden.

Proceeds shared with Berkshire Botanical Garden

HOUSATONIC

Under the Hemlocks
258 Great Barrington Road

Our bowl-shaped garden in the foothills of Tom Ball Mountain came with many natural gifts: boulders, hemlocks, black birch, pines, etc. Adding shrubs, bulbs and perennials rich in textures and color, Goshen stone paths, and various sculptures completed it. We were lucky to uncover a perfect place within the given ledge for water to gracefully fall into a small lily and fish-filled pond. This is a major focal point in the garden. It's the flow of these gardens that seems to please: from our "sunken "fairy woodland", with a succession of bluebells, foxgloves then echinacea, to our over-scale rock garden, topped out by plume poppies. Look for the secretive, mossy "Othello Boudoir" engulfed by ligularias, next to the outdoor living room. Going behind the huge rhodies up the secretive path to the "upstairs" hosta path garden and around back to view the water garden will complete your tour. **2006** ♿

Hours: 10 a.m. to 4 p.m.

From Route 7/Main Street in Great Barrington, follow Route 41 going towards West Stockbridge, going under the Housatonic Bridge. Continue straight and from the blinking light at Division Street, (passing the Williamsville Inn on left), go exactly 3.6 miles to #258. A diamond yellow curve arrow road sign is on the right side of the road – pointing into and across from our driveway.

From West Stockbridge, follow Route 41 South to Great Barrington. Go exactly 4.0 miles to 258 Great Barrington Road. The driveway and house are on the right just over the top of a hill. Look for Under the Hemlocks sign hanging from a tree.

Proceeds shared with Berkshire Botanical Garden

Public Gardens

BARNSTABLE COUNTY

SANDWICH

Heritage Museum & Gardens
67 Grove Street, (508) 888-3300
www.heritagemuseumsandgardens.org

Located in Historic Sandwich in beautiful Cape Cod, celebrate the American spirit amid 100 acres of gardens filled with award winning daylilies and Dexter rhododendrons. Sweeping lawns, annual gardens, heather, hosta, native and exotic trees and shrubs, and more than 7,000 labeled plants.

Hours: April 1 through October 31, daily, 10 a.m. to 5 p.m.; November 1 through December 31, Friday through Sunday, 10 a.m. to 4 p.m.

Admission: $12

One hour from Boston, take Route 3 to Route 6 to Exit 2. Take Route 130 to Grove Street.

BERKSHIRE COUNTY

HOUSATONIC

Project Native—Growing Nature's Gardens
342 North Plain Road/Route 41,
(413) 274-3433, www.projectnative.org

Project Native is a non-profit native plant nursery located on a fifty-four-acre farm in Housatonic. Native plants are available for sale at our garden shop and are displayed throughout the farm in seed banks and bird gardens. Project Native is currently growing

more than 150 varieties of native perennials, including wildflowers, shrubs, ferns, grasses, and vines.

Hours: April through October, Monday, Thursday, and Friday, 9 a.m. to 4 p.m.; Saturday, 9 a.m. to 5 p.m.; Sunday, 10 a.m. to 4 p.m. Special tours of the seed banks and nursery will be held on August 5 and 12.

Admission: Free

On Route 41/North Plain Road, is located 4.2 miles north of downtown Great Barrington on right.

From the Massachusetts Turnpike/I-90 take Exit 2. Turn left at end of exit, then right onto Route 102 south. In Stockbridge, turn left at Red Lion Inn onto Route 7 south. In Great Barrington cross brown bridge and take next right onto Route 41/North Plain Road.

From south, take Route 7 north to Route 41/North Plain Road.

LENOX

The Mount, Edith Wharton's Estate & Gardens
2 Plunkett Street, (413) 637-1899,
www.edithwharton.org

Edith Wharton was an authority on European landscape design as well as a passionate gardener. The Mount's three acres of formal gardens are strongly influenced by Wharton's travels in Europe and feature grass terraces, a sunken Italian garden, lime walk of linden trees, rock garden, unusual grass steps, fountains, and more. Since 1999, more than $3 million has been invested in the restoration of the historic gardens, including the 2005 revival of Edith Wharton's beloved flower garden.

Hours: May through October, daily, 9 a.m. to 5 p.m.

Admission: $16 adults, $8 students, children under 12 free.

The Mount is located in Lenox on corner of Route 7 and Plunkett Street.

PITTSFIELD

The Gardens at the Vincent J. Hebert Arboretum at Springside Park

North Street

The Memory Garden at Hebert Arboretum was established as a vehicle through which individuals could memorialize their loved ones. The Circular Garden features lilies, roses, and grasses, as well as appropriate annuals throughout the summer. The Butterfly Garden, filled with flowers and shrubs planted to lure butterflies, began its life only five years ago and has already become a garden of great beauty. It is a place where newlyweds often come for their wedding photographs as well as a nature lover's paradise. The eleven demonstration gardens planted and cared for by the Berkshire members of the Western Massachusetts Master Gardeners Association, funded in part by the Berkshire Environmental Fund, continues to be a place where gardening instruction and interaction with the gardening public takes place. The Demonstration Gardens boast an herb garden, two vegetable gardens, two shade gardens, a cutting garden, a perennial garden, a children's garden, a cottage garden, and a berry garden.

Hours: Year round, daily, dawn to dusk

Admission: Free

North Street is also Route 7, the main north/south artery of Berkshire County. The arboretum is just north of the city, about 0.5 mile north of the junction of Routes 9 and 7.

From the south, drive through Pittsfield past the Berkshire Medical Center. Springside Park, to the right is 0.5 mile on right.

From the north, go south on Route 7 past the entrance to Berkshire Mall on left and a large lake on right. The arboretum is 2 miles farther south of the lake, on the left.

STOCKBRIDGE

Berkshire Botanical Garden

Routes 102 & 183, (413) 298-3926, www.berkshirebotanical.org

Set in the heart of the Berkshires, this fifteen-acre botanical garden is known for its intimate landscapes with seasonal tapestries of fragrant and colorful perennials and annuals combined with the textures of shrubs and grasses. Featured are fourteen display gardens, three greenhouses, an arboretum, and a woodland preserve. Among the display gardens are two 100-foot-long perennial borders, a charming 1937 terraced herb garden, mixed border gardens—one featuring more than 2,000 annuals, a rock garden, rose garden, pond garden, and native plant garden. Also included is an ornamental vegetable garden and a children's garden. Educational programs and special events are offered year-round. The Berkshire Botanical Garden is a non-profit, membership supported organization. Please visit www.berkshirebotanical.org for more information.

♿ indicates parts of garden are handicapped accessible

Hours: May 1 through October 15, daily, 10 a.m. to 5 p.m. Guided tours available for groups by appointment.

Admission: $7 adults, $5 seniors, $5 students, members and children under 12 free.

From I-90/Massachusetts Turnpike take Lee exit and turn left off exit ramp onto Route 20. Almost immediately right onto Route 102. Go through center of Stockbridge and turn right, staying on Route 102. Just after intersection with Route 183, turn left into visitors' parking lot.

Chesterwood Estate & Museum
4 Williamsville Road, (413) 298-3579, www.chesterwood.org

Daniel Chester French, sculptor and landscape designer, created a landscape at Chesterwood typical of the Country Place Era of the late nineteenth to early twentieth centuries. The studio garden acts as an outdoor room and extension of the overall living space of the structure. The garden boasts a fountain and exedra, long border, a hydrangea walk, and extensive footpaths throughout the woodlands.

Hours: May 22 through October 15, daily, 10 a.m. to 5 p.m.

Admission: $10 adults, $9 seniors/military/college students, $5 children 6 to 18

From Stockbridge, go west on Route 102, turn left onto Route 183, and go 0.75 mile past the Norman Rockwell Museum. Turn right onto Mohawk Lake Road and then left onto Willow Street, which becomes Williamsville Road, unpaved road just before Chesterwood.

The Mission House
Main Street, (413) 298-3239, www.thetrustees.org

It is not by accident that the Mission House (1739) and its gardens are in perfect harmony. In the 1920s, landscape architect Fletcher Steele created a series of four garden rooms (the Dooryard and Orchard gardens, the Working Yard, and the East Lawn) that evoked the practical and comfortable gardens of the Colonial era.

Hours: Memorial Day weekend through Columbus Day, daily, 10 a.m. to 5 p.m.

Admission: Self-guided tour of the gardens is free; guided tour of the house is $6, children $3.

From I-90/Massachusetts Turnpike, take Exit 2. Follow Route 102 into Stockbridge. Continue past Red Lion Inn on Route 102/Main Street. The Mission House is on the right at the intersection with Sergeant Street.

Naumkeag
5 Prospect Hill Road, (413) 298-3239, www.thetrustees.org

From the Chinese Garden to the Blue Steps, Naumkeag rejuvenates the spirit. The South Lawn echoes the Berkshires; the Afternoon Garden provides a shady spot next to the 1885 mansion. They are the result of a brilliant collaboration between landscape architect Fletcher Steele and his patron, Mabel Choate, from 1926 until 1956.

Hours: Memorial Day weekend through Columbus Day, daily, 10 a.m. to 5 p.m.

Admission: $8 for self-guided tour of the gardens.

From I-90/Massachusetts Turnpike take Exit 2. Follow Route 102 into Stockbridge. From intersection of Routes 7 and 102 (at Red Lion Inn), take Pine Street north. Bear left onto Prospect Hill Road and follow for 0.5 mile to entrance on left.

TYRINGHAM
Ashintully
Sodem Road, (413) 298-3239, www.thetrustees.org

The gardens at Ashintully blend several natural features—a rushing stream, native deciduous trees, a rounded knoll, and rising flanking meadows—into an ordered arrangement with both formal and informal beauty. Garden features include the Fountain Pond, Pine Park, Rams Head Terrace, Bowling Green, Regency Bridge, and Trellis Triptych. Urns, columns, and statuary ornament the garden, while foot bridges, foot paths, stone stairs, and grassy terraces connect various parts of the garden.

In 1997, Ashintully Gardens received the H. Hollis Hunnewell Medal, established in 1870 by the Massachusetts Horticultural Society to recognize gardens of country residences embellished with rare and desirable ornamental trees and shrubs.

Hours: Mid-June through mid-September, Wednesday and Saturday, 1 p.m. to 5 p.m.

Admission: Free. Group garden tours of 15 or more are offered by prior appointment ($5 per person).

From I-90/Massachusetts Turnpike, take Exit 2/Route 20 east and bear right onto Route 102, and then immediately left onto Tyringham Road. Go about 6.5 miles, pass through Tyringham Center (road then becomes Main Road), to intersection with Sodem Road. Turn left and park on roadside as directed by signs. Parking available for 5 cars.

NANTUCKET COUNTY

NANTUCKET
The Gardens at Nantucket Wildflower Farm
84 Egan Lane, (508) 228-5551

Cinda Gaynor has created a series of whimsical gardens for pleasure, plant research, and sale in an unexpected spot on the island. Filling her gardens are indigenous Nantucket plants, some North American natives, and a diverse selection of annuals, perennials, and succulents, but none that harm—revealing her devotion to the conservation of Nantucket's fragile ecosystem. Cinda, a restoration horticulturalist, with a background in theater design, takes regular trips to Paris and California to seek an eclectic bounty of unusual garden pots, furniture, and accessories to fill an appealing retail space in a shed with a pergola.

Hours: Special Garden Conservancy Open Day on June 28, 9 a.m. to 5 p.m. Otherwise, May to early December, Monday through Saturday, 9 a.m. to 5 p.m.

Admission: Free

Follow Old South Road from Rotary toward Airport. Turn left onto Egan Lane. Follow curving road to the gardens on right. Park along Egan Lane and walk in.

SIASCONSET
Siasconset Union Chapel
18 New Street

This lovely open space in the heart of the historic village is a quiet area for reflection and remembrance. Simple privet hedges define the perimeter of the property; the stone walls along the rear of the garden form the columbarium making this place particularly important to 'Sconseters. Because of their architectural, historic, and cultural significance, both the chapel and the garden will be preserved by an historic preservation easement so that they will remain unchanged through the years to come. The chapel is open to garden visitors who may enjoy the interior architecture and the detailed needlepoint kneelers.

Hours: Special Garden Conservancy Open Day on June 28, 10 a.m. to 4 p.m.

Admission: Free

This garden is part of the walking tour. Maps will be available at "Hedged About," 10 Sankaty Road.

✦ indicates parts of garden are handicapped accessible

NEW HAMPSHIRE

New London Area Open Day
Saturday, June 9

There are gardens open on this date in nearby Vermont. See page 264 for details.

MERRIMACK COUNTY

ELKINS

Cottage Rock
346 Wilmot Center Road

Designed around several huge glacial erratics, this garden essentially evolved over the last thirteen years as the new home for my beloved perennials that I brought from a former garden. It has expanded as my "collection" has expanded. I am a dwarf conifer enthusiast as well, and this rural, edge-of-the-woods site has been an excellent site to experiment with all these plants in shady and sunny beds. I enjoy a few small "rock garden" plant areas also. **2001** ❢

Hours: 10 a.m. to 4 p.m.

From I-89, take Exit 11/New London. Go east on Route 11 from exit ramp. Follow for approximately 3 miles past Route 114 (Flying Goose Brew Pub on corner of Routes 114 & 11), past Lake Sunapee Country Club. Turn left onto Elkins Road. Go 1.3 miles on Elkins Road, which becomes Wilmot Center Road after you go through village of Elkins, (past post office, Pleasant Lake beach, etc.). My driveway is on right after you come up a small hill. My house is tan with white trim. Please park in small driveway or on street.

Proceeds shared with Friends of the John Hay National Wildlife Refuge

NEW LONDON

The Gardens of Carolyn & Peter Hager
99 Sugarhouse Road

Our gardens are an unexpected surprise in a woodland setting. The house was purchased in 1976 and the gardens begun in 1984. The land in front of the house was flat with a gradual slope to the road. As you walk up the drive you will notice the natural stream bed on right and a tower of *Hydrangea petioleris* on left. As you tour the gardens around the house you will notice a few unusual ideas. There is a *Prunus cistena* espaliered against the rear of the garage. The perennial garden with its meandering path is full of a variety of specimen evergreens, boxwood, and many Asiatic lilies. There is a bed to the right of the house and along the stream that has many different varieties of heather and a few more unusual evergreens. **NEW** ♿

Hours: 10 a.m. to 4 p.m.

From Concord, take I-89 north to Exit 11. Turn right off exit ramp onto Route 11 East. Turn left at flashing light onto Route 114 North/Main Street. Go past Colby Sawyer College, and turn right at flashing light onto North Pleasant Street (by Lake Sunapee Bank). Follow Pleasant Street down hill 1.6 miles and turn left into Slope n' Shore Club at Knollwood Road, which is right before the Inn at Pleasant Lake. After a few hundred yards turn left onto Sugarhouse Road and continue 0.2 mile. The garden is on left. Parking on one side of the street only.

The Hewitt Garden
1481 Route 103A

The long drive crosses a brook and ascends through meadows and woods to the house at the height of the land, which overlooks Lake Sunapee and the surrounding hills. Extensive woodland gardens with a profusion of native species, both rare and well-known, small rock gardens, a new large rockery, and a conservatory are features of this fifty-three-acre property. Kris Fenderson designed the continuously blooming front courtyard, back terrace, and other beds near the house and barn. The owners do all the gardening and fieldwork. **NEW** ♿

Hours: 10 a.m. to 4 p.m.

From the south on I-89, take Exit 11. Turn left off exit ramp onto King Hill Road, toward Newbury. Go about 2.6 miles to stop sign at intersection with Route 103A. Turn left and take second driveway on left, marked by stone post with number 1481.

From the north on I-89, take Exit 12 (not 12A). Turn right at end of exit ramp and in about 100 yards take an immediate left onto Route 103A toward Newbury. Go about 2.6 miles. You will have passed through intersection with King Hill Road on left and Soo Nipi Park Road on right. Turn left at second drive after this intersection, marked by a stone post as noted above.

From The Fells, turn left onto Route 103A for 2.8 miles to our driveway marked by a stone post on right with number 1481.

Proceeds shared with Friends of the John Hay National Wildlife Refuge & the New England Wildflower Society

SULLIVAN COUNTY

CORNISH

Northcôte

84 Lang Road

The garden of Bob Gordon and Marjorie Mann is named Northcôte. It was the home studio and garden of Stephen Parrish from his arrival in 1892 to his death in 1938. After a successful career as an etcher, he settled in Cornish to garden and paint. Fellow Philadelphian Wilson Eyre designed the house, which Parrish began planting vines against even before it was completed. For the next ten years, Parrish built a series of enclosed gardens stretching along the open hillside, using native materials and employing local craftsmen. Bob and Marjorie have restored the house and Bill Noble researched the garden and guided its restoration with his colleague Susan Howard, making Northcôte a gardener's garden once again. **NEW** ♿

Hours: 10 a.m. to 4 p.m.

Take I-89 north to Exit 20. Turn left at bottom of ramp onto 12A south. Eight miles is Plainfield. From center of Plainfield (a closed general store go 1 mile to Thrasher Road on left). Over a small iron bridge is Lang Road on left. Up Lang pass Burling Farm on right. Northcôte is next driveway on right after Burling Farm. After ascending driveway, first left and a quick right is best for parking. The driveway on right, in front of house should be left free for handicapped parking.

Public Gardens
MERRIMACK COUNTY

NEW LONDON
Community Garden at Tracy Library
155 Main Street, (603) 526-4656

The Olmsted Brothers designed this garden in 1927. It is a 198-foot-long and ninety-two-foot wide garden bordered on one side by a rustic stone wall and on the other by a tiered landscape. In the middle is a pool with a water sculpture designed by Dimitri Gerakiaris. An extensive collection of perennials (most from the original plantings) are in four "L"-shaped beds around the pool. Seven varieties of lilacs, some interspersed with flowering shrubs, are planted close by. There is also a rose garden featuring ten varieties. A shade garden with perennials and shrubs, frames the open lawn area where people are encouraged to stroll or sit on one of the ten benches placed throughout the garden. Garden guides with plant lists are made available to the public.

Hours: May through October, Monday through Friday, 9 a.m. to 5 p.m.; Saturday, 9 a.m. to 1 p.m. Closed Sunday.

Admission: Free

From I-91, take Exit 10 onto I-89 South. Go 26.6 miles to Exit 12/New London/Sunapee. Turn left at exit ramp onto Newport Road toward New London. Go 2.4 miles. Bear right onto Main Street/Route 114. Go 0.3 mile to Tracy Library on right. Parking is available across the road. The garden is down steps behind library.

♿ indicates parts of garden are handicapped accessible

From I-93, take Exit 12 onto I-89 North. Go 35 miles to Exit 12/New London/Sunapee. Turn right at exit ramp onto Newport Road toward New London. Go 2.4 miles. Bear right onto Main Street/Route 114. Go 0.3 mile to Tracy Library on right. Parking is available across road. The garden is down steps behind library.

The Fells at the John Hay National Wildlife Refuge
456 Route 103A, (603) 763-4789, www.thefells.org

A PROJECT OF
THE GARDEN
CONSERVANCY

These gardens, developed from 1914 to 1940 as a showplace country estate, have been restored by the Garden Conservancy and the site's nonprofit managing organization, The Fells. The historic design features formal, naturalized plantings, terraced lawns, native New Hampshire granite walls, and vistas of mountains and Lake Sunapee. The one-third-acre rock garden, in which Clarence Hay experimented with alpines for more than forty years, contrasts with a secret ruined woodland garden and a 100-foot perennial border. The on-site nursery raises perennials, including plants from the original gardens.

Hours: Year round, daily, dawn to dusk. Main house tours available Memorial Day through Columbus Day, and Wednesday through Friday in July and August.

Admission: $5 adults ($7 when Main House open), $2 children.

From I-89 north, take Exit 9/Route 103 and go west to Newbury. Take 103A north 2.2 miles. The Fells is on left.

From I-89 south, take Exit 12/Route 11. Turn right at end of ramp and immediate left onto Route 103A south. Go 5.6 miles to The Fells on right. Please park in lot and walk down driveway to gardens.

NEW JERSEY
Monmouth County Open Day
Saturday, April 28
MONMOUTH COUNTY

ATLANTIC HIGHLANDS
Mrs. Sverre Sorensen
1 Hill Road

Nestled in the hills (the highest coastal point from Maine to Florida) overlooking Sandy Hook Bay to New York City is a mature, natural woodland garden created by the owner and her late husband, Sev. Years ago plants were started by cuttings and seeds (many by daughter Sandy Sorensen Henning). Today, charming paths flanked with brunnera, epimediums, and phlox wind in and about rhododendrons, azaleas, skimmias, laurel, and dogwood—all with spectacular vistas of the ocean beyond. **2003**

Hours: 10 a.m. to 4 p.m.

Take Garden State Parkway south to Exit 114. Turn left at end of exit ramp and right onto Nutswamp Road at first light. Turn left onto Navesink River Road across Route 35, and continue to Locust Point Road. Do not go over Oceanic Bridge to Rumson. Go straight through intersection with Red Country Store entrance on right, bear right downhill, through traffic light at Route 36, up Grand Avenue, under Stone Bridge, and turn right onto Ocean Boulevard/Scenic Drive. Turn at second right onto Hill Road to # 1, first driveway on right. Look for high stone walls and gravel driveway. Please park along street.

Bergen County Open Day
Saturday, May 12
BERGEN COUNTY

RIDGEWOOD
The Handley Garden
342 Franklin Turnpike

John and Sue Handley's garden is set on a one-acre property. The front foundation planting is a mixed border of ornamental trees, shrubs, and flowers and prepares you only somewhat for the beauty of the garden behind the house. A water-and-rock garden is beside the deck. Sunny perennial borders punctuated by garden ornaments extend the length of the path that draws you to the open lawn. Sue Handley has planted a great variety of wonderful plants, some of which may be new to you. **2006** ♿

Hours: 10 a.m. to 4 p.m.

From Route 17 south, proceed past Ramsey, Allendale, and Waldwick to right turn at Ho-Ho-Kus/Racetrack Road exit. Proceed west 3 blocks and turn left onto Nagel. Proceed to Franklin Turnpike and turn right. Garden is on left.

From Route 17 north, go about 4 miles from Route 4 to Linwood Avenue overpass. Go under overpass and turn right. Continue to second traffic light at Pleasant Avenue and turn right. Follow to end and turn right onto Glen Avenue. Pass cemetery on left to a hairpin turn at beginning of Franklin Turnpike. Handley Garden is about 0.75 mile down on left. Please park on front lawn.

Proceeds shared with Citizens for Swimming

WOODCLIFF LAKE
Wiebke & Jan Hinsch
6 Willow Street

Wiebke's garden will horrify any lover of manicured lawns. "My controlled wilderness" she calls her islands of flower beds—including a rock garden and many rare trees—which attract bees, birds, hummingbirds, and butterflies. This is the work of one determined person. Flowers are Wiebke's lifeline. They now bloom 360 days a year but she is working on the remaining five. **2005** ❦

Hours: 10 a.m. to 4 p.m.

From the south, take the Garden State Parkway north to Exit 168/Westwood. Turn right onto Washington Avenue. At first traffic light, turn left (Seasons Restaurant on right) onto Pascack Road. Go about 1 mile to the reservoir on the right. Willow Street branches off to the left. Number 6 is the first house on the right (red brick).

From I-87/I-287, take Exit 14A onto the Garden State Parkway South. Go 1 mile to Exit 1/Schoolhouse Road. At ramp, turn left onto Spring Valley Road. Go straight through 2 traffic lights to end of road (Esty Restaurant) and turn left into Fremont Road. At end of road turn right onto Pascack Road. Go through one light. When lake appears on the left, Willow Street is the third road branching off to the right. Please park on the road.

Essex & Union County Open Day Saturday, May 20

Greenwood Gardens in Short Hills is also open on this date. See their listing on page 170. Read more about our preservation work at Greenwood Gardens on our website, www.gardenconservancy.org

ESSEX COUNTY

SHORT HILLS

Garden of Dr. & Mrs. George E. Staehle
83 Old Hollow Road

Our garden is in an old quarry. Over the years we have cleared and planted it ourselves, after a local landscaper told us it was impossible and to let it stay wild. We started about forty years ago with azaleas, rhododendrons, and wildflowers, then went on to hostas, hellebores, daylilies, geraniums, primulas, and other perennials. We continue to collect and plant experimentally. **2006**

Hours: 10 a.m. to 2 p.m.

From Route 24 west, take Hobart Gap Road exit. Turn right at traffic light onto Hobart Gap Road. At blinking light, road name changes to White Oak Ridge Road. At next light (1 mile), turn right onto Parsonage Hill Road. Continue to "T" junction. Turn left onto Old Short Hills Road and go about 0.5 mile to second street on right, Old Hollow Road. Garden is at #83, fifth house on right. Please park along street.

UNION COUNTY

SUMMIT

Regina Carlson (with help from Kenneth Carlson)
105 Mountain Avenue

Our quarter-acre suburban garden has more than 4,000 square feet of beds with more than 300 varieties of plants, laid out in bold, sweeping, and functional curves. I taught myself gardening (library books, visiting dozens of English gardens) and designed, made, and maintain our garden outside a busy work life. Features include a two-level deck high above the yard, enclosed with vine-covered lattice; flowery balcony; patio nestled into a flowerbed; arbor and two-story trellis; stone "loveseat" built into a bank; bridges over gully; weed-free grass; garden and kitchen composting; and many labor-saving features. **NEW** ♿

Hours: 10 a.m. to 4 p.m.

Take Route 24 to Summit Avenue exit. Route 24 runs between Route 78 and Route 287. This exit is about 10 miles west of New Jersey Turnpike Exit 14, about 5 miles west of Garden State Parkway Exit 142, and about 10 miles east of Route 286 Exit 37. From the east, this is third Summit exit. Go south on Summit Avenue through downtown and as it curves left and becomes Elm Street. Within 2 blocks turn right onto Mountain Avenue, at stop sign, about 1.8 miles from Highway 24. Go through 2 intersections on Mountain Avenue to #105, on right; a yellow, stucco house with front porch benches and house numbers on red door. Montview Road, directly opposite #105, is a good place to park. There is no parking on east side of Mountain Avenue; park on Montview Road or west side of Mountain Avenue.

Hunterdon County Open Days
Saturday & Sunday June 2 & 3
HUNTERDON COUNTY

CALIFON
Frog Pond Farm
26 Beavers Road

In a peaceful countryside hollow, a half-acre spring-fed pond reflects the beauty of the natural scene. Everywhere in this mature garden, both native and introduced trees and shrubs combine to add beauty. Some of them are rather rare. The garden includes a wide variety of rhododendrons, azaleas, and mountain laurel. The Japanese primroses and iris expand prolifically (especially in rainy summers) along several ever-running spring-fed brooks. For added horticultural interest, many tender potted plants are displayed on the patio. They are grown by the homeowner in her small greenhouse. Crossing on a foot bridge to the meadow garden, many new perennials are to be seen adding color and form to beds and borders. This year, a new brookside planting has been added which replaces invasive shrubbery. There is a rock garden, too, where Ruby and Martin Weinberg, the homeowners, have lowered maintenance by eliminating some short-lived alpines and adding a few low-growing shrubs. It is all part of their garden renovation. Ruby is the author, and Martin, the photographer, of their recently published book *The Garden Reborn: Bringing New Life to Your Aging Landscape.* **2006**

Hours: 10 a.m. to 4 p.m.

From I-78, take Exit 24. Turn right (if coming from east) onto Route 523 toward Oldwick. Continue straight ahead as road becomes Route 517. Continue through village of Oldwick and on, with no turns (6 miles from interstate), to traffic light. This is Fairmont, with Fairmont Church on right corner. Turn left onto Route 512 and go about 1 mile to Beavers Road (bend in road with fence). Turn right and go about 1 mile to #26 at foot of hill. Number is on mailbox and there is a pond in front. Please park on Beavers Road.

Somerset County Open Day
Saturday, June 2
SOMERSET COUNTY

BEDMINSTER
River Run Farm
455 Bunn Road

River Run Farm is a horse farm estate dating from the 1920s. John Smith designed the current formal gardens in the 1980s. The garden rooms are filled with many flowering trees and shrubs that bloom year round, complementing spring bulbs and perennials. The walled pool garden features a wisteria-covered gazebo, a ten-foot-high holly hedge, a trumpet-vine-covered pergola underplanted with peonies, liriope, and crabapple trees. The fountain garden features a circular fountain surrounded by lawn and mixed perennial beds. A *Cornus kousa* dogwood highlights the sunny perennial garden, backed by tall grasses and traversed by a slate path. The shade garden features two long, deep beds backed by stone walls and bisected by a grass path. A courtyard garden and a woodland garden complete the garden. Other features include brick walls covered with English ivy, a vast collection of shade plants, an espaliered fire thorn, a small apple orchard, and an old pet cemetery. **2006**

Hours: 10 a.m. to 4 p.m.

From Route 287 north, take Exit 22A/Pluckermin to Route 202/206 south. Turn right onto Route 620/Burnt Mills Road. Turn right onto Bunn Road 3.2 miles from Route 287.

From Route 287 south, take Exit 22/Bedminster/Pluckemin. Make a U-turn at River Road onto Route 620/Burnt Mills Road. Turn right onto Bunn Road 4.2 miles from Route 287.

From Route 78 east, take Exit 26/Route 523/Lamington/North Branch to Route 665/Rattlesnake Bridge Road. Turn left onto Route

620/Burnt Mills Road. Turn left onto Bunn Road 4.6 miles from Route 78.

From Route 78 west, take Exit 29 to Route 287 north, and proceed as directed above.

Proceeds shared with Somerset Regional Animal Shelter

Essex County Open Day
Sunday, June 3

ESSEX COUNTY

SHORT HILLS
George Sternlieb
66 Old Short Hills Road

You will find a great variety of shade and sun lovers in troughs, pots, raised beds, and distinct gardens. Roses, clematis, dahlias, and hostas abound, framed by magnolias and Japanese maples. Non-hardy features include orchids, succulents, and a substantial range of vines, as well as begonias and other house/greenhouse plants. Four small pools are featured, as well as thirty-foot climbing hydrangeas. **2005** ❘

Hours: 10 a.m. to 2 p.m.

From Garden State Parkway, take Exit 142. Take I-78 west to Millburn and get off at Exit 50B. At top of exit ramp, turn right onto Vauxhall Road and go to end, about 0.8 mile (Vauxhall twists, so watch out). Turn left onto Millburn Avenue. In about 0.5 mile, the road jogs slightly to right. Take this road (now called Essex) to third traffic light at Old Short Hills Road (also called Main Street). Turn right and go uphill about 0.4 mile to #66 on right.

From New York City, take Lincoln Tunnel to New Jersey Turnpike/I-95 south. Take Exit 14/Newark Airport. Stay right through tollbooth and take I-78 local west to Millburn. Take Exit 50B. Proceed as directed above.

Spring Lake
Open Day
Sunday, June 3

MONMOUTH COUNTY

SPRING LAKE
McMullen Garden
1 St. Clair Avenue

Our garden by-the-sea was designed, planted, and is cared for by landscaper, Jaymee Carey, about ten years ago. Walled and elevated, one enters into a special world. Hundreds of Oriental and Asiatic lilies bloom all summer long. Hydrangea, butterfly bushes and other flowering shrubs along with ornamental grasses and annuals thrive. Three sides of this one-and-one-half-acre garden are devoted to perennial borders: one borders the croquet court, another to the east has a lovely view of the ocean beyond. Trees are few, but we cherish an old Russian olive, a Southern magnolia, and a Japanese umbrella pine. A koi pond, small shade and herb gardens complete the landscape. Mr. Carey wanted to create a garden that bloomed from February to December and he has. **2004**

Hours: 10 a.m. to 4 p.m.

From the north, take the Garden State Parkway south to Exit 98. Stay left on Route 34 south toward Point Pleasant/Spring Lake. Go south 1.8 miles to traffic circle. Go 3/4 of the way around circle to East Route 524/Allaire Road. Continue 4.8 miles, past Route 35 and Route 71 and across railroad tracks into Spring Lake. Allaire becomes Ludlow. Travel to First Avenue. Turn right and go 2 blocks to St. Clair. Turn left. We are the last house on right, #1 (brick and wood frame).

From the west, take the New Jersey Turnpike to I-95 East. Go just over 30 miles, I-95 becomes Route 138 after going under the Garden State Parkway. Go 3 traffic lights and turn right onto New Bedford Road. Go 2 lights to Allaire Road and turn left. Pass Routes 35 and 71 and railroad tracks onto First Avenue. Proceed as directed above.

From the south, take the Garden State Parkway north to Exit 98. Take Route 138 East and proceed as directed above.

Richard & Barbara Nelson
115 Passaic Avenue

Meander through the bricked pathways of this formal English garden overflowing with dozens of varieties of perennials and herbs. The centerpiece, a stone urn, rises in the midst of the garden's quadrants, and serves as the focal point. Its base is encircled by Oriental lilies, Asiatic lilies, tetraploid daylilies, and poppies. A treat for the vigilant eye is the occasional hummingbird visiting the buddleia. A quiet brick courtyard features equally beautiful containers brimming with unusual annuals such as plumbago, taros, clerodendrum, tibouchina, strobilanthes, and pentas. Beneath hibiscus topiaries are various shades of listianthus. On a raised stone bed surrounding the garden is a G-gauge outdoor railroad which runs along 400 feet of track. Villages are nestled among dwarf shrubs and groundcovers along with automobiles and characters, depicting scenes from the 1930s and 40s. Other plants of interest are brugmansia, alliums, agapanthus, digitalis, delphiniums, passifloras, scented geraniums, several salvia species, Gerbera daisies, and *Begonia grandis*. In full view below his art studio, this colorful vista serves as a constant source of inspiration for the owner and serves as a living canvas for all who visit. **2004**

Hours: 10 a.m. to 4 p.m.

From the north, take the Garden State Parkway south to Exit 98. Stay left on Route 34 south toward Point Pleasant/Spring Lake. Go south 1.8 miles to traffic circle. Go 3/4 of the way around circle to East Route 524/Allaire Road. Continue 4.8 miles, past Route 35 and Route 71 and across railroad tracks into Spring Lake. Allaire becomes Ludlow. Continue to Ocean Avenue. Turn right and go 9 blocks (0.5 mile) to Passaic Avenue. Turn right. Our house (gray with trim), #115, is 3/4 block in on left.

From the west, take the New Jersey Turnpike to I-95 East. Go just over 30 miles, I-95 becomes Route 138 after going under the Garden State Parkway. Go 2.25 miles to New Bedford Road South. Turn right at 2nd traffic light, then left onto Allaire Road/Route 524 East. Go 2 miles to Ocean Avenue. Crossing onto Ocean Avenue, go 9 blocks (0.5 mile to Passaic Avenue. Turn right. Our house (gray with white trim), #115, is almost 2 blocks in on left.

Jules & Jane Plangere
106 Morris Avenue

Following in the footsteps of my father, who was the gardener and superintendent of the "garden rich" Martin Maloney estate in Spring Lake, after retirement I became a "casual" gardener on one-quarter of the block that was the original estate. The estate property, one block from the Atlantic Ocean, is distinguished by a six-foot-high black wrought-iron fence that still encircles the entire block and by holly bushes and forty-foot holly and pin oak trees planted by my father more than seventy years ago. In keeping with the elevation of the house on the property, a three-foot-high fieldstone wall was constructed within the iron fence. An elevated border atop the wall was planted with salt resistant mixed perennials. This design gives privacy and frames the rose-bush-encircled gazebo of this corner property. A putting green and sand trap highlight a grass plot that fronts a pool house. The border plantings are interspersed with flowering Japanese cherry and pear trees. **2004** ♿

Hours: 10 a.m. to 4 p.m.

From the north, take the Garden State Parkway south to Exit 98. Stay left on Route 34 south toward Point Pleasant/Spring Lake. Go south 1.8 miles to traffic circle. Go 3/4 of the way around circle to East Route 524/Allaire Road. Go 4.8 miles into Spring Lake to the beach. Turn right onto Ocean Avenue and go 9 blocks to Morris Avenue. Turn right and go to first house on right in second block, #106.

From the south, take the Garden State Parkway North to Exit 98. Take Route 138 east and proceed as directed above.

From the west, take I-195 east to the end. I-195 becomes Route 138. Continue to end. Turn right onto Route 35 at Belmar. At the second traffic light turn left onto Route 524/Allair Road. Proceed as directed above.

Bergen County Open Day Saturday, June 16

BERGEN COUNTY

Maywood
Dail & Tony's Garden
66 West Magnolia Avenue

Our sunny front gardens spill over with China blue agastache and kalimeris, yellow heliopsis, assorted geraniums, heaths and heathers, an handmade copper trellis clothed in *Clematis viticella* 'Etolle Violette', and several varieties of alliums, punctuated by deep blue brodiaea and golden California poppies. The handmade copper arch, inviting you into the back gardens, elevates a mature tangutica clematis as well as several other clematises. There, under two towering maples, we are surrounded with the joys of textured gardening. The mature weeping crabapple Malus 'Red Jade', *Stewartia pseudocamellia*, out charming collection of both large and small hostas and hellebores, unusual ferns, and a collage of colorful mature astilbes encourages you to linger in this tapestry of green, and enjoy the whimsy that is all about. When our many houseplants are summering outside, they enhance the feeling of rooms ithin the garden, have a seat in any of the several nooks around. Just beyond the shade canopy is our woodland streambed and pond, enhanced with many unusual perennials, deciduous azaleas and rhododendrons and a 'new' baker's rack covered with a number of different clematis, both climbing and shrubby. And just beyond is our newest, a true red tree form *Lagerstroemia indica* 'Dynamite', with its crimson new leaves. **2005** ♿

Hours: 10 a.m. to 4 p.m.

From George Washington Bridge, take Route 4 west to Forest Avenue, turn left onto Forest at the light and go back over Route 4 where it becomes Maywood Avenue. Continue south for 1 mile and turn right onto West Magnolia Avenue.

From 208 East, take Forest Avenue exit off Route 4 East to the right then left onto Forest Avenue. Proceed as directed above.

From 17, take Route 4 East and proceed as directed above. Ours is thirteenth house on left, second up from corner of Ramapo Avenue.

Ridgewood
The Handley Garden
342 Franklin Turnpike

John and Sue Handley's garden is set on a one-acre property. The front foundation planting is a mixed border of ornamental trees, shrubs, and flowers and prepares you only somewhat for the beauty of the garden behind the house. A water-and-rock garden is beside the deck. Sunny perennial borders punctuated by garden ornaments extend the length of the path that draws you to the open lawn. Sue Handley has planted a great variety of wonderful plants, some of which may be new to you. **2006** ♿

Hours: 10 a.m. to 4 p.m.

From Route 17 south, proceed past Ramsey, Allendale, and Waldwick to right turn at Ho-Ho-Kus/Racetrack Road exit. Proceed west 3 blocks and turn left onto Nagel. Proceed to Franklin Turnpike and turn right. Garden is on left.

From Route 17 north, go about 4 miles from Route 4 to Linwood Avenue overpass. Go under overpass and turn right. Continue to second traffic light at Pleasant Avenue and turn right. Follow to end and turn right onto Glen Avenue. Pass cemetery on left to a hairpin turn at beginning of Franklin Turnpike. Handley Garden is about 0.75 mile down on left. Please park on front lawn.

Proceeds shared with Citizens for Swimming

River Edge
Anthony "Bud" & Virginia Korteweg
800 Summit Avenue

Edgecroft is a unique terraced property laid out in 1910 by Italian artisans, with 100 Carrara marble stairs to a swimming pool with a Venetian bridge surrounded by a stone-columned pergola draped in roses, wisteria, and honeysuckle. The property has five garden rooms: a gated brick courtyard entrance with a slowly maturing allée of hydrangeas to greet the guest entering the Edgecroft gardens. Like old time capsules, hydrangeas provide a warm welcome with hues of pinks and lavender interspersed with a variety of mixed perennials. Rare *Cryptomeria 'Lobbii'*, rhododendrons, azaleas, and *Magnolia virginiana*; a centerpiece tiered bronze angel fountain; a Victorian perennial garden with David Austin antique roses and favorite perennials; a formal garden with crape myrtles, azaleas, and a fountain with a copy of Verrocchio's fifteenth-century bronze Cupid with dolphin. A series of three koi ponds interspersed with nine waterfalls cascade down terraces edged with aged pines, golden larches, flowering cherry trees, dogwoods, *Styrax japonicus*, hydrangeas, wild strawberries, and creeping roses. Bronze water statuary, stone benches, and stone statuary are throughout the grounds. An all-white Bridal Room is in progress. Heritage white birches and dogwoods, rhododendrons, hydrangeas, azaleas, buddleia, and creeping cushion white roses will provide the backdrop for white perennials and annuals of the season. **2006** ₺

Hours: 8 a.m. to 4 p.m.

From George Washington Bridge, take Route 4 west to Route 17 north. Take Midland Avenue/River Edge exit. Go east about 2 miles to "T" junction and turn right onto Kinderkamack Road. Travel south to first traffic light. Turn right onto Lincoln Avenue up a cobblestone hill. Walled property on right is Edgecroft. Turn right onto Summit Avenue. Number 800 is immediately on right.

From I-80 or Garden State Parkway, get on Route 17 north and proceed as directed above. Please park along street and enter through open gates.

Proceeds shared with Beautification Foundation of River Edge

TENAFLY

Linda Singer
170 *Tekening Drive*

I designed this romantic garden to include bluestone walks and patios, fieldstone sitting walls, rose-and-vine-covered arbors and trellises, stone ornaments, a swimming pool, and a small vegetable garden enclosed by a white picket fence. There are perennial and mixed borders. A cottage garden is of special interest for a wide variety of flowering shrubs. The greatest challenge is thwarting the legions of deer, moles, voles, field mice, and rabbits that love the garden as much as I do. I have lots of volunteer plants to give away if you do the bending. **2006** ⚲

Hours: 10 a.m. to 4 p.m.

From Palisades Parkway, take Exit 1/Englewood/Palisades Avenue. Turn right at first traffic light onto Sylvan Avenue/ Route 9W, drive north about 3 miles. Turn left at light onto East Clinton Avenue. Drive 0.5 mile and turn right onto Ridge Road. Drive 1 block and turn right onto Berkeley Drive. Drive 1 block and turn left onto Highwood Road. Drive 2 blocks and turn right onto Tekening Drive. House is third on right. A sign with #170 is high on a tree. Please park on street.

Proceeds shared with PFLAG of Bergen County

Monmouth County Open Day Saturday, June 23
MONMOUTH COUNTY

RUMSON

Beliza Ann Furman
8 *Woods End Road*

Over the past years, my late husband, Sam, and I replaced horticultural clichés with our interpretation of a real garden. The focal point is the pond-like swimming pool and waterfall, which are surrounded by several planted areas. In spring, bulbs, azaleas, viburnums, lilacs, astilbes, and rhododendrons stand out. In summer, assorted lilies, spirea, crape myrtle, hydrangea, old roses, and gazillions of perennials fill in the gaps. We are in bloom from February to November. Behind the pool, climbing roses and crabapple standards enhance a columned pergola and seating area. A formal parterre features a stone dining set, standard 'Fairy' roses, and assorted annuals. **2006**

Hours: 10 a.m. to 4 p.m.

From Garden State Parkway, take Exit 109. Coming from north, turn left (east) onto Newman Springs Road; from south, bear right. Go through five traffic lights to end. Turn right onto Broad Street/Route 35. Go to next light and turn left onto White Road. Go to end. Turn left onto Branch Avenue. At blinking light, turn right onto Rumson Road. Continue straight to sign "Rumson, Settled 1665." Second left is Woods End Road. Our house is third on left. Please park on street, not in driveway.

King & Leigh Sorensen
7 North Ward Avenue

The house is a former windmill adjacent to a river. The landscape design includes a raised perennial bed with shrubs and flowering trees in the background. The garden was featured in the January 1983 issue of *House Beautiful*. There are espaliered apple trees near King's vegetable garden, which features five varieties of lettuce. Leigh has a collection of bonsai and King raises honeybees. Many ornamental grasses are incorporated into the gardens, which flood at times of extreme high tides. **2005** ♿

Hours: 10 a.m. to 4 p.m.

From Garden State Parkway, take Exit 109. Turn east onto Newman Springs Road and after 1.5 miles turn left onto Broad Street. After 0.75 mile turn right onto Harding Place and continue east 5 miles (road name changes to Ridge, then Hartchorne). At end, turn left onto North Ward Avenue. Our driveway is a continuation of North Ward Avenue. The house, #7, is marked on an oar in a grass garden.

Bergen & Morris County Open Day
Saturday, August 11

BERGEN COUNTY

TENAFLY

Linda Singer
170 Tekening Drive

I designed this romantic garden to include bluestone walks and patios, fieldstone sitting walls, rose-and-vine-covered arbors and trellises, stone ornaments, a swimming pool, and a small vegetable garden enclosed by a white picket fence. There are perennial and mixed borders. A cottage garden is of special interest for a wide variety of flowering shrubs. The greatest challenge is thwarting the legions of deer, moles, voles, field mice, and rabbits that love the garden as much as I do. I have lots of volunteer plants to give away if you do the bending. **2006** ♿

Hours: 10 a.m. to 4 p.m.

From Palisades Parkway, take Exit 1/Englewood/Palisades Avenue. Turn right at first traffic light onto Sylvan Avenue/ Route 9W, drive north about 3 miles, and turn left at light onto East Clinton Avenue. Drive 0.5 mile and turn right onto Ridge Road. Drive 1 block and turn right onto Berkeley Drive. Drive 1 block and turn left onto Highwood Road. Drive 2 blocks and turn right onto Tekening Drive. House is third on right. A sign with #170 is high on a tree. Please park on street.

Proceeds shared with PFLAG of Bergen County

MORRIS COUNTY

RANDOLPH

Jones Garden
123 Mountainside Drive

Our garden covers about one half of our one-acre property. After thirty-seven years, the garden has evolved from a collection of more than 500 different specimens to a more designed setting. I have created sunny borders by the pool which are inspired by Christopher

Lloyd and Fergus Garrett, and by Piet Oudolf's books. The backyard shade garden features many plants with interesting foliage characteristics: variegation, color, texture, structure. Other features include a small bog garden and deer-resistant plantings at the front. **2006**

Hours: 10 a.m. to 4 p.m.

From I-287, take Exit 39 to Route 10 west for 5 miles to Franklin Road (traffic light, Exxon gas station on right). Proceed through light, taking Shongum exit onto Franklin Road (south), which becomes Openaki Road. One mile from Route 10 turn right onto Mountainside Drive. We are on left, 0.3 mile from Openaki, at #123. Please park on street.

Essex County
Open Day
Saturday, September 8

Greenwood Gardens in Short Hills is also open on this date. See their listing on page 170. Read more about our preservation work at Greenwood Gardens on our website, www.gardenconservancy.org

ESSEX COUNTY

NUTLEY
Graeme Hardie
210 Rutgers Place

New Jersey? When you step into my garden, you are transported to a world far from what most imagine is a "typical" New Jersey garden. I call it my "jungle." This is a forty- by sixty-foot walled contemporary garden, designed by Richard Hartlage. For its size, it is richly planted in perennials and tropicals—a mix that works to great effect. My garden is one of texture and contrasting leaf form and color. Good use has been made of level changes, affording the garden the experience of, at one point, having an overview of the garden and the next, walking under and surrounded by it. The garden boasts bold sculpture, terraces, and a well-hidden hot tub. It was featured in *Garden Design* magazine in February 2005 and awarded a Golden Trowel Award in the Professional category. It was

also featured in *Traditional Home* magazine in September 2000. **2005**

Hours: 10 a.m. to 4 p.m.

From Lincoln Tunnel or Exit 16 from the New Jersey Turnpike/I-95, go west on Route 3. From the Garden State Parkway, go east on Route 3. From either direction, go to exit marked Main Avenue/Nutley/Passaic exit. At end of exit ramp, turn left and go through 2 traffic lights (3 lights if coming from west). After this traffic light, continue straight ahead. Rutgers Place is the fourth street on the left. Come up Rutgers Place to top of hill; when road flattens, #210 is on left.

Proceeds shared with Essex County Master Gardeners

Silas Mountsier
205 Rutgers Place

With the help of Seattle landscape gardener Richard Hartlage, my garden has grown in the last few years from one half acre to one acre. I like drifts of plants and the interplay of strong lines; contrasting leaf texture and color gives this mostly shade garden a strong, almost architectural, form. But, too, my garden has many nooks and crannies, each with its own surprise to delight the eye. Sculpted objects abound and complement the rich botanical mix. My garden brings me joy and has for over fifty years; I find it hard to believe it's mine—truly a long-held dream come true. This garden is featured in *Garden Design's* December 2003 issue. **2005** ♿

Hours: 10 a.m. to 4 p.m

From Lincoln Tunnel or Exit 16 from the New Jersey Turnpike/I-95, go west on Route 3. From the Garden State Parkway, go east on Route 3. From both directions, go to exit marked Main Avenue/Nutley/Passaic exit. At end of exit ramp, turn left and proceed through 2 traffic lights (3 lights if coming from west). After this traffic light, continue straight ahead. Rutgers Place is the fourth street on the left. Come up Rutgers Place to top of hill; when road flattens, #205 is on right.

Proceeds shared with Essex County Master Gardeners

♿ indicates parts of garden are handicapped accessible

SHORT HILLS
George Sternlieb
66 Old Short Hills Road

You will find a great variety of shade and sun lovers in troughs, pots, raised beds, and distinct gardens. Roses, clematis, dahlias, and hostas abound, framed by magnolias and Japanese maples. Non-hardy features include orchids, succulents, and a substantial range of vines, as well as begonias and other house/greenhouse plants. Four small pools are featured, as well as thirty-foot climbing hydrangeas. **2005** ♿

Hours: 10 a.m. to 2 p.m.

From Garden State Parkway, take Exit 142. Take I-78 west to Millburn and get off at Exit 50B. At top of exit ramp, go right on Vauxhall Road and go to end, about 0.8 mile (Vauxhall twists, so watch out). Turn left onto Millburn Avenue. In about 0.5 mile, the road jogs slightly to right. Take this road (now called Essex) to third traffic light at Old Short Hills Road (also called Main Street). Turn right and go uphill about 0.4 mile to #66 on right.

From New York City, take Lincoln Tunnel to New Jersey Turnpike/I-95 south. Take Exit 14/Newark Airport. Stay right through tollbooth and take I-78 local west to Millburn. Take Exit 50B. Proceed as directed above.

Public Gardens
BERGEN COUNTY

TENAFLY
Davis Johnson Park & Gardens
137 Engle Street, (201) 569-7275

Featuring an award-winning rose garden recognized by the American Rose Society, this seven-and-one-half-acre park has many floral beds, paths, and benches. Our gazebo is a favorite place for wedding ceremonies and photos. This former estate has several mature beech trees.

Hours: Year round, daily, dawn to dusk

Admission: Free

Take Route 9W to East Clinton Avenue. Go west downhill to first traffic light (Engle Street). Turn left. Park entrance is on right, 0.25 mile from Clinton.

WAYNE
Laurelwood Arboretum
725 Pines Lake Drive West,
(973) 835-5683,
www.laurelwoodarboretum.org

Laurelwood Arboretum is a thirty-plus-acre, botanically diverse property located in the Pines Lake section of Wayne Township in northwestern New Jersey. Laurelwood features woodland trails, wildlife, two ponds, and hundreds of varieties of rhododendrons, azaleas and other unusual species of plants and trees. Once a commercial nursery, Laurelwood Arboretum is now maintained as a public park through a partnership between Friends of Laurelwood Arboretum and the Township of Wayne, and is funded through memberships, bequests, and donations.

Hours: Year round, daily, dawn to dusk. Closed federal and state holidays.

Admission: Free

From the south take Route 287 north to Exit 53 (third Riverdale exit, past the exit for Route 23). Turn right onto Hamburg Turnpike at end of exit ramp. Go about 1 mile and turn left onto Route 202/Terhune Avenue, then first right onto Colfax Road. Turn left onto Vale Road, then right onto Pines Lake Drive.

From the north take Route 287 south to Route 208 South Exit/Franklin Lakes. Turn right at end of exit ramp, another right and a quick left onto Colonial Road. Go to "T" intersection and blinking traffic light and turn right onto Franklin Lakes Road. Turn left at second light onto Breakneck Road (becomes Berdan Avenue). Go about 0.5 mile, make sharp right onto Indian Road. Turn left onto Osceola then left onto Pines Lake Drive, about 0.5 mile. Continue until just before Vale Road then turn left into gated parking lot in the arboretum.

The arboretum is between Colfax Road and Pines Lake Drive, bordered on one end by Vale Road. Parking lot is through gate on Pines Lake Drive.

ESSEX COUNTY

BLOOMFIELD

Oakeside-Bloomfield Cultural Center

240 Belleville Avenue, (973) 429-0960

A three-acre garden, Oakeside is on both the state and national Register of Historic Places. The grounds are currently undergoing restoration. A formal rose garden (1913) and large kitchen garden (1922) were designed by Vitale, Brinckerhoff, and Geiffert. A naturalistic water garden and terrace garden near the solarium date from about 1929.

Hours: Year round, daily, dawn to dusk, except during private events; groups by appointment

Admission: Free

From Garden State Parkway south, take Exit 148. Stay straight on J.F.K. Drive to end, then turn left and make quick right back onto J.F.K. Drive. At first traffic light, turn right onto Belleville Avenue. Take second entrance on right for parking.

From Garden State Parkway north, take Exit 149. Turn right off exit ramp onto J.F.K. Drive. Proceed as directed above.

MAPLEWOOD

Durand-Hedden House & Garden

523 Ridgewood Road, (973) 763-7712

The historic Durand-Hedden House sits on two picturesque acres that include a sloping meadow edged with trees and shrubs, a perennial bed, and a children's garden. It also boasts a large herb collection with many species and cultivated varieties of thyme, sage, and mint.

Hours: Year round, daily, dawn to dusk.

Admission: Free

From I-78 west and Route 24 west, take Exit 50B/Millburn/Maplewood. At top of exit ramp, turn right onto Vauxhall Road. Continue to intersection of Millburn Avenue at third traffic light. Cross Millburn onto Ridgewood Road. Go 1 mile, past blinking light. House is first on left after Durand Road and opposite Jefferson School.

MONTCLAIR

Van Vleck House & Gardens

21 Van Vleck Street, (973) 744-4752,
www.vanvleck.org

A PROJECT OF
THE GARDEN
CONSERVANCY

Begun at the turn of the century, these gardens have been developed by several generations of committed horticulturists. The plan is largely formal, responding to the Mediterranean style of the house. The extensive collection of rhododendrons and azaleas, including several named for family members, is renowned. Also of note are the many mature plant specimens.

Hours: Year round, daily, 9 a.m. to 5 p.m.

Admission: $3 suggested donation

From Garden State Parkway north, take Exit 148/Bloomfield Avenue. Stay in left lane of exit ramp through first traffic light and take "jug-handle" under the parkway back to Bloomfield Avenue; turn right at light. Go 2.5 miles through Bloomfield, Glen Ridge, and Montclair town centers. Turn right onto North Mountain Avenue (Montclair Art Museum is on left). Go through one light (Claremont Avenue) and take next left onto Van Vleck Street; Van Vleck House & Gardens is on left.

From Garden State Parkway south, take Exit 148/Bloomfield Avenue. Follow service road through one stop sign and two lights. Turn right, (west) at the third light onto Bloomfield Avenue. Proceed as directed above.

From New York City, take Lincoln Tunnel to Route 3 west. Exit at Grove Street, Montclair. Turn left at top of exit ramp onto Grove, proceed 3.9 miles to Claremont Avenue, turn right. Go 0.9 mile to fifth light. Turn right onto North Mountain Avenue and proceed as directed above.

From I-280, take Exit 8B/Prospect Avenue. Proceed north 2 miles to Bloomfield Avenue, turn right, and go 0.5 mile to third light. Turn left onto North Mountain Avenue. Go through 1 light, (Claremont Avenue) and take next left onto Van Vleck Street. Van Vleck House & Gardens is on left.

RIDGEWOOD
The James Rose Center
506 East Ridgewood Avenue,
(201) 446-6017, www.jamesrosecenter.org

James Rose was a pioneer of applying modern design principles to landscape architecture in the 1930s. Built in 1953, his house and garden were designed to change over time and now reflect more than forty years of evolution. It is a unique environment of interwoven spaces formed by structure, plants, and water to create a strong fusion between house and garden.

Hours: May through October, first and third Saturday, 10 a.m. to 4 p.m., by appointment only

Admission: $8

From George Washington Bridge, take Route 4 west to Route 17 north to Ridgewood Avenue/Ridgewood exit. Follow East Ridgewood Avenue towards Ridgewood. House is on corner of East Ridgewood Avenue and Southern.

SHORT HILLS
Greenwood Gardens
274 Old Short Hills Road, (973) 258-4026,
www.greenwoodgardens.org

A PROJECT OF
THE GARDEN
CONSERVANCY

The Garden Conservancy is assisting Greenwood in the restoration of this historic twenty-two-acre garden. Since the early twentieth century, Greenwood Gardens has been a private retreat with formal Italianate gardens graced with colorful tiles, rustic stone tea houses, mossy-pebbled walks and vistas stretching for miles into the surrounding wooded hillsides. Though the beauty of Greenwood remains partially hidden beneath chipping stucco and overgrown vegetation, careful preservation work and imaginative horticulture is bringing the gardens back to life.

Hours: Special Garden Conservancy Open Day, May 20, 12 p.m. to 4 p.m. and September 8, 1 p.m. to 3 p.m.; otherwise, May through October by appointment only.

Admission: $5

From Garden State Parkway, take Exit 142. Take I-78 west to Millburn and take Exit 50B. At top of exit ramp, turn right onto Vauxhall Road and proceed to its end, about 0.8 mile. At end of Vauxhall, turn left onto Millburn Avenue. In about 1 mile, road jogs slightly to right and changes to Essex. At third traffic light turn right onto Old Short Hills Road and go up hill about 0.5 mile to stone gateposts marking entrance of Old Short Hills Park, #274, on right. Turn here and follow signs to parking lot.

From New Jersey Turnpike/I-95 south, take Exit 14/Newark Airport. Stay right through tollbooth, and take I-78 local west to Millburn, and get off at Exit 50B. Proceed as directed above.

From Route 24 west, take Hobart Gap Road exit. Turn right at light onto Hobart Gap Road. At blinking light, road name changes to White Oak Ridge Road. At next light (1 mile), turn right onto Parsonage Hill Road. Continue to "T" junction. Turn left onto Old Short Hills Road and go about 0.6 mile where road widens at stone gate marked with signs for #274. Greenwood Gardens shares this entrance with Old Short Hills Park. Proceed into park for parking directions.

UPPER MONTCLAIR
The Presby Memorial Iris Gardens
474 Upper Mountain Avenue,
(973) 783-5974, www.presbyiris.tripod.com

The Presby Memorial Iris Gardens is the world's largest display garden of irises, with over 100,000 blooms throughout the season (three weeks). The collection of more than 2,000 varieties in thirty beds, mostly tall bearded iris, also contains miniature dwarf bearded, Louisiana, Siberian, Japanese, remontant, and historic irises. A display bed demonstrates the varied landscapes in which irises can grow.

Hours: Garden open during bloom season, mid-May through early June, 10 a.m. to 8 p.m., daily, weekends and holidays.

Admission: Free

Upper Mountain Avenue is bounded by Route 46 on the north, Route 23 to the west, Bloomfield Avenue, Montclair, on the south and is easily reached from Route 3, I-80, I-280, I-287, and Garden State Parkway. Please call for directions.

MERCER COUNTY

PRINCETON
Morven Museum & Garden
55 Stockton Street, (609) 924-8144,
www.morven.org

Home to a signer of the Declaration of Independence and five New Jersey governors, the Morven landscape is a composite of 200 years of American history. Its gardens interpret three periods in Morven's history: a nineteenth-century picturesque entrance lawn, an eighteenth-century horsechestnut walk, and an early twentieth-century Colonial Revival garden.

Hours: Year round, Wednesday through Friday, 11 a.m. to 3 p.m.; Saturday and Sunday, 12 p.m. to 4 p.m.

Admission: $5 adults, $4 seniors and students

From Somerville Circle/Route 202/I-287, take Route 206 south about 17 miles into Princeton. The road (called Bayard Road in Princeton) ends at traffic light, with Nassau Street/Route 27 to left and Stockton Street (continuation of Route 206) to right. Turn right onto Stockton. Morven's driveway is second on right just past Princeton Borough Hall and Police Station.

MIDDLESEX COUNTY

NEW BRUNSWICK
The Rutgers Gardens
112 Ryders Lane, (732) 932-8451
http://rutgersgardens.rutgers.edu/nj

The Rutgers Gardens' first collections were begun during the 1920s so that students, educators, researchers, and plant aficionados would have access to an extensive collection of mature plant specimens. Many years and plant collections later (including the American Holly Collection and Donald B. Lacey Display Garden), the gardens still serve as an outdoor classroom where students and horticultural

enthusiasts of all ages can discover and enjoy a diverse range of landscape plants in a variety of garden settings.

Hours: Year round, daily, 8 a.m. to dusk

Admission: Free

Take Route 1 to Ryders Lane/East Brunswick exit. At end of exit ramp, get in left lane and take first left onto Log Cabin Road, which will take you into Rutgers Gardens.

MORRIS COUNTY

BOONTON
The Emilie K. Hammond Wildflower Trail
McCaffrey Lane, (973) 326-7600

This 463-acre park of hilly terrain and granite boulders includes mountain trails that wind their way through a forest of white oaks, maples, beeches, and hemlocks, and a series of niches provides specific microclimates suitable for more than 250 different wildflowers and shrubs native to the eastern United States.

Hours: Year round, daily, dawn to dusk

Admission: Free

From I-80 west, take Route 46/Denville exit east to Mountain Lakes exit. Turn left onto the Boulevard. Bear left onto Powerville Road. Take first left onto McCaffrey Lane.

MORRISTOWN
Acorn Hall
68 Morris Avenue, (973) 267-3465,
www.acornhall.org

Acorn Hall, the headquarters of the Morris County Historical Society, is a Victorian Italianate mansion (circa 1853-1860). The gardens have been restored by the Home Garden Club of Morristown to be reflective of the 1853-1888 period. Features include spring-flowering trees, shrubs, and bulbs; authentic Victorian roses; an herb garden and traditional knot garden; and a fern garden.

Hours: Year round, daily, dawn to dusk

Admission: Free

From I-287 south, take Exit 37/Route 24 east/Springfield to Exit 2A and follow signs to Morristown. Follow Columbia Road to end

---

♿ indicates parts of garden are handicapped accessible

traffic light (in front of Governor Morris Hotel). Turn left into second driveway on right.

From I-287 north, take Exit 36A onto Morris Avenue. Take first right fork onto Columbia Turnpike and turn left immediately at light. Turn left into second driveway on right.

Delbarton—
St. Mary's Abbey School
230 Mendham Road, (973) 538-3231,
www.delbarton.org

Delbarton, the largest estate of Morris County's Gilded Age, is now a private boys school run by Benedictine monks and occupies more than 380 acres of the original four thousand. A splendid Italian garden with a pergola and statuary flanks the west side of Old Main, the imposing old residence.

Hours: Year round, weekdays, 9 a.m. to 5 p.m., weekends, 9 a.m. to dusk

Admission: Free

From I-287, take Exit 35/Route 124/ Madison Avenue. Bear right at end of exit ramp onto Route 124 west/South Street. Proceed straight to Morristown Green. Follow signs for Route 510 west/Washington Street. This becomes Route 24/Mendham Road. Delbarton is on left, 2.5 miles from Morristown Green.

MORRIS TOWNSHIP
The Frelinghuysen Arboretum
53 East Hanover Avenue,
(973) 326-7600, www.morrisparks.net

The 127-acre Frelinghuysen Arboretum displays a wide range of native and exotic plants in demonstration gardens of perennials, annuals, plants for shade, ferns, vegetables, and roses. Collections include conifers, dogwoods, crabapples, cherries, and hollies set around a splendid 1890s Colonial Revival-style mansion.

Hours: Grounds open year round, daily, 9 a.m. to dusk. Closed Thanksgiving, Christmas, and New Year's Day.

Admission: Free

From I-287 north, take Exit 36A. Proceed to Whippany Road. At second traffic light, turn left onto East Hanover Avenue. Entrance is on right.

From I-287 south, take Exit 36. Turn right onto Ridgedale Avenue. Turn right at second light onto East Hanover Avenue. Entrance is on right.

PASSAIC COUNTY

RINGWOOD
New Jersey State
Botanical Garden at Skylands
Morris Road, (973) 962-9534,
www.njbg.org

This ninety-six-acre Historical Landmark Garden is surrounded by 4,084 acres of woodland with hiking and biking trails. The garden includes a forty-four-room Tudor-style manor house, an arboretum, formal gardens, lilac garden, crabapple allée, water gardens, statuary, wildflower area, rhododendron garden, and heath and heather garden.

Hours: Year round, daily, 8 a.m. to 8 p.m.

Admission: $5 for parking on weekends, Memorial Day through Labor Day

From Route 208 and Skyline Drive, turn right at end of Skyline Drive onto Route 511. Take second right onto Sloatsburg Road. Pass Hewitt School and Carletondale Road. Turn right onto Morris Road; Skylands is 1.5 miles up Morris Road.

From I-287, take Exit 57. Follow signs to Skyline Drive and proceed as directed above.

From New York State Thruway/I-87, take Exit 15A/Route 17 and follow to Route 72 west, which becomes Sloatsburg Road in New Jersey. Take Sloatsburg past Ringwood Manor; Morris Road is on left. Proceed as directed above.

SOMERSET COUNTY

BERNARDSVILLE
The Cross Estate Gardens
Leddell Road, (973) 539-2016,
www.nps.gov\morr

Tucked away along the headwaters of the Passaic River, Cross Estate Gardens go back to the early years of this century when wealthy people built grand country mansions as summer

the new york
garden

a magazine dedicated to gardening in the New York metro area
newyorkgardenmagazine.com

retreats in the "Mountain Colony" located in Bernardsville. Its gardens and buildings include a walled garden, pergola, native garden, and woodlands and provide a glimpse of a lifestyle that is now but a memory.

Hours: Year round, daily, dawn to dusk

Admission: Free

From I-287 south, take Harter Road exit. Turn left at stop sign onto Harter Road, then left at stop sign onto Route 202 south/Mount Kemble Avenue. Go 0.9 mile, turn right at traffic light onto Tempe Wick Road 2 miles (past entrance for Jockey Hollow). Turn left onto Leddell Road at waterfall and go 1.1 miles. Turn left onto long driveway at sign "New Jersey Brigade Area—Cross Estate Gardens."

From I-287 north, take Route 202/North Maple Avenue/Jockey Hollow exit. Turn right at light onto Route 202 north/Mount Kemble Avenue. Go 1.7 miles and turn left at light onto Tempe Wick Road. Proceed as directed above.

Far Hills
Leonard J. Buck Garden
11 Layton Road, (908) 234-2677,
www.somersetcountyparks.org

The Leonard J. Buck Garden is a nationally known rock garden, developed by its namesake in the 1930s. It lies in a woodland stream valley where natural rock outcroppings have been uncovered. There are extensive collections of pink and white dogwoods, azaleas, rhododendrons, wildflowers, ferns, and rock-loving plants.

Hours: April through November, weekdays, 10 a.m. to 4 p.m.; Saturday, 10 a.m. to 5 p.m.; Sunday, 12 p.m. to 5 p.m. December through March, weekdays, 10 a.m. to 4 p.m. Closed major holidays. Group tours available.

Admission: $3 suggested donation; $1 seniors and children.

From I-287 north, take Exit 22B; from I-287 south, take Exit 22. At end of exit ramp, take Route 202/206 north, staying right to continue north on 202. Follow signs to Far Hills and Morristown. At Far Hills train station, turn right before tracks onto Liberty Corner/Far

Hills Road. Travel 0.9 mile to Layton Road and turn right. Garden is on left.

Gladstone
Fairview Farm Wildlife Preserve Bird & Butterfly Garden
2121 Larger Cross Road, (908) 234-1852,
www.urwa.org

The Upper Raritan Watershed Association (URWA) has established a garden on Fairview Farm Wildlife Preserve to promote the conservation of birds and butterflies, to provide environmental and horticultural education, and to foster an appreciation of nature. Daytime visitors, school groups, artists, garden, birding, and butterfly clubs can explore small shrubs, perennials, and annuals that have been selected as a host or nectar plant to a vast array of birds and butterflies. A small kiosk offers a butterfly inventory, descriptions and photographs of likely sightings and the various stages of metamorphosis. Children delight in discovering a Black Swallowtail caterpillar munching away on parsley, while a hummingbird moth hovers nearby looking much like the ruby-throated variety that feeds on the trumpet vine.

Hours: Year round, daily, dawn to dusk

Admission: Free

From I-287, take Bedminster exit to Route 202/206 north. Go 6 traffic lights from exit ramp, bearing left on Route 206 towards Chester. Turn left onto Pottersville Road. Go 0.8 mile and turn left onto Larger Cross Road. Go 0.5 mile to URWA's stone pillars on right.

Somerset
Colonial Park Arboretum, Fragrance & Sensory Garden, Perennial Garden & Rudolf W. van der Goot Rose Garden
156 Mettlers Road, (732) 873-2459,
www.somersetcountyparks.org

The 144-acre arboretum contains labeled specimens of flowering trees and shrubs, evergreens, and shade trees that grow well in central New Jersey. The five-acre Perennial

Garden contains beds of flowering bulbs, perennials, annuals, trees, and shrubs that provide year-round interest. The Rose garden offers a formal display of more than 3,000 roses of 325 varieties. The Fragrance & Sensory Garden is designed especially for those with visual impairment or physical handicaps. Use N.J. Relay Service@711 (individuals with hearing or speech impairment).

Hours: Year round, daily, 8 a.m. to dusk; Wednesday, 12 p.m. to dusk. Guided tours can be arranged for groups on weekdays for a small fee.

Admission: $1 suggested donation per person

From I-287, take Exit 12. At end of exit ramp, turn left onto Weston Canal Road. After 2 miles, turn left before bridge (do not cross canal). Continue along Weston Canal Road, which becomes Weston Road. Turn right onto Mettlers Road. Continue to Colonial Park.

From Route 206 south, go to Dukes Parkway "jug handle," (sign reads "Manville/Somerville"). Follow to end and turn right onto Main Street. Go through center of Manville on Route 533 towards Millstone. Turn left onto Route 623/Wilhousky Street. Go over a small bridge and turn right onto West Canal Road. Proceed as directed above.

From Route 206 north, turn right at traffic light onto Amwell Road. After 2.3 miles, you will see sign for Colonial Park on right. Turn left onto Mettlers Road. Proceed as directed above.

UNION COUNTY

SUMMIT
Reeves-Reed Arboretum
165 Hobart Avenue, (908) 273-8787, www.reeves-reedarboretum.org

A thirteen-acre historic country estate, the arboretum is a nature conservancy with a focus on horticultural and environmental education for children and adults. There are azalea, rose, rock, and herb gardens designed by Calvert Vaux, Carl F. Pilat, and Ellen Biddle Shipman, thousands of April-blooming daffodils, an herb garden, and a perennial border that flowers April through October. Naturalistic

♿ indicates parts of garden are handicapped accessible

areas provide wildlife habitat. Walk the trails through our woodland forest or explore the wildlife habitat garden.

Hours: Year round, daily, dawn to dusk

Admission: Free

From New Jersey Turnpike/I-95, take Exit 14/Newark Airport onto I-78 west. After several miles, take right fork onto Route 24 west toward Morristown/Springfield. Take Exit 9B/Hobart Avenue to first traffic light. Turn left and cross back over Route 24. Go through next traffic light onto Hobart Avenue. Arboretum is 0.5 mile on left.

Mindowaskin Park

11 Kimball Circle, (908) 233-8110

Mindowaskin Park was established in 1918 and includes a large lake, fountains, waterways, winding paths, hardwood trees, a bird sanctuary, and a new granite balustrade overlooks flowering gardens. A large gazebo offers opportunities for walking and watching, ice skating, model boat sailing, performances, art shows, picnics, and relaxation.

Hours: Year round, daily, 7 a.m. to 10 p.m.

Admission: Free

From Garden State Parkway, take Exit 137 and head towards Westfield on North Avenue. After 3.1 miles, turn right onto Elmer Street and right again onto East Broad Street. Mindowaskin Park is within 1 block on left.

NEW YORK
Westchester County Open Day
Saturday, April 14
WESTCHESTER COUNTY

LEWISBORO
The White Garden
199 Elmwood Road

The native oak-hickory forest provides a "sacred grove" setting for the modern Greek Revival-style house. The gardens, completed in 1999, were designed by Patrick Chassé, ASLA, and nearest the house are classically inspired, including a nymphaeum, pergola garden, labryinth, and theater court. Additional hidden gardens include a perennial ellipse, a conservatory garden, and an Asian-inspired moss garden. Several water features accent the landscape, and native plantings dominate in areas outside the gardens. Many sculptures and water features enrich this landscape and swans guard the Temple of Apollo on an island in the main pond. In spring, more than 100,000 daffodils bloom in the woodland. Woodland walking paths lead through a shaded dell. A state-of-the-art greenhouse supports the gardens, administered by gardener Eric Schmidt, who ably orchestrates the rich garden plantings throughout the property. **2006**

Hours: 10 a.m. to 3 p.m.

From Merritt Parkway/Route 15, take Exit 38 and follow Route 123 north through New Canaan to New York state line. Town of Lewisboro and village of Vista are first signs encountered. Go past Vista Fire Department about 0.25 mile. Just after shingled Episcopal church on right, Route 123 bears left and Elmwood Road bears right. Go about another 0.25 mile just over a hill. At beginning of a gray stockade fence on right is driveway at #199.

Suffolk County Open Day
Saturday, April 28
SUFFOLK COUNTY

EAST HAMPTON
Abby Jane Brody
44 Glade Road

This is primarily a woodland garden in which the native oaks are the upper story. I am an inveterate plant collector with a special interest in rare or unusual flowering trees and shrubs as well as herbaceous plants. The half-acre site has something in flower, preferably fragrant, almost every day of the year. In late April the last of the camellias and hellebores may be in bloom. The daphnes, epimediums, and hundreds of other woodland plants should be flowering. In June the Japanese azaleas should be flowering. **2006**

Hours: 10 a.m. to 4 p.m.

From Montauk Highway/Route 27, turn left at traffic light in East Hampton. Pass town pond, go through village, and turn left at windmill. Pass under railroad bridge and take right at fork to Springs Fireplace Road. About 3 miles, turn left onto Woodbine and take an immediate right onto Glade Road. Please park along road, not on grass.

Proceeds shared with LongHouse Reserve

Margaret Kerr
1006 Springs Fireplace Road

The garden, designed by Kerr, surrounds the house and studios on two acres that extend down to the wetlands of Accabonac Harbor. Kerr's brick rug sculptures, inspired by tribal Middle Eastern carpets, are placed throughout the garden. One, a brick prayer rug, lies in a contemplative glade below the studios. Kerr collects plants grown in the Middle Ages in a courtyard around a fountain and lily pool highlighted with espaliered pear trees. In the spring, drifts of thousands of daffodils bloom in the fields around the house and are left unmown until late fall. Native grasses and wildflowers make islands of meadow during the summer. **2006**

Hours: 10 a.m. to 2 p.m.

From Montauk Highway/Route 27, turn left at traffic light in East Hampton. Pass town pond. Continue 0.9 mile past next light, taking an immediate left onto North Main Street. Pass windmill on right. Go 0.3 mile, bearing right at fork onto Springs Fireplace Road. Go 5 miles. Driveway is marked by mailbox #1006. Please park along Springs Fireplace Road and walk down dirt road to second house on left.

Proceeds shared with Horticultural Alliance of the Hamptons & Bridge Gardens Trust

WAINSCOTT

Biercuk/Luckey Garden
18 Sayres Path

Our four-season woodland garden shelters, under a high oak canopy, a collection of rhododendrons, azaleas, kalmia, pieris, understory trees, perennials, bulbs, and tropicals in season. A mostly sunny rear corner contains a pool designed as a pond with a waterfall and is surrounded with plantings which peak mid-July through October. Winding paths and stone walls enhance a sense of depth and elevation change on a mostly flat acre. There is something in bloom every season. **NEW**

Hours: 10 a.m. to 4 p.m.

From Montauk Highway/Route 27 turn right onto Sayre's Path. House is first driveway on right. Please park along roadside.

Suffolk County Open Day Saturday, May 5

SUFFOLK COUNTY

CUTCHOGUE

Jacqueline Penney Art Gallery & Studio
270 North Street

This seventeen-year-old garden, pond, and waterfall was designed by Conni Cross of Environmentals and is maintained by Mino Illescas.

The garden maximizes the available space through the liberal use of miniature plants and accents. There are more than 147 varieties of perennials and shrubs and demonstrates what can be done with a small site. The garden is a constant source of beauty year round for the artist and visitors to the Jacqueline Penney Art Gallery and Studio. **NEW** ♿

Hours: 10 a.m. to 4 p.m.

One very short block east of first traffic light heading east on Route 25. North Street is directly across from Fisherman's Restaurant. Please park on the street.

Manfred & Roberta Lee
26850 Main Road, Route 25

Located in the village of Cutchogue, these two-and-one-half acres of gardens complement the Victorian house and outbuildings. Four large tulip trees punctuate the front lawn. Deep perennial gardens surround the property. Mature azaleas, rhododendrons, roses, hydrangeas, and lilacs are spread throughout the garden. There are unusual conifers and Japanese maples as well as golden chain trees. This year, some mature specimens of mountain laurel and other shade-loving shrubs have been planted under the tulip trees to attain a more biodiverse environment. In addition, if the weather permits, 1,000 tulips will be in bloom as well as a spectacular old redbud. **2006** ♿

Hours: 10 a.m. to 4 p.m.

From Long Island Expressway/I-495, take Exit 73/Route 58. Take Route 58, which leads into Route 25. Continue to Cutchogue. We are five houses past North Fork Country Club on right (south) side of Route 25. Please park on street.

Westchester County Open Day Saturday, May 5

WESTCHESTER COUNTY

BEDFORD
Mr. & Mrs. Coleman Burke
52 Hook Road

This is a simple, formal, country garden with old stone walls complementing a nineteenth-century house. A rock garden frames a naturalistic swimming pool with views of the perennial garden and Beaver Dam River. **2004**

Hours: 10 a.m. to 4 p.m.

From I-684, take Exit 4 north. Follow Route 172 to Route 22 north through Bedford Village. Bear left onto Route 22 and continue to Hook Road, on right beyond golf course. Follow 0.25 mile. House, #52, is on left. It is beige with black shutters and a cobblestone driveway. Please park along Hook Road.

Penelope & John Maynard
210 Hook Road

We created a garden among rock ledges and oak woods on the steep shoulder of Mount Aspetong. The site is fragmented; thus, the garden areas are designed to flow from one to another, linked together by a ribbon of stone walls. The greatest challenge has been to create some flat, restful spaces. The wide variety of plants must meet one criterion—to prove themselves in dry woodland conditions. **2006**

Hours: 10 a.m. to 6 p.m.

From I-684, take Exit 4. Turn east onto Route 172. Go 1.5 miles to Route 22. Turn left and drive through Bedford. Just beyond Bedford Oak Tree, 2.1 miles from Routes 172 and 22, turn right onto Hook Road. Garden (#210) is almost at top of hill. Park along road.

BEDFORD HILLS
Sandra & Roger Goldman
289 McLain Street

Our gardens are an act of love and will always be a work in progress. We have created different outdoor living areas on our property, defined to a great extent by the natural resources we are blessed with. Specifically, our 1907 Dutch Colonial stone house built around a magnificent linden tree. It provides wonderful shade and allowed us to build stone terraces and share gardens around a portion of our house. Also, under the linden tree grows a rare evergreen which helps define the different terrace levels we have built. Due east off the terrace grows an absolutely magnificent copper beech which separates the house and terrace area from our pool, lily pond, and our vegetable and cutting gardens. Our vegetable garden cannot be seen from the house as it is up the hill just past the stone outcropping east of our swimming pool. It has been a labor

🔥 indicates parts of garden are handicapped accessible

of love for both of us. Beginning with started seeds of unusual varieties of vegetables in our basement in February, we set out the seedlings in May. This garden is something we work at for a good seven months of the year and it provides us with enjoyment of the fruits of our labor year round. **2006**

Hours: 10 a.m. to 2 p.m.

From I-684, take Exit 4/Route 172. Turn west onto Route 172 (towards Mount Kisco). Go about 1 mile to West Patent Road and turn right (just after school crossing sign). Go about 1.5 miles to second stop sign and turn left onto Broad Brook Road. Broad Brook Road becomes McLain Street. Follow to #289.

Phillis Warden
531 Bedford Center Road

This garden of many facets includes perennial borders, two water gardens, a formal vegetable garden, wildflower garden, fern garden, marsh garden, tree platform overlooking the marshlands, woodland walk, and formal croquet court. The garden extends over seven acres. **2006**

Hours: 10 a.m. to 6 p.m.

From Bedford Village, take Route 22 towards Katonah to intersection at Bedford Cross. Garden is on left. Please park at Rippowam School and walk to #531.

Proceeds shared with The Native Plant Center at Westchester Community College

LARCHMONT
Forest Court—
Joanna & Mark Friedman
5 Forest Court

This one-acre woodland garden was established in 1938 by the world-renowned horticulturist Harold Epstein. It is home to hundreds of hardy plants from Asia, and the oldest *Metasequoia glyptostroboides* in the United States. Well represented genera of enkianthus and epimedium create a mainstay of the garden. Massive oaks support fifty-year-old climbing hydrangeas. **NEW** ♿

Hours: 10 a.m. to 4 p.m.

From the Hutchinson Parkway north, exit at Larchmont. Turn left onto Weaver Street. Turn right onto Forest Avenue. Turn right again onto Larchwood/Devonshire Street. Make an immediate right onto Forest Court.

From I-95 south, take the Larchmont exit. Take exit ramp onto New Jefferson. Turn left onto Chatsworth Avenue. At the fork, stay left onto Rockinstone Avenue. At the boulder, go around onto Poplar Road. Cross Forest Avenue onto Larchwood/Devonshire Street. Make an immediate right onto Forest Court. There is limited parking on street.

Westchester County Open Day
Sunday, May 6

WESTCHESTER COUNTY

MOUNT KISCO
Judy & Michael Steinhardt
433 Croton Lake Road

The Steinhardts' love of plants is evident throughout this fifty-five-acre estate. More than 2,000 species of trees, shrubs, and perennials have been incorporated into the gardens. Landscape designer Jerome Rocherolle has created a naturalistic setting with walkways, stream beds, bridges, and ponds where plants can be appreciated and nurtured. There is a fern garden, a woodland garden, a yellow garden, an alpine garden, a maple garden, an experimental garden, fruit orchards, and a mature perennial bed. Plants and trees are labeled throughout the gardens. Look for extensive use of ferns, moss (including a moss bridge), more than 350 cultivars of Japanese maples, and hundreds of varieties of *Hemerocallis*. Woodland plants and groundcovers are well established. The experimental beds are filled with mail-order plants that will be integrated into the gardens when they mature. Antique apple trees abound in the fruit orchards. No two are alike. Exotic waterfowl inhabit the many ponds, and some unusual animals roam the generous fields and hillsides. The Steinhardt garden has been featured in *Architectural*

Digest (Germany), *Vogue Country Living* (Australia), *Garden Design, House Beautiful,* and many local publications. **2006** ⅃

Hours: 10 a.m. to 4 p.m.

From I-684 take Exit 6/Katonah/Route 35. If coming from south, turn left onto Route 35; turn right if coming from north. Go about 0.25 mile to traffic light at Cherry Street and turn left. Go less than 0.5 mile to Croton Lake Road and turn right. Look for #433 on right.

From Saw Mill River Parkway, take Exit 37/Kisco Avenue (1 exit beyond Mount Kisco). Turn right at end of exit ramp and, after a few hundred feet, turn right onto Croton Lake Road. Number 433 is less than 2 miles ahead on left. Please do not park on Croton Lake Road; park on property, where directed.

Rocky Hills—The Garden of William & Henriette Suhr
95 Old Roaring Brook Road

At Rocky Hills, planting among the stone walls began some fifty years ago and continues to this day. You will find mature specimen of black walnut and ash, complimented by recent additions of weeping beech, dawn redwood, stewartia, dogwood and an impressive collection of magnolia and conifers. Tree peonies and an extensive planting of rhododendron and azalea compete for attention with carpet of bulbs throughout the eight acres. Most impressive in May and June are the forget-me-nots, which are alllowed full freedom throughout the garden. Starting on the hillside meadow, clouds of perfect blue flowers appear among ever expanding rock garden, through the hills and terraces, walls and paths, through fern woodlands, finding good company with self sown primula along the natural brook that serves as the heart of the garden. **2006** ⅃

Hours: 12 p.m. to 4 p.m.

From Saw Mill River Parkway, go north to Exit 33/Reader's Digest Road. At traffic light, turn left, then make a sharp right onto Old Roaring Brook Road. Rocky Hills, #95, is 1 mile on right.

From Merritt Parkway/Route 15, travel to I-287 west and exit at Saw Mill River Parkway north. Proceed as directed above. Please park along Old Roaring Brook Road or Lawrence Farms Crossways as directed.

Proceeds shared with Friends of Lasdon

Dutchess County Open Day
Saturday, May 12
DUTCHESS COUNTY

AMENIA
Broccoli Hall—Maxine Paetro
23 Flint Hill Road

Visitors to Broccoli Hall describe this English-style cottage garden as "incredible," "inspirational," "magical"—and they come back again and again. Starting in 1986 with an acre and a half of bare earth, Maxine Paetro collaborated with horticulturist Tim Steinhoff to create a series of enchanting garden rooms. Broccoli Hall offers an apple tunnel, a brick courtyard, a lavish display of spring bulbs blooming with crabapples in May, an extensive border of iris, peonies, and old shrub roses flowering in June, a tree house with long views, and a secret woodland garden with a teddy bears' picnic. Photos of Broccoli Hall can be seen at www.broccolihall.com. **2006**

Hours: 10 a.m. to 4 p.m.

From Route 22 north, go towards Amenia. Go west on Route 44 to Route 83 north/Smithfield Road. Go 2.5 miles to dirt road on right, Flint Hill Road. Turn right. House (#23) is first on left. Please park on Flint Hill Road. Be careful of ditches.

Proceeds shared with Amenia Free Library

Mead Farm House Garden
224 Perry's Corners Road

On the site of a 250-year-old farmyard, this mature garden winds around a fair approximation of a nineteenth-century horse barn and utilizes rocky outcroppingss and the stone foundations of long-gone farm buildings as the visual anchors of the perennial beds. The base of an old silo has become a deck from which one can gaze over a small pond at the distant landscape. Features include a bog garden, and some interesting trees, including a sizeable Japanese umbrella pine planted about 1966. **2006** ♿

Hours: 10 a.m. to 4 p.m.

From Routes 22, 44 & 343 at only traffic light in Amenia, take Route 22/44 north about 1 mile. Turn left at Maplebrook School onto Perry's Corners Road. Go about 1 mile to clapboard farmhouse on right. Please park on street.

Tompkins County Open Day Saturday, May 19

TOMPKINS COUNTY

TRUMANSBURG
Hitch Lyman's Garden
3441 Krums Corners Road

With luck the collection of 200 lilac varieties will be in full flower as well as species of peonies, daphnes, and crabapples. The 1848 Greek Revival-style farmhouse was moved to this site in 1990 and the garden, pond-side Doric temple, rustic fountain, and odd assembly of trees are slowly reaching out into the surrounding meadow. Architectural building by Glenn Wilder, stonework by Kevin Reilly, and metalwork by Durand Van Doren showcase our area's talent. **2006** ♿

Hours: 10 a.m. to 4 p.m.

From Ithaca, go north on Route 96 about 6 miles. Turn right onto Krums Corners Road. Go to sixth driveway on left. Please park on road.

ROCKY HILLS

SCHEDULE OF EVENTS

April 26th, Thursday
7:00—9:00 p.m.
Rocky Hills Lecture Series
Chappaqua Library
195 South Greeley Avenue
Chappaqua, New York

May 6th, Sunday
12:00—4:00 p.m.
Garden Conservancy's Open Day
Focus on Bulbs in the Garden

May 13th, Sunday
12:00—4:30 p.m.
Mother's Day In the Garden at
Rocky Hills
Hosted by the Friends of Rocky Hills

May 26th, Saturday
2:00—6:00 p.m.
Garden Conservancy's Open Day

June 2nd, Saturday
6:00—8:00 p.m.
Cocktail Party and Silent Auction
*Hosted by Henriette Suhr and the
Friends of Rocky Hills*

For more information about
Rocky Hills and these events,
contact the Garden Conservancy
at (845) 265-2029.

♿ indicates parts of garden are handicapped accessible

Remsenberg Open Day
Sunday, May 20
SUFFOLK COUNTY

REMSENBURG
Little Birdstone—
Mr. & Mrs. Howard Finkelstein
3 Kingfisher Cove

This is a garden of sun and shade that has been developing and changing over thirty-six years. My main objective has been to keep the garden fresh and interesting twelve months of the year by planting trees, shrubs, and perennials that will provide interest at different times year round. This allows the garden to present a different appearance with each season. We have many specimen trees, rhododendrons, and azaleas. There is a pond and rock garden and paths leading you to different points of interest. **2006**

Hours: 10 a.m. to 4 p.m.

From west, take Sunrise Highway to Eastport exit to Montauk Highway/Route 27 through Eastport to Speok traffic light at Phillips Avenue, about 4 miles. Turn right onto Phillips Avenue to South Country Road and turn left. Turn right again onto Basket Neck Lane to Kingfisher Cove. We are first house on left. Please park on Basket Neck Lane or Kingfisher Cove.

From east, take Sunrise Highway to Westhampton Beach south to Montauk Highway/Route 27, and go to Speok traffic light. Proceed as directed above.

The Gardens of
Fred & Monica Meyer
7 Tuthill Lane

This secret garden is located off a long driveway. Here the owners have created separate garden rooms that were often done in English gardens. Each is quite distinctive and surprises the viewer upon entry. The entire property was once a native cedar forest that has now been entirely converted to gardens. Just through the gates is a typical perennial border with iris, peonies, hollyhock, and Shasta daisies. One of the

"rooms" is surrounded with mature cedars and underplanted with ericaceous shrubs. Within is a knot garden outlined with dwarf boxwood together with dwarfred barberry. Another "room" contains a two-level pond with goldfish. Either side of a long pergola is an astilbe and foxglove garden and a green and yellow grass garden. At the end of the pergola is another surprise, but that must wait for your arrival. **NEW** ⅄

Hours: 10 a.m. to 4 p.m.

From the west, take Sunrise Highway to Exit 62. Turn right at the stop sign to Montauk Highway. Turn left and go through Eastport Hamlet. After the railroad underpass and just past Speonk sign, bear right onto South Country Road. Continue past the post office, two streets to Tuthill Lane. The garden is the third driveway on right.

From the east, take Sunrise Highway to Exit 63/Westhampton Beach. Go south on Montauk Highway and turn right at the traffic light. Go west 2.8 miles to Nidgyn Avenue to end. Turn right and then left onto Tuthill Lane. Park on Tuthill Lane and walk down driveway.

Mara J. Urshel &
Ronald R. Rothstein
172 South Country Road

These country gardens are on three acres of groomed landscape surrounding a 200-year-old wooden farmhouse, a once working barn from the 1700s, and a small guest house with a white picket fence. As you come up the driveway, you are greeted by beautiful old trees. American elm, linden, maple, beech, and apple trees. One was hit by a 1930s hurricane and replanted itself, laying down on the ground. At the end of the driveway is a living couch with trimmed accessory tables. The garden areas are all individual and are all with different plantings: perennial, shade, pool gardens, and an organic vegetable garden. **NEW** ⅄

Hours: 10 a.m. to 4 p.m.

Take the Long Island Expressway/I-495 east for 58.5 miles. Take Exit 68 towards William Floyd Parkway/CR-46/Wading River/Shirley and go 0.2 mile. Go straight on Long Island Expressway south and go 0.1 mile. Turn right onto William Floyd Parkway South towards CR-46 S/Shirley/Smith Point Park and go 3.1 miles. Take Route 27 east towards Montauk and go 6.6 miles. Take Exit 61 towards CR-51/East Moriches/Riverhead and go 0.2 miles. Keep left at the fork and go toward CR-51 N/Riverhead/Eastport. Go 0.3 mile. Keep left at the fork toward Eastport. Go 0.2 mile. Go straight toward Sunrise Highway Service Road South. Go 0.1 mile and turn right onto CR-55 heading southeast. Go 0.7 mile and turn left onto Montauk Highway. Go 1.2 miles, straight on South Country Road. The garden is at #172.

Westchester County
Open Day
Saturday, May 26

WESTCHESTER COUNTY

Mount Kisco
Rocky Hills—The Garden of William & Henriette Suhr
95 Old Roaring Brook Road

A Project of
The Garden
Conservancy

At Rocky Hills, planting among the stone walls began some fifty years ago and continues to this day. You will find mature specimen of black walnut and ash, complimented by recent additions of weeping beech, dawn redwood, stewartia, dogwood and an impressive collection of magnolia and conifers. Tree peonies and an extensive planting of rhododendron and azalea compete for attention with carpet of bulbs throughout the eight acres. Most impressive in May and June are the forget-me-nots, which are alllowed full freedom throughout the garden. Starting on the hillside meadow, clouds of perfect blue flowers appear among ever expanding rock garden, through the hills and terraces, walls and paths, through fern woodlands, finding good company with self sown primula along the natural brook that serves as the heart of the garden. **2006** ♿

Hours: 2 p.m. to 6 p.m.

From Saw Mill River Parkway, travel north to Exit 33/Reader's Digest Road. At traffic light, turn left, then make a sharp right onto Old Roaring Brook Road. Rocky Hills, #95, is 1 mile on right.

From Merritt Parkway/Route 15, travel to I-287 west and exit at Saw Mill River Parkway north. Proceed as directed above. Please park along Old Roaring Brook Road or Lawrence Farms Crossways as directed.

Proceeds shared with Friends of Lasdon

Westchester County
Open Day
Sunday, May 27

WESTCHESTER COUNTY

Armonk
Cobamong Pond
15 Middle Patent Road

This is one of the great woodland gardens of the world, a twelve-acre pond is surrounded by twelve acres of naturalistic woodlands with an abundance of flowering shrubs that has been enhanced for more than forty years. It is featured in the book *The Beckoning Path*, with eighty color photographs. The garden has a wealth of rhododendrons on June 2, and flowering trees, shrubs, and Japanese maples. It is rough terrain and someone with a wheelchair or a cane is not advised to attend approximately a half-mile walk/hike around the lake. **2006**

Hours: 10 a.m. to 4 p.m.

From I-684 south, take Exit 4/Route 172. Turn left (east) and continue to end. Turn right (south) at Shell gas station onto Route 22. Go 2.2 miles, then turn left onto Middle Patent Road. Take second driveway on right, marked by four mailboxes. House, #15, is at end of a long driveway.

From I-684 north, take Exit 3N and go north on Route 22 for 4 miles, then turn right onto Middle Patent Road and proceed as directed above.

Proceeds shared with Mount Kisco Day Care Center/Scholarship Program

---

♿ indicates parts of garden are handicapped accessible

Tompkins County Open Day
Saturday, June 9

The gardens at Hospicare in Ithaca are also open today. See their listing on page 222.

TOMPKINS COUNTY

DANBY
Myers Gardens
1071 Michigan Hollow Road

Six acres of rolling lawn and perennial beds contain more than 550 different varieties of perennials nestled behind and between fieldstone walls and structures. Features include a covered bridge, a working water wheel on a post-and-beam constructed feed mill, a blacksmith shop, and a huge glass sponge fossil rock enclosed in a unique display case. There is also a thirty-foot-diameter stone sundial and a potting shed garden with four raised beds. **2005** ♿

Hours: 10 a.m. to 4 p.m.

From downtown Ithaca, take Route 13/34/96 south. About 3 miles south of Ithaca, take left exit onto Route 34/96 and go about 9 miles. Turn left onto Hill View Road and go to stop sign (2 miles) at intersection of Michigan Hollow Road. Garden is directly in front on opposite side of intersection. Please park on road or on lawn as posted.

Proceeds shared with Tompkins County Community Beautification Program

ITHACA
Jim Eavenson
1117 Trumansburg Road

This garden evolved over many years, one bed at a time. What was initially a sloping hillside filled with weeds and brush is now a multitude of perennial beds and borders planted around small trees and shrubs. The slope is divided by shrubs, hedges, and stone walls into garden rooms, with many nooks and crannies to explore. A pyramidal arbor is covered by wisteria and makes a great place to sit in the shade and take in the view of the lake below and Ithaca Falls off in the distance. **NEW**

Hours: 10 a.m. to 4 p.m.

Located on Route 96 towards Cayuga Medical Center, the garden is 1.3 miles from the old "octopus" or what is known as the convergence of Routes 96, 89, and 13. Driving up hill, house is on right. A busy road, parking is allowed on east side of Route 96. A small parking lot to hold about 12 cars exists on west side of road about 3 houses down the hill.

Proceeds shared with Tompkins County Community Beautification Program

Posner Garden
212 Bundy Road

Perennial beds and borders completely envelop the beautifully restored farmhouse on this country property. The gardens have been designed to create many little vignettes of endearing plant combinations. Plants were carefully chosen to thrive in varying light conditions, ranging from full sun to dry shade under evergreens, to deepest shade against a north-facing wall. Stone walls and rustic fences define the edges of the garden yet still provide views of the neighboring fields and woods. The garden is a delight for children as well, as there are frogs with attitude just about everywhere you look. **NEW** ♿

Hours: 10 a.m. to 4 p.m.

Go 1.5 miles up Route 96 toward hospital. Turn left onto Bundy (Alterra Adult Care Facility on corner). Go 1 mile. The house is on right at top of hill.

NEWFIELD
Medicine Tree Farm
91 Shaffer Road

A combination of whimsy and "funkiness" defines this garden's style. A series of arbors lead you through the picket fence and across two miniature ponds on a plank bridge. A rustic locust arbor draped in grapevines and hops is underplanted with naturalizing perennials and ornamentals and lead to the peafowl enclosures. Rare java green peafowl and many uncommon hybrid color and pattern mutations of peafowl are bred here. The birds will be at the peak of their annual display and many new chicks are expected in early June. **NEW**

Hours: 10 a.m. to 4 p.m.

Take Route 13 south out of Ithaca towards Elmira. About 4 miles out, watch for the Gulf Station on the right at top of a long hill. Just beyond, turn left onto Main Street, Newfield. About 1 mile down, turn left onto Shaffer Road/County 131. Tioga Bank is on corner. Take first left (also marked Shaffer Road). My drive is on left between second and third house, marked with a post #91. Garden sits 0.25 mile back. Please drive to house to turn around and park.

Proceeds shared with Tompkins County Community Beautification Program

Ulster County Open Day
Saturday, June 9

ULSTER COUNTY

NEW PALTZ

Lee Reich

387 Springtown Road

A writer once proclaimed my garden to be very much a "man's garden"; perhaps it is. The emphasis is on fruits and vegetables but the whole works is woven into planting of flowers and ornamental shrubs. I try to grow a year-round supply of pretty much every kind of vegetable except rhubarb and Jerusalem artichoke. Fruits include many varieties of dwarf apples and pears, grapes, and numerous uncommon fruits such as pawpaws, persimmons, gooseberries (twenty or so varieties), currants, and medlars. Out in the adjoining hayfield is a 100-foot trellis of hardy kiwis and a swale bordered by chestnut and hazelnut trees. **2005** ♿

Hours: 10 a.m. to 4 p.m.

From New York State Thruway/I-87, take New Paltz/Route 299 west exit through New Paltz. Cross bridge and take first right onto Springtown Road. Bear right at fork; house is #387, about 3 miles on left.

From Kingston, take 32 south. Go about 2 miles, after passing Rosendale, to Tillson Road. (Postage Inn is on left). Turn right. Turn left at stop sign onto Springtown Road. House is #387 and is about 1.5 miles on right. Please park along street or driveway.

SAUGERTIES

Riverhill Garden—
Joe & Tamara DiMattio

Patterson Lane

Riverhill is a five-acre hillside sloping down to a rocky beach on the Hudson River. It is the result of thirty years of weekend taming and gardening. Views of the Hudson are a defining feature, as is the park-like landscape, sculpted into terraces and gentle slopes. The gardens include an alpine scree slope, a terraced perennial garden, an outcrop rockery, a shrub walk, a tiered stone wall garden, and a conifer collection. Also of interest is a koi canal with the beginnings of aquatic planting, several hundred potted cacti and succulents, and a sprinkling of homegrown sculpture. Recently, our attention has been drawn back to the riverbank where we have begun stone work and terracing using on-site materials. Not to be missed is eagle spotting and watching the river flow. **2006**

Hours: 10 a.m. to 4 p.m.

From New York State Thruway/I-87, take Exit 20. Turn right onto Route 212 east to Main Street, Saugerties. Follow to 9W north (past movie theater); turn left and continue 3.2 miles (just past a white steepled church on left) to Patterson Road and turn right. Go 0.3 mile to first right after railroad tracks which is Patterson Lane (not marked). Go 0.2 mile to first house on left (white picket fence, no number). Turn left at top of driveway into parking area.

Putnam County
Open Day
Sunday, June 10

Manitoga/The Russel Wright Design Center in Garrison and Stonecrop Gardens in Cold Spring are also open on this date. See their listings on pages 218 & 220.

PUTNAM COUNTY

GARRISON
Ross Gardens
43 Snake Hill Road (Travis Corners)
This garden is a series of vignettes that flow into each other on five acres overlooking the Hudson River. The gardens are designed and maintained by the owner, Arthur Ross, and include a water garden, a moon (white) garden, meditation garden, rock garden, interesting daylilies, a fern garden, shrub garden (azaleas, rhododendrons, mountain laurels), cutting gardens, and garden sculptures, along with a waterfall and a new koi pond. Garden paths give easy access to many unusual flowers. **2005**
Hours: 10 a.m. to 4 p.m.
Take Route 9 to Garrison Golf Course. Turn west onto Snake Hill Road. Garden is 0.25 mile on left. Parking is available for 30 cars at any one time.
Proceeds shared with The Philipstown Garden Club

Suffolk County
Open Day
Sunday, June 10

SUFFOLK COUNTY

ST. JAMES
Head of the Harbor—
Alexandra Leighton's Garden
54 Harbor Hill Road
Alexandra's gardens surround the (c. 1830) house where she lives and works as a landscape designer and owner of Garden Schemes. In 1895, the house became the superintendent's cottage for the Wetherell estate 'Head of the Harbor' designed by Stanford White for his sister-in-law. Twenty-plus acres in all—consisting of upland, woodland, pond, seeps, marsh, orchard and meadow—the farmhouse and gardens sit at the front corner. All of the gardens open onto an old pear and quince orchard, which in turn frames a view of Stony Brook Harbor. A perennial border in front of a deep blue fence and curved brick wall is where Alexandra experiments with color and textural combinations. It consists of deep blues, violets, and glaucus greens accented with chalky apricots. On the same northwest side under an enormous silver beech canopy, is a moss and fern garden. A brick wall winds past a silver-gray wall garden. The wall is Connecticut brownstone, a material brought to Long Island on trade ships on ballast. Also included area small oval parterre of germander and berberis, and a bank of various lavenders underplanted with ice blue muscari 'Valerie Finnis'. Alchemist roses, striped morning glories and a tiny leafed Japanese elm frame the side steps and entry while the quince, boxwood, and *Magnolia grandiflora* in the front yard are suggest her family ties to Virginia. **2006**
Hours: 10 a.m. to 4 p.m.
Take the Long Island Expressway/I-495 to Exit 56. Go down the ramp, turn left and go north on Route 111. In Smithtown at a classic crossroad (church, library, bank and diner) Route 111 turns into Route 25A. Continue straight (east) under a train trestle. At the second traffic light, turn left onto Moriches Road. Turn right at the second street, Harbor Hill Road (next to the St. James General Store). Alexandra Leighton's gardens are at the bottom of the hill on right with a long privet hedge and orchard. Pull in and park in field.

Westchester County
Open Day
Sunday, June 10

WESTCHESTER COUNTY

BEDFORD

High and Low Farm
649 South Bedford Road

A French inspired garden that *House & Garden* says "combines echoes of antiquity with a startling modernism that is rare in a private landscape." Integrating the physical changes in the land into garden features, High and Low Farm is a balance of geometry and nature.
NEW

Hours: 10 a.m. to 4 p.m.

From the north, take I-684 south to Exit 4. Turn left off the exit ramp. After about 0.5 mile, Foxlane High School will be on right and Succabone Road on left. The house is first driveway on left after Succabone Road.

From Connecticut, take I-95, exit at Stamford and get onto Route 104. Follow Route 104 into New York. The road turns into Long Ridge Road. Long Ridge Road ends at a "T" intersection with Route 172/Pound Ridge Road. Turn left. At a blinking traffic light at Shell station, turn right onto South Bedford Road (which is a continuation of Route 172). The next blinking light is Foxlane High School. Proceed as directed above.

Keith & Susan Kroeger—
Pook's Hill
621 Guard Hill Road

This minimalist garden and house, created by the owner/architect, are spatially inspired by a lifelong interest in American and European farm building complexes. They are set between the road, two side property lines, and the edge of a meadow, and consist of six spaces formed by the walls of the buildings and freestanding wood, stone, and stucco walls. The spaces are furnished with a limited palette of material consisting of gravel, grass, several varieties of vines, shrubbery and trees, and feature a number of ornaments, including a lap pool.
2006 ♿

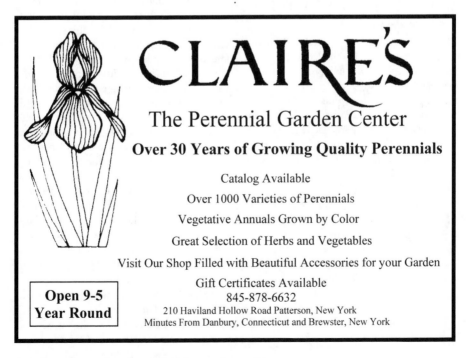

CLAIRE'S

The Perennial Garden Center

Over 30 Years of Growing Quality Perennials

Catalog Available

Over 1000 Varieties of Perennials

Vegetative Annuals Grown by Color

Great Selection of Herbs and Vegetables

Visit Our Shop Filled with Beautiful Accessories for your Garden

Gift Certificates Available
845-878-6632
210 Haviland Hollow Road Patterson, New York
Minutes From Danbury, Connecticut and Brewster, New York

Open 9-5
Year Round

♿ indicates parts of garden are handicapped accessible

Hours: 10 a.m. to 4 p.m.

From Route 684, take Exit 4 to Route 172 toward Bedford. Go 1 mile and turn left onto Clark Road. Continue to dead end (0.5 mile) and turn right onto Guard Hill Road. The garden is on right, #621, in about 0.5 mile. Please park along one side of road only, do not enter driveway.

From Saw Mill River Parkway, take Exit 39/Bedford Hills/Route 117 east of parkway to traffic light. Turn left past firehouse, and turn right onto Main Street/Bedford Center Road. Go about 3 miles and merge right at stop sign onto Route 22. Go 0.25 mile and turn right onto Clinton Road. Turn left at dead end (about 0.5 mile) onto Guard Hill Road. Proceed as directed above.

From Merritt Parkway, take Exit 34/Long Ridge Road towards Bedford. At dead end (about 8 to 10 miles), turn left at traffic light into Bedford Village. Bear right in village alongside green, past row of shops, and merge onto Route 22 north. Go about 0.25 mile and turn left onto Guard Hill Road. House is on left after third road hump, about 0.5 mile.

Michael & Katherine Takata
100 Little Town Lane

The garden was designed by Penelope Maynard to take advantage of this challenging site on a rocky hillside with a natural spring and a series of ponds. Walls, hedges, and focal points draw the visitor around the natural contours. Walks flow from one area to another, past native and exotic plant materials chosen for their texture, pattern, color, form, and fragrance. Birds have become an integral part of the garden since it was planted. **2006**

Hours: 10 a.m. to 4 p.m.

From Bedford Village, follow Route 172 east, and take first right onto Middle Patent Road. Then take fifth right onto Little Town Lane, a one-lane dirt road. Number 100 is last driveway on left. Please follow shared driveway and proceed past pond and gate.

BEDFORD HILLS
Phillis Warden
531 Bedford Center Road

This garden of many facets includes perennial borders, two water gardens, a formal vegetable garden, wildflower garden, fern garden, marsh garden, tree platform overlooking the marshlands, woodland walk, and formal croquet court. The garden extends over seven acres. **2006**

Hours: 10 a.m. to 6 p.m.

From Bedford Village, take Route 22 towards Katonah to intersection at Bedford Cross. Garden is on left. Please park at Rippowam School and walk to 531 Bedford Center Road.

Proceeds shared with The Native Plant Center at Westchester Community College

CORTLANDT MANOR
Vivian & Ed Merrin
2547 Maple Avenue

This garden was featured in House & Garden's 100th anniversary issue, October 2001 and in *The New Garden Paradise—Great Private Gardens of the World* by Dominique Browning. Overlooking a small lake, this garden has unfolded over a rocky wooded site over the last fifteen years, under the guidance of designer Patrick Chassé. New additions include a large variety of azaleas, a tempered glass-enclosed lookout over the lake, and a wooden lotus bridge for perfect lotus viewing on a private pond. Mixed borders line garden rooms that flow among the landforms. Native plants form the framework for a collection that embraces many unusual and rare plants, as well as a large tree peony garden. Several water gardens enhance the site, and greenhouses and a formal kitchen garden provide additional plants, both ornamental and edible. A new entrance garden has been planted and there is a new woodland walk by a stream. **2006**

Hours: 10 a.m. to 2 p.m.

From Taconic State Parkway, take Route 202 exit. Turn left towards Peekskill. Go 2.5 miles, then turn left at traffic light onto Croton

Avenue, just past Cortland Farm Market. Go 1.2 miles to blinking light/stop sign and turn right onto Furnace Dock Road. Go 0.8 mile to blinking light/stop sign and turn left onto Maple Avenue. Go 0.9 mile to private road on right. Go 0.2 mile to #2547 on left. Please park at house.

NORTH SALEM

Artemis Farm—
Carol & Jesse Goldberg
22 Wallace Road

Eight years ago, I dismantled an unused barn on our farm and designed a formal garden on the site. It has eight beds surrounded by boxwood and it is furnished with many nineteenth-century garden antiques. There are two other adjoining large border gardens. All have a sweeping view of the bucolic back pasture. A small intimate garden off the kitchen is the main summer eating area and a gravel stable courtyard has a trough garden complemented by more unusual pieces of stone and terra cotta. The front of our circa 1869 farmhouse, surrounded by maples, has primarily shade-loving plants. Additions in 2003 included a vegetable garden in one of the former paddocks and a pergola-covered outdoor dining room was constructed off the living room of the house. In 2006 a new "Secret Garden" behind a barn was created from an area that was used for dumping garden debris. It has become a charming oasis with meandering paths, a seasonal stream and predominantly shade plants. **2006** ♿

Hours: 10 a.m. to 4 p.m.

From I-684, take Exit 7/Purdys. Follow Route 116 east, bearing left where it joins Route 121 north. Travel about 2 miles and turn right onto Route 116 east. Vox Restaurant is on corner. Go 0.1 mile to Wallace Road and turn left. It is first house on left. Note Artemis Farm sign on tree. Please park as directed.

Proceeds shared with Adopt a Dog

Page Dickey & Francis Schell— Duck Hill
23 Baxter Road

At Duck Hill, a series of hedged-in gardens are related to the nineteenth-century farmhouse they surround. They include an herb garden, a white garden, and a crabapple courtyard, all described in Page Dickey's *Duck Hill Journal*, *Breaking Ground*, and *Inside Out*. There is also a pool with rose pergola, and a vegetable/cutting garden centered on a Greek Revival-style chicken house. **2006**

Hours: 10 a.m. to 6 p.m.

From I-684 North, take Exit 7/Purdys. Follow Route 116 east to North Salem. After Route 121 joins Route 116, go 0.4 mile. At flagpole, turn left onto Baxter Road. Go to top of hill and turn right onto a private road. Duck Hill, #23, is second house on left. Please park along road.

From I-684 South, take Exit 8/Hardscrabble Road. Turn right onto Hardscrabble, go over highway, and continue to end at a "T." Turn

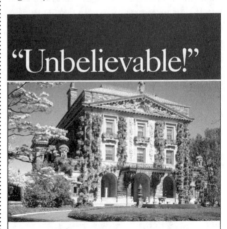

♿ indicates parts of garden are handicapped accessible

right onto June Road, then take first left onto Baxter Road. Go about one mile, at white picket fence turn left onto private drive. We are the next house in on the left.

Keeler Hill Farm
64 Keeler Lane

Although the land has been farmed since 1731, it is just in the last fifteen years that gardens have been developed, including the perennial garden, green garden, and white garden. A friendship garden, which provides swimming pool privacy, was planted with friends' castoffs. The vegetable and fruit gardens were placed among the farm buildings. A cutting garden and a lilac walk were added in 1999. In 2003, a new hornbeam hedge replaced the lilac hedge in the perennial garden. **2005**

Hours: 10 a.m. to 4 p.m.

From I-684 north, take Exit 7/Purdys. Turn right off exit ramp onto Route 116 east and go about 5 miles. Cross over Old Route 124/June Road. Route 116 will join up with Route 121 about 1 mile after June Road intersection. Bear left at that intersection. About 1 mile up the road, turn right onto Keeler Lane. Continue 0.5 mile. On left, you will see 7 yellow barns. Turn in gate with the sign on left pillar that reads "Keeler Hill Farm" and "Keeler Homestead" on right pillar. Proceed up driveway to parking.

Proceeds shared with the North Salem Open Lands Foundation

Yorktown
Barbara & John Schumacher
315-317 Crow Hill Road

At least four acres of this fifty-acre property have been developed into gardens by Barbara and John Schumacher, owners of the garden antique shop Fleur. The large rose garden below the house colors the landscape with 400 roses. A perennial garden features hostas, tree peonies, and sweeps of Asiatic lilies. Other attractions are a fern garden and a generous and varied collection of hydrangeas. **NEW**

Hours: 10 a.m. to 4 p.m.

From I-684 south take Exit 6 for Route 35/Cross River/Katonah. Turn right onto Route

35. Go 1.6 miles and turn left onto Route 100. Go 4.6 miles and turn left onto Crow Hill Road. Parking is not allowed on Crow Hill Road. Please park on side streets and take care walking to garden.

From the Saw Mill River Parkway, take the exit for Route 133/Millwood Road in Mount Kisco. Go west on Route 133 (an extension of Main Street) toward Millbrook and turn right onto Crow Hill Road. The Schumacher's driveway will be on left. Parking is not allowed on Crow Hill Road. Please park on side streets and take care walking to garden.

Columbia & Dutchess County Open Day Saturday, June 16

COLUMBIA COUNTY

Claverack
Peter Bevacqua & Stephen King
Willmon Road & Route 23B

Step through the gate of this garden and you'll find yourself in a private, magical world. This two-acre garden, located in the hamlet of Claverack, feels much larger because of its division into many garden spaces–spaces designed with a careful eye to color and especially texture. One area unfolds upon the next with its own sense of individuality. This ever-evolving garden has gone through a period of rethinking over the past year, reflecting not only the tastes of the owners, but also the natural life cycle of plants. **2005**

Hours: 10 a.m. to 4 p.m.

From Taconic State Parkway, take Exit 82 and go northwest towards Hudson and Rip Van Winkle Bridge. At first traffic light, turn right (north) onto Route 9H/23. At next light, (Claverack Market and post office will be on right), turn left onto Route 23B. After about 0.8 mile turn right onto Willmon Road. Please park along left side of road.

COPAKE FALLS
Margaret Roach
99 Valley View Road

This eighteen-year-old homemade garden reflects my obsession with plants, particularly those with good foliage or of interest to wildlife. Sixty species of birds visit annually. Informal mixed borders, frog-filled water gardens, a paved garden, and a bluestem meadow cover my two-and-a-half-acre hillside, a former orchard dotted with simple, Victorian-era farm buildings and house, surrounded by Taconic State Park land. Expansion continues and this year visitors are welcome to walk next door to see the beginnings of a landscape I started in 2002 around a new, modern guest house. Even I am shocked at the stark contrast between the two places, the new one featuring a large, enclosed gravel courtyard with formal lines. **2006**

Hours: 10 a.m. to 4 p.m.

Off Route 22 (5 miles south of Hillsdale, 13 miles north of Millerton) take Route 344 towards Taconic State Park signs. Bear right after park entrance and blue store, over metal bridge and past camp. After High Valley Road intersection on left, continue right another 100 feet to green barn and house on left (park on that side only, please).

EAST TAGHKANIC
Grant & Alice Platt
46 Tibbet Lane

This garden, which won a Golden Trowel Award from *Garden Design* magazine in 2005, is nestled in the woods at the end of a country lane. It takes advantage of a widely varied landscape to create a series of informal gardens that attempt to exploit the beauty of the natural setting. The site contains woodland paths, which wander over bridges across a creek and past the remains of old stone walls and natural rock formations. Included in the gardens are sunny herbaceous borders, a rock garden, shade garden, and park-like hillside garden including a pergola. Out of sight but just over a rise is a path that leads to a swimming pond. **2006**

Hours: 10 a.m. to 4 p.m.

From Taconic State Parkway north, pass Route 82/Ancram/Hudson exit and go 1.6 miles. Turn right onto Post Hill Road (from north, turn left). Go 0.8 mile to a silo at Nostrand Road. Turn left and go 0.3 mile to Route 27 (no sign). Turn left and go 1 mile to Taconic Parkway underpass. Go 0.5 mile to Tibbet Lane. Turn left. Proceed to parking area.

GERMANTOWN
Tailings—Robert Montgomery
404 White Birch Road

The gardens at Tailings comprise a series of bulb, perennial, and rose plantings closely integrated with the natural landscape and joined to each other by woodland paths. Axial cuts have been made through the woods to offer views in all directions and to complement the architecture. These culminate in a prospect of the Hudson River and the entire Catskill Mountain range. **2004** ♿

Hours: 10 a.m. to 2 p.m.

From Germantown, take Route 9G north from traffic light to intersection with Route 10; turn right. Go 0.25 mile to White Birch Road and turn left. Go 1 mile to Tailings' driveway on right; look for #404 on mailbox. Please park at top of driveway.

HILLSDALE
Shale Hill—Douglas Hunt
120 Underhill Road

When I bought a house named Shale Hill at the end of 1999 I had no idea how prophetic that name would be. The next spring, armed with a design from Sara Stein, I found out. Through the intervention of a bulldozer and pick axe, the half-acre now includes shade plantings near the house, a cottage-style border and a classic clipped-box herbary. One hillside is planted with more than seventy hybrid *Rosa rugosa*, another is covered with hay-scented fern. A daylily-lined path leads to a rustic arbor affording an impressive view of the Taconic Hills. **NEW**

Hours: 10 a.m. to 4 p.m.

From the intersection of Routes 22 & 23 in Hillsdale, take Maple Street (adjacent to

♿ indicates parts of garden are handicapped accessible

Sunoco Station) south until it intersects with Anthony Street. Turn left onto Anthony Street and then right onto Underhill Road. Go exactly 0.7 mile, passing Deer Track Lane twice. Shale Hill is the fouth house on right past second entrance to Deer Track Lane. Please park on east side of road, near the mailbox marked #120.

HUDSON
Hudson Bush Farm
154 Yates Road

Formal gardens surrounding the eighteenth-century house include color-oriented parterres, a double red border, rock garden, long walk leading to a summerhouse, small pool, and vegetable garden on three acres surrounded by old-growth woods. **2006** ♿

Hours: 10 a.m. to 4 p.m.

From Taconic State Parkway, take Hudson/Ancram exit. Take Route 82 west to traffic light at Bells Pond. Go west on Route 9/Route 23 to Yates Road, about 1 mile. Turn right. Go 0.25 mile to driveway on right at old brick house. Please park at top of or along drive.

Proceeds shared with the Hudson Area Association Library

Antony Nagelmann & Helen Faraday Young
68 Fingar Road

Surrounding a 1740s farmhouse, this garden, on the site of an Indian settlement above the Taconic Creek, has evolved and expanded over years of gradual use and attention. Approach along a quiet poplar-lined road, 150-year-old maples stand sentry in front of the house. Enter through wrought iron gates onto shaded lawns flanked by well-established borders of bulbs, shrubs and perennials. The large organic vegetable patch, surrounded by sunflowers produces a wide range of heirloom vegetables for the house and neighbors. A sunken garden bordered by many varieties of hostas, leads onto a sloping meadow and access to the creek through a woodland walk. From the terrace of the house the land falls away with clear views of the gardens, fields, and creek woodland.

Specimen trees including reintroduced chestnuts divide the gardens and its banks and walls into several peaceful areas. In recent years more than 100 trees have been added, as well as an orchard to the south. **2006**

Hours; 10 a.m. to 4 p.m.

From I-90, take the Catskill Exit and turn left towards Hudson. Take Route 9/Route 23 over bridge. Continue straight, ignoring signs for Hudson, 5.8 miles. Pass Williams Hardware on right. Start to slow down, Pizza Café will be on right. Turn left onto Yates Road. Go 0.5 mile and make first left onto Fingar Road. House and garden will be first property on right. Please park by barns on left or as directed.

From Route 9H in Claverack, go south 2.8 miles and turn right onto Stone Mill Road (by Hildebrandt Trucking and big corner). Go 0.8 mile. Make slight right, then first right onto Fingar Road. House and garden will be first property on right.

From Route 9H/Bells Pond Crossroads travel north 1 mile. Pass Bryant Farms produce stand (and golf). Turn left onto Stone Mill Road. Continue as directed above.

LIVINGSTON
River School Farm—Owen Davidson & Mark Prezorski
80 Hill Road

River School Farm has been protected as part of the Olana Viewshed by Scenic Hudson. The property has views of Olana and the entire Catskill range. The central landscape, designed around an 1830s farmhouse, consists of four rolling acres carved out of an 150-acre working apple orchard on Blue Hill. The five-year-old garden is exuberant, eclectic, experimental, and very much a work-in-progress. It features two ponds, long rose hedges, a rock garden, large perennial and shrub borders, and an extensive specimen tree collection. **NEW**

Hours: 10 a.m. to 4 p.m.

River School Farm is 2 miles southeast of Olana State Historic Site. From Routes 14 & 31, follow Route 31 south for 0.3 mile. Turn right at Hill Road. House is 0.25 mile further on right in midst of an orchard.

WEST TAGHKANIC
Arcadia—Ronald Wagner & Timothy Van Dam
733 Taghkanic Road

Our early Greek Revival-style farmhouse is surrounded by a pastoral landscape. An avenue of sweet gum trees, lining the formal drive, is planted in forced perspective to extend the approach to the house. The gently rolling hillside is punctuated by a magnificent grove of black locust trees; a wildflower meadow rises to the northeast. The emerging, informal plantings include the lilac walk, rhododendron and hydrangea beds, and a forest grotto. A large pond is the focus of surrounding naturalistic plantings giving to views of the bog beyond. **2005** ♿

Hours: 10 a.m. to 4 p.m.

From center of village of Livingston/Route 9, go east on Church/Livingston Road, passing red brick Dutch Reformed Church, and go east about 2 miles, to Taghkanic Road. Turn right and go to second house on right, #733.

From Taconic State Parkway, take Hudson/Route 82 exit. Drive northwest on Route 82, past Taconic Diner with neon Indian. About 1 mile from Taconic Parkway, turn left onto Livingston Road. Go 1 mile up a winding hill to Taghkanic Road on left. Turn left and go to second house on right, #733.

DUTCHESS COUNTY

AMENIA
Broccoli Hall—Maxine Paetro
23 Flint Hill Road

Visitors to Broccoli Hall describe this English-style cottage garden as "incredible," "inspirational," "magical"—and they come back again and again. Starting in 1986 with an acre and a half of bare earth, Maxine Paetro collaborated with horticulturist Tim Steinhoff to create a series of enchanting garden rooms. Broccoli Hall offers an apple tunnel, a brick courtyard, a lavish display of spring bulbs blooming with crabapples in May, an extensive border of iris, peonies, and old shrub roses flowering in June, a tree house with long views, and a secret woodland garden with a teddy bears'

picnic. Photos of Broccoli Hall can be seen at www.broccolihall.com. **2006**

Hours: 10 a.m. to 4 p.m.

From Route 22 north, go towards Amenia. Go west on Route 44 to Route 83 north/Smithfield Road. Go 2.5 miles to dirt road on right, Flint Hill Road. Turn right. House (#23) is first on left. Please park on Flint Hill Road. Be careful of ditches.

Proceeds shared with Amenia Free Library

Bronx County Open Day Saturday, June 23

Parking is very limited in this neighborhood. Please check www.opendaysprogram.org or call our toll-free number 1 (888) 842-2442 for instructions

BRONX COUNTY

BRONX
Byrns Garden
4602 Palisade Avenue

This one-and-one-half-acre Bronx garden, featured in *Metropolitan Home* magazine, contains many surprises. Located on a gentle hillside

Wave Hill
A public garden & cultural center
Bronx, New York 718.549.3200
www.wavehill.org

♿ indicates parts of garden are handicapped accessible

across from Riverdale Park and overlooking the Hudson River, the setting is private in the extreme. A woodland path winds through giant *Rhododendron maximum* to a stream and waterfall. This is offset by the upper garden, a formal ninety-foot double perennial border. The swimming pool is formal yet natural in its own room. The final surprise is a hidden garden, located in an 1829 limestone quarry with ferns, some petasites, and many other woodland plants. **NEW**

Hours: 12 p.m. to 4 p.m.

From south, take the Henry Hudson Parkway to 232nd Street. Exit left onto 232nd Street and continue to Palisade Avenue. Turn right and go 0.6 mile to garden.

From north, take the Henry Hudson Parkway to 246th Street exit. From across road, turn right onto 247th Street (look carefully for sign). Go to Palisade Avenue and turn left. The garden is second on left.

Parking is available here for all three gardens open today, which are within walking distance of one another.

Riverdale
The Weinroth Gardens at Quarrytop
700 West 247th Street

The gardens are set on multiple levels overlooking the Hudson River. Although unintended, the levels create a fairly formal setting which result from an attempt to terrace down to street level on what had been a steep drop off. Two spectacular trees, a huge oak and a copper beech, are the stars of the property, although our expanding outdoor sculpture collection is very special to us. We have tried to create all-season gardens and are particularly proud of our shade borders. **NEW**

Hours: 12 p.m. to 4 p.m.

From New York City, take the Westside Highway to Henry Hudson Parkway to Exit 21/West 246th Street turn left at light and cross over highway. Continue straight through the next light for 1 block. Make a sharp right turn onto Arlington (street sign is on the left) continue straight to stop sign, turn left (this

is 247th Street) and continue straight to 700 West 247th on left. (If you hit Palisade Avenue. you have gone 1 house too far).

From the north, take the Henry Hudson Parkway to Exit 21/West 246th Street. Turn right onto service road to 247th Street. Continue straight to #700 on left. Cars may park on 247th Street or in driveway.

Parking is also available near the Byrns Garden for all three gardens open today, which are within walking distance of one another.

Proceeds shared with Wave Hill

Riverside
Morgenthau
4682 Dodgewood Road

This is a one-acre garden situated on the Dodge Estate in Riverdale. The house was a wing originally attached to the Dodge mansion and moved in 1949 to create a separate residence. The gardens had been planted by two generations of Dodge women and then reworked, beginning in 1993 by the current owners. Large

specimen trees and shrubs continue to thrive amidst new plantings including a vegetable/cutting garden enclosed by espaliered apple trees. A work in progress that underlines the transition this property has made from country estate to suburban garden. **NEW**

Hours: 12 p.m. to 4 p.m.

The garden is located between 246th and 247th Streets on the west side of the Henry Hudson Parkway, on Dodgewood Road. Please see directions to the Byrns Garden.

Suffolk County Open Day Saturday, June 23

SUFFOLK COUNTY

EAST HAMPTON

Abby Jane Brody

44 Glade Road

This is primarily a woodland garden in which the native oaks are the upper story. I am an inveterate plant collector with a special interest in rare or unusual flowering trees and shrubs as well as herbaceous plants. The half-acre site has something in flower, preferably fragrant, almost every day of the year. In late April the last of the camellias and hellebores may be in bloom. The daphnes, epimediums, and hundreds of other woodland plants should be flowering. In June the Japanese azaleas should be flowering. **2006**

Hours: 10 a.m. to 4 p.m.

From Montauk Highway/Route 27, turn left at traffic light in East Hampton. Pass town pond, go through village, and turn left at windmill. Pass under railroad bridge and take right at fork to Springs Fireplace Road. About 3 miles, turn left onto Woodbine and take an immediate right onto Glade Road. Please park along road, not on grass.

Proceeds shared with LongHouse Reserve

Garden of Arlene Bujese

40 Whooping Hollow Road

Situated on a sloping half-acre, the landscape comprises four areas. A flower garden, bordered by evergreens, surrounds a goldfish pond in the rear of the house. Brick walkways weave throughout. The front property is terraced into three levels. Ten or so outdoor sculptures are strategically placed throughout. Favored trees are flowering cherry, pear, maple, and red leaf plum, and others. This garden, completely created and maintained by the owner, has been growing over seventeen years with the aim of creating a meditative "walk around—sit here and there" environment for all seasons. We continue to work on our property and have recently decided to have a vegetable garden behind our main perennial garden. For the past year we have had to do major work on our house and property and although it is still a work in progress we have decided to be a part of the Open Days Program for 2007. Our gardens and house have been featured in *Country Living Gardener, Early Homes* issue of *Old House Interiors*, and *Westport Magazine*. **2006**

Hours: 10 a.m. to 2 p.m.

Take Route 114 from Sag Harbor or East Hampton, about 4 miles. Turn right onto Whooping Hollow Road. Please park along street.

Margaret Kerr

1006 Springs Fireplace Road

The garden, designed by Kerr, surrounds the house and studios on two acres that extend down to the wetlands of Accabonac Harbor. Kerr's brick rug sculptures, inspired by tribal Middle Eastern carpets, are placed throughout the garden. One, a brick prayer rug, lies in a contemplative glade below the studios. Kerr collects plants grown in the Middle Ages in a courtyard around a fountain and lily pool highlighted with espaliered pear trees. In the spring, drifts of thousands of daffodils bloom in the fields around the house and are left unmown until late fall. Native grasses and wildflowers make islands of meadow during the summer. **2006**

Hours: 10 a.m. to 2 p.m.

From Montauk Highway/Route 27, turn left at traffic light in East Hampton. Pass town pond. Continue 0.9 mile past next light, taking an immediate left onto North Main Street. Pass windmill on right. Go 0.3 mile, bearing right at fork onto Springs Fireplace Road. Go 5 miles. Driveway is marked by mailbox #1006. Please park along Springs Fireplace Road and walk down dirt road to second house on left.

Proceeds shared with The Horticultural Alliance of the Hamptons and Bridge Gardens Trust

Carol Mercer
33 Ocean Avenue

An undeniable partnering of pattern, movement, and color makes this garden seem to glow and come alive. Mercer and her partner, Lisa Verderosa, have a thriving garden design business called the Secret Garden, Ltd.; they received accolades for the design of the roof garden at the 2003 Kips Bay Designer Showhouse in New York City. Previous years' recognition includes the Gate House Gardens at the 2002 Villa Maria Designer Showhouse, Water Mill, New York and gold medal awards at several of the New York City flower shows. The garden was a cover story in *Garden Design* magazine, and appeared in *House Beautiful, Garden Style, Victoria, Martha Stewart Living,* and *Design Times* magazines, as well as in *Seaside Gardening, The Garden Design Book, Sanctuary: Gardening for the Soul, The Natural Shade Garden,* and, most recently, in *Landscape with Roses, Garden Stone,* and *Hot Plants for Cool Climates.* It was also featured in *Newsday* in 1999 and appeared in the Time/Life book series, *Beds & Borders, Gardening Weekends,* and *Shade Gardening.* **2004** ♿

Hours: 10 a.m. to 4 p.m.

From Montauk Highway/Route 27, proceed east through Water Mill, Bridgehampton, and Wainscott to East Hampton. At traffic light at head of pond, turn right onto Ocean Avenue. House, #33, is fourth on left. White stone driveway is marked by a small gray sign. Please park as directed.

Proceeds shared with East End Hospice

Ulster County Open Day
Saturday, July 7
ULSTER COUNTY

BEARSVILLE
Gayle Burbank Garden
203 Cooper Lake Road

This garden is a twenty-eight-year effort which took me from novice to professional landscape designer. It has evolved from a few flower beds to a total development of the property on which my house sits. There are many garden areas incorporating shrubs, perennials, and ornamental trees. There is a large mixed border and shade garden, a three-tiered perennial bed, a gazebo garden, and a large pool area with stone walkways and a small pond. Strewn throughout are the ceramic bird baths, planters, and fountains that I make. Birds singing; the fragrance of honeysuckle, viburnum or peony; wind chimes in the breeze; the sounds of the pool waterfall; the scurry of the frogs as you approach the pond—I have tried to create paradise. **2006** ♿

Hours: 10 a.m. to 4 p.m.

Take New York State Thruway to Exit 19. Take traffic circle to Route 28/Pine Hill. Go to Route 375 and turn right and follow to end. Turn left onto Route 212. Go through town of Woodstock. After Bear Café restaurant on left, cross small bridge and bear left. Then take first right onto Cooper Lake Road. The garden is 0.75 mile on left at #203.

WEST HURLEY
Bebe & Dan Turck
33 Clover Street

When we purchased this property there was grass to mow. Over the years we transformed it into a spring-to-autumn showcase. Pink and white flowering fruit trees set against a living fence of red flowering quince, started from one bush, surround the property. Currants, blueberries, grapes, gooseberries, kiwi, raspberries, high bush cranberries, and honeyberries attract many birds. Our butterfly koi pond is very relaxing and the bog garden attracts many creatures. Other gardens include annuals, ornamental grasses, herbs, rhubarb, asparagus, cacti, vegetables, and perennials. **2006** ♿

Hours: 10 a.m. to 4 p.m.

From Kingston, go west on Route 28 to fourth traffic light. There is a green and white sign that reads "Woodstock Exit Only/Route 375". Turn right onto Route 375. Go 0.2 mile to third right and turn onto Mosher Place. The garden is located at top of hill at #33 Clover Street. Please park on street.

Suffolk County Open Day Saturday, July 14

SUFFOLK COUNTY

CUTCHOGUE
Conni Cross Garden Designer
Route 25

This is a twenty-three year old garden on approximately five acres. It is three-quarters shade garden with light, sandy soil, designed by garden designer Conni Cross. This unusual solar house is surrounded by a tufa garden featuring dwarf and miniature conifers and alpines. Look for a waterfall, four ponds, an aviary and barnyard, beautiful stonework, children's playhouse, natural-style pool, rare plants, lush gardens, and many other unusual garden features. **2006** ♿

Hours: 10 a.m. to 2 p.m.

Take Long Island Expressway/I-495 to Exit 73. Go east on Route 58 through Riverhead business district. Route 58 turns into Route 25 where it intersects with Route 105. Continue east on to Mattituck. Pass Waldbaums on left. Go 2 miles. Entrance to Environmentals and Conni Cross' garden is just around bend from Trimble's of Cutchogue and Wagon Wheel Lane, on left. Approximate distance from Riverhead to Cutchogue is 13 miles.

MATTITUCK
Maurice Isaac & Ellen Coster Isaac
4835 Oregon Road

This early 1900s country farmhouse has been designed with two major borders incorporating extensive plantings of unusual combinations of bulbs, perennials, trees, shrubs, and annuals. A pond adds a beautiful and soothing touch. A path leads to a swimming pool and plantings, as well as an old restored barn adjacent to an arbor planted with wisteria, clematis, and several vines offering tranquility, shade, and a view of the extensive nearby vineyards. **2006** ♿

Hours: 10 a.m. to 4 p.m.

From Long Island Expressway/I-495, take Exit 73/Route 58 and follow to Route 25. Go through Mattituck past Love Lane to Wickham Avenue. Turn left and go past railroad tracks and traffic light. Stay straight on Wickham; it will turn into Grand Avenue. Take Grand about 0.25 mile to East Mill Road. Turn right, keeping to left; this will turn into Oregon Road.

Dennis Schrader & Bill Smith
1200 East Mill Road

Set in the heart of the North Fork wineries, the two-plus-acre garden surrounds a restored 1850 farmhouse. The gardens are encircled by fourteen acres of fields. The decks, porches, and terraces are filled with container plantings. There are many perennial and mixed shrub borders, vegetable, herb, and dwarf fruit tree plantings, a formal knot garden, and a woodland shade area. The garden has rustic arbors, trellises, stone walls, a garden pavilion, many sitting areas, and a natural clay pond with a stream and bridge. There are other ponds for water lilies and papyrus. Many of the plantings contain tropicals, subtropicals, tender perennials, and annuals. Dennis is co-author of the book *Hot Plants for Cool Climates: Gardening with Tropical Plants in Temperate Zones*. **2006** ♿

Hours: 10 a.m. to 4 p.m.

From Long Island Expressway/I-495, take Exit 73/Route 58 and follow to Route 25. Go through town of Mattituck past Love Lane

---

♿ indicates parts of garden are handicapped accessible

to Wickham Avenue. Turn left and go past railroad tracks and traffic light. Stay straight on Wickham and it will turn into Grand Avenue. Take Grand about 0.25 mile to East Mill Road. Turn left and look for #1200. Please park along street.

Proceeds shared with The Horticultural Alliance of the Hamptons

SOUTHOLD
Milford Garden
1200 Bay View Road

Our garden is an integral part of our old farmhouse, barn, and field complex. We have a little pond, a number of perennial gardens, a vegetable garden, small fruits, and an herb and cutting garden. **2005** ♿

Hours: 10 a.m. to 4 p.m.

Located between hamlets of Peconic and Southold, just off Route 25 on Bay View Road. Turn at Empire gas station and drive 0.3 mile to Indian Museum on right. We are next house, #1200. Please park along road.

Tompkins County Open Day
Saturday, July 14

TOMPKINS COUNTY

DANBY
Myers Gardens
1071 Michigan Hollow Road

Six acres of rolling lawn and perennial beds contain more than 550 different varieties of perennials nestled behind and between fieldstone walls and structures. Features include a covered bridge, a working water wheel on a post-and-beam constructed feed mill, a blacksmith shop, and a huge glass sponge fossil rock enclosed in a unique display case. There is also a thirty-foot-diameter stone sundial and a potting shed garden with four raised beds. **2005** ⚑

Hours: 10 a.m. to 4 p.m.

From downtown Ithaca, take Route 13/34/96 south. About 3 miles south of Ithaca, take left exit onto Route 34/96 and go about 9 miles. Turn left onto Hill View Road and go to stop sign (2 miles) at intersection of Michigan Hollow Road. Garden is directly in front on opposite side of intersection. Please park on road or on lawn as posted.

Proceeds shared with Tompkins County Community Beautification Program

FREEVILLE
Ann M. & Carlton J. Manzano Garden
418 Caswell Road

This property has an old-fashioned charm. Cottage garden perennials mingle with native plants in large beds surrounding the restored 1860 Greek revival-style house. A stone terrace sits below natural looking stonework, and the back of the property is a broad expanse of lawn, framed with mature trees. Carlton is a plein air artist, and his studio, located in a barn-type structure on the property, will also be open for viewing. **NEW** ♿

Hours: 10 a.m. to 4 p.m.

From Ithaca, take Route 13 north about 8 miles to Hanshaw Road and turn left. Go 2.7 miles to West Dryden Road and turn right. Go 3 miles to Caswell Road and turn left. Go 0.5 mile to #418. House is on left.

Proceeds shared with Tompkins County Community Beautification Program

ITHACA
Cayuga Daylilies
77 Halseyville Road

My garden features more than 250 labeled varieties of daylilies, most of which will be in bud or bloom at this time of year. The large display beds containing just daylilies are breathtaking when in bloom. Stone paths meander through large cottage garden borders, filled with a wide variety of perennials, shrubs, small trees, and of course, more daylilies. A pond borders the property and features an unusual, locally made fountain. **NEW**

Hours: 10 a.m. to 4 p.m.

From Ithaca, take Route 79 West for 7 miles to the blinking traffic light. Turn right onto Halseyville Road. Cayuga Daylilies is first house on right (0.5 mile).

Proceeds shared with Tompkins County Community Beautification Program

Roseanne & Joe Moresco
7 Highland Park Lane

The garden exhibits the many horticultural passions of its creators. Joe's garden of hardy cactus thrives above a stone wall next to the drive, and dozens of Roseanne's bonsai plants are on display, many of them created from cuttings from the garden. A bark-mulched path meanders through a woodland planting of shrubs and perennials. Other features include flowering perennial borders, a small pond with water plants, and a greenhouse for the collection of orchids, cactus and other exotic plants. **NEW** ♿

Hours: 10 a.m. to 4 p.m.

From Route 13 take Cayuga Heights Road exit. At the end of ramp turn left onto Highland Road. Go 0.1 mile and turn left onto Berkshire Road. Go 0.4 mile and bear right onto Highland Road. Go 0.1 mile and turn left onto Highland Park Lane. Proceed 0.1 mile up to top of hill. House is on right just before the circle. Park along road on both sides (including the circle) being careful not to block any driveways.

Proceeds shared with Tompkins County Community Beautification Program

Mount Garden
303 East Upland Road

This deep village lot has been designed by Elizabeth and Tim to create a feeling of spaciousness and calm. Stone paths and walls frame beds planted with an all-season mix of early bulbs, perennials, and shrubs. All hardy to this area, plants are chosen as much for texture, shape, foliage, and bloom. Several arbors lead from the sunny front to the rear of the property where plantings shift to a more naturalistic style, featuring mature trees, shade-loving perennials, touches of whimsy, and a dry stream bed. **NEW** ♿

Hours: 10 a.m. to 4 p.m.

From downtown Ithaca, East Upland Road can be reached by taking Route 13N, exiting right onto Triphammer Road, and passing directly through the Community Corners. Park only on the south side of Upland, or on adjacent streets. A white picket fence identifies the house.

Proceeds shared with Tompkins County Community Beautification Program

LANSING
Lion Garden
219 Lansing Station Road

Flowers welcome you from the moment you arrive at this garden. Entrance plantings embrace the street and line the brick driveway, filled with hundreds of blooming perennials. Large beds around the house are filled with perennials, and dozens of planted pots grace the deck on the shady hillside. The gardens continue down a steep, wooded hill, where borders of shade-loving perennials, groundcovers and shrubs surround a gazebo and folly. Woodland trails lead to a small ravine below the garden. **NEW** ♿

Hours: 10 a.m. to 4 p.m.

From Ithaca, take Route 34 north along Cayuga Lake to where the road runs into Route 34B at Rogue's Harbor Inn. Turn left onto Route 34B and go 5.5 miles to Cecil's Tavern on right. Turn left onto Lansing Station Road and go 1 mile. The grey, modern-style house is on left, and wooden mailbox reads #219. Please park on left past driveway. Use brakes as there is a steep incline. For handicap access, park in driveway.

Proceeds shared with Tompkins County Community Beautification Program

---

♿ indicates parts of garden are handicapped accessible

Suffolk County Open Day Sunday, July 15

SUFFOLK COUNTY

EAST HAMPTON

Alexandra Munroe & Robert Rosenkranz Gardens
19 West End Road

This young garden around a 1928 beach-front house combines formal and naturalistic landscaping. An exuberant meadow with many varieties of perennials, self-seeding annuals, and grasses is adjacent to a cottage garden and rose bed enclosed by a yew exedra. Nearby, a visitor strolls through a woodland walk, border with cryptomeria, cypress, and rhododendron underplanted with arisarum, ferns, and trillium, and concludes as the trail ends near the dunes with ornamental grasses. The house overlooks a parterre and croquet lawn where lead urns planted informally with various annuals serve as focal points. The kitchen terrace leads to a formal vegetable and cutting garden. **2006**

Hours: 11 a.m. to 4 p.m.

From Montauk Highway/Route 27, proceed to East Hampton. At traffic light at head of pond, turn right off Ocean Avenue. Take third right onto Lily Pond Lane and drive to end. At stop sign, turn left onto West End Road. House is fifth on left (ocean side), marked with cedar gate and privet hedge. Please park along West End Road or at Georgica Beach.

Bob & Mimi Schwarz
8 Lilla Lane

An explosion of color! The rainbow daylily garden is a sight to see in mid-July. More than 600 named varieties of daylilies are grown in undulating herbaceous borders, backed by cedars, hemlocks, and masses of rhododendrons. More than 5,000 of our own seedlings bloom in the seedling patch. There is also an ornamental grass garden with clumps of miscanthus, panicum, and other grasses. The entire garden has inviting benches and shade. **2005**

Hours: 10 a.m. to 2 p.m.

From Montauk Highway/Route 27, go to East Hampton. Pass movie theater and continue to traffic light. Turn left after light, going under railroad bridge, with windmill on right. Continue 0.5 mile, bearing right at fork onto Springs/County Road 41. Go 3 miles and turn right onto Hildreth Place. At end, turn left onto Accabonac. Go 0.25 mile and turn right onto Lilla Lane. House (#8) is 200 yards down on right. Please park on street.

MONTAUK

Richard Kahn & Elaine Peterson
224 West Lake Drive

Originally landscaped in 1931 soon after the house was completed, this garden had withstood a multitude of nor'easters and hurricanes as well as alternating periods of attention and neglect before we started slowly to leave our own imprint in 1977. Situated on the Montauk peninsula where it is surrounded by an endless expanse of water and sky, the property is protected by the original non-native plantings of oak, silver maple, and privet, which buffer the gardens on all sides except the east, which faces on Lake Montauk. This protective enclosure within an often inhospitable, very exposed geography gives the place its alluring lushness and its delight to those who first (or repeatedly) enter here from outside. It gives the illusion of total retreat, peace, and safety while still holding onto some of the romance and mystery of former days. Throughout the gardens we have tried to allow space for quiet observation and contemplation, space which shelters one from the nearby sounds of neighbors and traffic. We have encouraged the local bird and insect populations by growing what they like and not using poisons, and they have rewarded us, filling the air with their sounds and movements. We have indulged a love of trees and shrubs by planting a great variety of them. An ongoing exploration of perennials and bulbs is pursued as different appropriate settings for them appear. Herb and vegetable gardens extend the repertoire. Garden design and materials are determined by the persistent challenges of heavy wind and salt spray. **2005** ♿

Hours: 10 a.m. to 2 p.m.

From Montauk Highway/Route 27, go past village of Montauk 0.8 mile. Turn left onto West Lake Drive (signs for Montauk Harbor/Route 77/Montauk Downs). Garden, #224, is 1.2 miles on right. Please park along road, not on grass.

Dutchess County
Open Day
Saturday, July 21

DUTCHESS COUNTY

AMENIA
Jade Hill—Paul Arcario & Don Walker
13 Lake Amenia Road

Jade Hill is a hillside stroll garden with a varied collection of exotic plant material. A partial list includes dwarf yellow-stripe bamboo, fountain bamboo, lotus, magnolias, Japanese maples, and conifers. Trees, shrubs, and perennials have been planted to form a tapestry of color and texture. Features include a walk-through bamboo grove and goldfish ponds. An Oriental viewing pavilion cantilevered over a ledge overlooks a gold-themed garden. The rose garden has more than fifty varieties of hardy shrub roses. Garden was featured in the September 2006 issue of *Better Homes & Gardens*. **2006**

Hours: 10 a.m. to 4 p.m.

From traffic light in Amenia at intersection of Routes 22, 44, and 343, take Route 44 west. Make first left after 55 mph sign onto Lake Amenia Road. A gated driveway is after fifth house on right. Please park on Lake Amenia Road.

Mead Farm House Garden
224 Perry's Corners Road

On the site of a 250-year-old farmyard, this mature garden winds around a fair approximation of a nineteenth-century horse barn and utilizes rocky outcrops and the stone foundations of long-gone farm buildings as the visual anchors of the perennial beds. The base of the old silo has become a deck from which one can gaze over a small pond at the more distant landscape. Features include a bog garden, and some interesting trees, including a sizeable Japanese umbrella pine, planted about 1966. **2006** ♿

Hours: 10 a.m. to 4 p.m.

From intersection of Routes 22, 44 and 343 at only traffic light in Amenia, take Route 22/44 north about 1 mile. Turn left at Maplebrook School onto Perry's Corners Road. Proceed about 1 mile. House is a clapboard farmhouse on right. Please park on street.

MILLBROOK
309 Route 343
309 Route 343

This Millbrook garden has been a work in progress since 1970, when the owners purchased twenty-eight acres of hillside with four magnificent oak trees on it. A long driveway is screened with white pines on one side, and rows of sugar maples on the other, marking the edge of the field. Through the maples, the field can be seen with its groves of white pines, birches, and other trees. A perennial border at the top of the drive curves towards the house, creating a splash of color in the summer. Winding paths through the fields and woods complement the array of perennials, wildflower gardens, shrubs, and trees. **NEW**

Hours: 12 p.m. to 4 p.m.

From the Taconic Parkway north, take the Route 44 exit. Turn right onto Route 44 and continue to first traffic light. Go straight through light onto Route 343. Go exactly 1.6 miles and look on the left for a blue sign that read "Jay Van Alen". If you see Dutchess Day School you have gone too far.

From Route 22 go to Dover Plains and take Route 343 west. After 6 miles you will see Dutchess Day School on the right. Look for blue sign that reads "Jay Van Alen" on the right at the top of the hill. If you see Nine Partners Lane you have gone too far.

♿ indicates parts of garden are handicapped accessible

Belinda & Stephen Kaye
658 Deep Hollow Road

This farmhouse garden, designed around a lily pond and Carpenter Gothic-style potting shed, incorporates unusual combinations of annuals, ornamental vegetables, herbs, and perennials. Along the nearby roadside, native shrubs, grasses, and favorite weeds are naturalized to provide a screen. Other features include a petasites grove, a recently completed fountain by a local sculptor, and a strictly utilitarian vegetable garden. **2006** ♿

Hours: 8:30 a.m. to 4 p.m.

From Millbrook, take Route 44 east towards Amenia. Continue through Mabbettsville and, about 3 miles beyond, look for Charlotte's Restaurant on right. Take next right onto Deep Hollow Road. Farm is first on left after church. It is yellow with a yellow barn.

From Amenia, take Route 44 west towards Millbrook about 5 miles to hamlet of Lithgow. Turn left onto Deep Hollow Road. Please park along Deep Hollow Road.

MILLERTON
Hyland/Wente Garden
95 Taylor Road

The property consists of a modern barn-like structure located on rolling farmland overlooking Indian Mountain and lake views. The house has eight doors leading to a series of distinct gardens, intentionally blurring house and gardens. Emphasizing grasses, textures, colors and plant combinations, the gardens blend with surrounding wildflower meadows and are designed for interest in all seasons. There is a rill with bamboo, a secret garden, a pool garden, a garden of solar panels, and a wooded walk down to Indian Lake. **2006** ♿

Hours: 10 a.m. to 4 p.m.

From Route 22 in Amenia, drive north 4.1 miles to Coleman Station Road/Route 58, and turn right. Go 1.1 miles, crossing Harlem Valley Rail Trail. Turn left immediately onto Regan Road, which, after 0.8 mile, dead-ends into Taylor Road. Turn right and go 0.1 mile up hill, and driveway, #95, is on left.

From clock tower in Sharon, Connecticut, drive north on Route 41 along Sharon Green. Turn left onto Route 361 west at stop sign 0.1 mile in middle of Sharon Green, then make an immediate right, just after fire station, remaining on Route 361/Millerton Road. Follow for 2.1 miles and turn left onto Dakin Road (at a sign for Mole's Hill Farm Stables). Go up hill on Dakin Road, which becomes Taylor Road 0.4 mile from Route 361; #95 is on right.

PAWLING
The Brine Garden— Duncan & Julia Brine
21 Bluebird Inn Road

Underway since 1990, this six-acre garden and arboretum reflect both naturalism and structure. Two 1920s farmhouses establish an old-fashioned ambience. They sit on a cliff over a marsh and glade and enjoy long vistas of distant ridges. Gravel pathways connect horticulturally diverse areas. Native plants from the owner's nursery are featured. Garden and naturalistic areas blend. Dramatic, large-leaved, and floriferous perennials accent an allée of taxodium, groupings of *Acer triflorum*, *Betula nigra* and parrotia, as well as a hedge of *Miscanthus giganteus*. A map and plant list are provided. **2006**

Hours: 2 p.m. to 6 p.m.

From Route 22 toward Pawling. Continue past Trinity Pawling School. Turn right onto Route 68. Bear left at the first intersection onto Hurd's Corner Road. Go 0.5 mile. Please park on the right of Hurd's Corner Road across from Bluebird Inn Road on the left. Walk in to the last house on left.

From Route 7 in Gaylordsville, Connecticut, go east on Route 55 towards New York. At the "T" intersection turn left and continue to Route 22. Turn left (south) onto Route 22 and go 4 miles. Turn left onto Route 68. Bear left at the first intersection onto Hurd's Corner Road. Go 0.5 mile. Please park on the right of Hurd's Corner Road across from Bluebird Inn Road on the left. Walk in to the last house on left.

Proceeds shared with Friends of the Great Swamp (FROGS)

STANFORDVILLE
Ellen & Eric Petersen
378 Conklin Hill Road

This is a sunny country garden maintained by the owners. It is a collector's garden with many interesting and unusual plants. To balance the "one of everything" chaos, we have added structure with rock walls and arbors as well as by placing small trees directly into perennial beds. The trees are big enough now to give structure and scale to the garden beds and include conifers and flowering, deciduous trees. Plants that seed in provide continuity and act as informal ground covers: feverfew, columbine, poppies and many others. I try to blend the garden into its wild surroundings with vigorous native shrubs and perennials but close to the house I use fancier plants. I love yellow, purple, silver and variegated foliage and any perennial that tops six feet. **2004** ♿

Hours: 12 p.m. to 4 p.m.

From Route 82 north, pass firehouse in Stanfordville. Go 5 miles to Old Conklin Hill Road and turn right. You will come to a "T" very soon. Turn right again there. Now you are on Conklin Hill Road. Continue about 2 miles up hill. We are on the right after a sharp uphill turn. Please pull into the field on the left. The house and garden are on the right.

Proceeds shared with Bartram's Gardens

Columbia County
Open Day
Sunday, July 22

There are also gardens open on this date in nearby Berkshire County, Massachusetts. See their listings on page 144.

COLUMBIA COUNTY

CANAAN
Rockland Farm
180 Stony Kill Road

Our garden was wild land when we arrived, and trees and scrub had taken over since the sheep-farmers moved west. Now, we think we have created, with help from many talented people over the years, a variety of gardens that flow pleasingly one from another over about six acres. They include a 150-foot-long rock ledge, a fifty-foot-long rock garden, perennial beds around our pool, a lavender garden, a water garden, plus a vegetable garden and a "Marrakitchen" container-garden supported by a greenhouse, and a woodland garden in development. **NEW** ♿

Hours: 10 a.m. to 4 p.m.

From west, take Route 295 (the last exit before the toll going north on the Taconic) through East Chatham to the flashing traffic light at the intersection of Route 5 in Canaan. Immediately after the intersection, take the dirt road on left (Upper Queechy Road) and then turn left at end and look for a wooden gate on right that leads to a red barn.

From east, take Route 295 from Route 41 in Massachusetts or from Route 22 in New York past the tip of Queechy Lake and the Canaan Market (both on right), and then take first dirt road on right (Stony Kill Road). Turn right after about 0.5 mile through a wooden gate leading to a red barn.

Proceeds shared with Berkshire Botanical Garden

Westchester County
Open Day
Sunday, July 22

WESTCHESTER COUNTY

BEDFORD HILLS
Phillis Warden
531 Bedford Center Road

This garden of many facets includes perennial borders, two water gardens, a formal vegetable garden, wildflower garden, fern garden, marsh garden, tree platform overlooking the marshlands, woodland walk, and formal croquet court. The garden extends over seven acres. **2006**

Hours: 10 a.m. to 6 p.m.

From Bedford Village, take Route 22 towards Katonah to intersection at Bedford Cross. Garden is on left. Please park at Rip-

♿ indicates parts of garden are handicapped accessible

powam School and walk to 531 Bedford Center Road.

Proceeds shared with The Native Plant Center of Westchester Community College

KATONAH
Michael Fuchs
33 Reyburn Road

Originally part of the pre-Revolutionary War Van Cortland estate, this country home includes an early 1800s icehouse and a meticulously maintained, century-old, clay tennis court. Old-fashioned vase-grafted apple trees remain from what was a large orchard planted in the late 1880s. Very large, formal perennial gardens surround a restful antique gazebo nestled against the reservoir woodland. A dining patio, outdoor fireplace, and pergola were carefully constructed around century-old wisteria. Old growth and specimen trees, as well as bronze statuary and huge beautifully planted antique urns accent this very private property. **2006** ⚲

Hours: 10 a.m. to 4 p.m.

From I-684, take Exit 6 to Route 35 west. At second traffic light, turn left onto Cherry Street. The first right is Reyburn Road. Bear left at fork. House is on right with white picket fence. Please park on street.

LARCHMONT
Premium Pond Garden
10 Pryer Lane

This garden has been planted to take advantage of water views. The 1908 stucco house sits on Premium Pond. Landscape designer Barbara Paca has created two undulating beds which enclose an expanse of lawn leading to the water. Blue, pink, purple, and white perennials and annuals bloom from June to August. Pale pink roses and dark purple clematis climb a wooden pergola, offering a shady respite at the pool terrace in June. As the season progresses, hydrangeas, hollyhocks, and dahlias provide an abundance of color throughout the wide beds. **NEW** ⚲

Hours: 10 a.m. to 2 p.m.

From the Hutchinson River Parkway heading south, take Exit 20/Weaver Street/Scarsdale. Turn left onto Weaver Street. At end of Weaver Street turn right onto Boston Post Road (about 5 minutes on Weaver) and turn left onto Larchmont Avenue. Turn right onto Magnolia Avenue and go to end. Turn left on Pryer Lane to #10 on right.

NORTH SALEM
Hilltop
122 Nash Road

The landscape design is intended to marry natural beauty of the site to the drama of the house. Note how intimate garden areas east of the house are extensions of major architectural features. To maintain abundant sunlight, trees are kept away from the house and used only for specific effect. The cork tree that separates the foreground from the entry garden is an example. Native perennials and grasses create an active outdoor space that seamlessly flows from the house and extends to and becomes integral with the meadow. **NEW** ⚲

Hours: 10 a.m. to 4 p.m.

From south on Route 684, take Exit 6A/Golden's Bridge. Turn left onto Route 22. Go 1.4 miles to Nash Road and turn right. Go 1 mile to #122 on left.

From north on Route 684, take Exit 8/Hardscrabble Road/Golden's Bridge. Turn left at stop sign at end of exit ramp. Turn left at first traffic light onto Route 22 South towards Purdy's. Go about 3.1 miles to Nash Road, just past second Valeria Road. Turn left onto Nash Road and go 1 mile to #122. Turn left into driveway at mahogany gate. Please park along

SCARSDALE
Fran & Alan Zimbard
91 Penn Road

The subtle harmony of Eastern gardens have long inspired us, and we strive to incorporate these rhythms in our own designs. Meandering pathways lead to island gardens overflowing with perennials and shade gardens with diverse hosta and ferns. Muted color, texture, and form are important considerations for the choice of plantings. Elements such as rock, stone sculpture, and antiquary add depth. Water features capture peaceful reflections amid gentle sounds. Arches, with their repeating forms, add visual interest while benches offer an invitation for relaxation and quiet thought. **NEW** ♿

Hours: 10 a.m. to 4 p.m.

From South of Westchester County, take the Hutchinson River Parkway North to Exit 21/Weaver Street. Follow the service road up the traffic light and turn right onto Weaver Street. Cross over the parkway and go 2 additional blocks to Penn Boulevard and turn right. Proceed on Penn Boulevard which becomes Penn Road. The garden is on left, #91.

From Northern Westchester, take I-684 to Hutchinson River Parkway South. Go to Exit 20/Weaver Street. Turn right off exit and go 2 blocks to Penn Boulevard. Proceed as directed above.

From Connecticut, take the Merritt Parkway or I-95 to I-287 West to Hutchinson River Parkway South to Exit 20/Weaver Street. Proceed as directed above.

Columbia & Dutchess County Open Day Sunday, September 9

COLUMBIA COUNTY

ANCRAM
Adams-Westlake
681 Route 7

Two writers, garden writer Abby Adams and crime novelist Donald Westlake, authored the various plantings on this former farm in a pastoral Columbia County valley. Perennial borders, a walled swimming pool garden, a cutting/vegetable garden, a fruit orchard and an ornamental frog pond frame the 1835 farmhouse. A new stone courtyard garden behind the house opens up to hillside views. Paths and strategically placed sitting areas guide a visitor through the landscape to a deep natural ravine, where a spring-fed pond faces a field of wildflowers. Trails lead up the ravine, past wetlands and a creek, to high meadows. **2005**

Hours: 10 a.m. to 4 p.m.

From Taconic State Parkway, exit at Jackson Corners (mile 71); go east on Route 2. At first "Y," turn left onto Route 7, following signs for Ancram. At second "Y," turn left, staying on Route 7. Our house is just past the Gallatin Town Hall (about 7 minutes from Taconic), on left; look for #681 on a red mailbox.

CLAVERACK
Loomis Creek–Gardens of Andrew Beckman & Bob Hyland
29 Van Deusen Road

We purchased our twenty-five-acre property, a former dairy farm, seven years ago. We continue to "hack away" at the invasive thugs (buckthorn, multiflora rose, brambles, etc.) around the 1830s farmhouse, outbuildings, hayed fields and one-acre retail nursery—featured in the February 2006 issue of the British magazine *Gardens Illustrated*. Our mixed borders and meadows reflect our passion for "great" sun and shade perennials, shrubs, ornamental grasses, tender perennials and tropicals. Highlights include the nursery demonstration borders, pool garden, a cooperative vegetable garden, shade borders, and the "evolving" wetland walk to Loomis Creek. We like to share our eclectic gardens in early September when composites, meadow grasses, fruiting shrubs, and seasonal containers are lush and exuberant as summer winds down. **2006**

Hours: 10 a.m. to 4 p.m.

From New York State Thruway/I-87, take Exit 21. After tollbooth, turn left and go east on Route 23. Cross Hudson River on Rip Van Winkle toll bridge. Proceed east on Route 23 to second traffic light (about 5.6 miles). Turn left onto Route 23 and Route 9H and go north 3.9 miles to first light in Claverack. Claverack Post Office and Market will be on right. Turn left, Route 23B, and go west about 0.5 mile. Take first left onto Stone Mill Road and go 1 mile to intersection of Van Deusen Road. Look for Loomis Creek Nursery sign and turn right onto Van Deusen Road. Come down to parking area and greenhouses on left.

♿ indicates parts of garden are handicapped accessible

From Taconic State Parkway, take Route 23/Hillsdale/Claverack exit. At top of exit ramp, turn right (from north) or left (from south) onto Route 23 west towards Claverack. Go about 5.5 miles to first light in Claverack (Xtra Mart will be on right; Claverack Market and Post Office on left). Go through light. Route 23 changes to Route 23B on other side of intersection; continue for about 0.5 mile.

Take first left turn onto Stone Mill Road and go about 1 mile to intersection of Van Deusen Road. Look for Loomis Creek Nursery sign and turn right onto Van Deusen Road. Come down to parking area and greenhouses onto left.

COPAKE FALLS
Margaret Roach
99 Valley View Road

This eighteen-year-old homemade garden reflects my obsession with plants, particularly those with good foliage or of interest to wildlife. Sixty species of birds visit annually. Informal mixed borders, frog-filled water gardens, a paved garden, and a bluestem meadow cover my two-and-a-half-acre hillside, a former orchard dotted with simple, Victorian-era farm buildings and house, surrounded by Taconic State Park land. Expansion continues and this year visitors are welcome to walk next door to see the beginnings of a landscape I started in 2002 around a new, modern guest house. Even I am shocked at the stark contrast between the two places, the new one featuring a large, enclosed gravel courtyard with formal lines. **2006**

Hours: 10 a.m. to 4 p.m.

Off Route 22 (5 miles south of Hillsdale, 13 miles north of Millerton) take Route 344 towards Taconic State Park signs. Bear right after park entrance and blue store, over metal bridge and past camp. After High Valley Road intersection on left, continue right another 100 feet to green barn and house on left (park on that side only, please).

CRARYVILLE
Susan Anthony & Richard Galef
158 Maiers Road

A long ledge of white, whale-shaped rock dubbed "Moby Dick" (both because of its form and because our obsession may equal Captain Ahab's) dominates the eastern edge of the lawn. From the grassy plateau atop the ledge, the view to the east is of the Taconic Hills and the Berkshires. Looking west, a new house addition is set into the wooded hill, displacing Susan's large perennial bed. New beds now edge the woodland grove and the shrub border. The beds (once a painter, Susan uses plants as her palette) provide cascades of color across the lawn through the seasons. Stone walls, steps, terraces, and paths built with found stone by myself and a helper over the years, surround the house and court yard. (We are presently extending the wall and terrace around the new addition.) The woodland grove, a large wooded area with tall native trees, is underplanted with many shade-loving plants, ground covers, shrubs, and rare and unusual ornamental trees. There are many species and varieties of maples. Bounded by the perennial beds, a craggy extension of the rock ledge, and an allée on three sides, the fourth side is woods, which the grove seems to encroach upon more each year. Pond-side beds and a peninsula planted with perennials, evergreens, and deciduous shrubs and specimen trees surround the pond at the north edge of the lawn. And, where there once was a large swamp filled with dead trees, we have made a five-acre, naturally landscaped, secluded lake for wildfowl, wildlife, and—sometimes—ourselves. We think it is beautiful. Come see for yourselves. **2006** ♿

Hours: 10 a.m. to 4 p.m.

From Taconic State Parkway, exit east at Manor Rock Road. Go 1 mile to fork and turn right onto Maiers Road. Twenty feet on left are 5 mailboxes and our driveway with a sign, "158 Maiers Road."

From junction of Routes 22 and 23 at Hillsdale, proceed west on Route 23 exactly 4 miles to County Route 11/Beauty Award Highway.

Go south 2.2 miles to Craryville Road. Turn right and go 0.8 mile to fork. Bear right onto Manor Rock Road and proceed 1.5 miles to Maiers Road fork. Keep left for about 20 feet. Our driveway is just past 5 mailboxes. Please park on Maiers Road and walk in.

MILLERTON
Helen Bodian
Carson Road

This is an eclectic set of four gardens on an old farmstead high on a forested ridge above the Harlem Valley. Standing above the house and garden are broad, open fields crowned by deciduous woodland. Each of the four gardens has its own character and season, permitting a wide range of horticultural experiment and planting style. The rural landscape frames everything; the rock garden, set into the meadow hill by the house, and the square border and shrub borders, stationed below a slope of mature oaks, birch, and maple. Fields rise above the ornamental vegetable garden and the walled "tropical" garden, so that no matter what picture is created, the wild place always hangs above it. For this reason (with the exception of the tropical garden), planting has carefully combined appropriate exotic and native or native-looking plants. The connections between gardens also serve as transitions between man-made and natural space. Grass paths cutting through fields lead from garden to garden, from barn to deep forest and from garden and pond into light woodland. **2006** ♿

Hours: 2 p.m. to 6 p.m.

From Millerton, take Route 22 to intersection of Routes 44 and 22 and continue north on Route 22 for 4 miles. On right, you will see a sign for Columbia County and on left, Carson Road. Turn onto Carson Road and go up hill for 1 mile. On left are a tennis court and a metal barn, on right a white farm house with a modern addition. Please park in field next to barn.

From Hillsdale, take Route 22 south about 14 miles from traffic light in Hillsdale. Look for a sign on left for Dutchess County and Carson Road on right.

DUTCHESS COUNTY

RHINEBECK
Cedar Heights Orchard— William & Arvia Morris
8 Crosby Lane

The gardens near the house and pool have informal plantings of shrubs and perennials for all seasons. They are surrounded by a variety of unusual specimen trees. The large vegetable garden nearby includes peach trees and annuals for cutting. From there mowed paths lead down a hillside to ponds that have been extensively planted over the years. We have a wild garden containing more smaller ponds, a stand of bamboo, shrubs, and trees both native and introduced. There are various structures to provide focus and rest along the way. The garden is not fenced. The orchard hillside faces west with views to the Catskills **2006** ♿

Hours: 10 a.m. to 4 p.m.

From Taconic State Parkway, take Rhinebeck/Red Hook exit and follow Route 199 west to traffic light (about 4 miles). Take Route 308 straight for 2 miles to Cedar Heights Road. Turn right and take second right onto Crosby Lane. Follow to dead end and into Cedar Heights Orchard. Please park in barnyard and in marked areas. Please call (845) 876-3231 for more information.

Westchester County Open Day
Sunday, September 9

WESTCHESTER COUNTY

LEWISBORO
The White Garden
199 Elmwood Road

The native oak-hickory forest provides a "sacred grove" setting for the modern Greek Revival-style house. The gardens, completed in 1999, were designed by Patrick Chassé, ASLA, and nearest the house are classically inspired, including a nymphaeum, pergola garden, labrynth, and theater court. Additional hidden gardens include a perennial ellipse, a conservatory garden, and an Asian-inspired moss garden. Several water features accent the landscape, and native plantings dominate in areas outside the gardens. Many sculptures and water features enrich this landscape and swans guard the Temple of Apollo on an island in the main pond. In spring, more than 100,000 daffodils bloom in the woodland. Woodland walking paths lead through a shaded dell. A state-of-the-art greenhouse supports the gardens, administered by gardener Eric Schmidt, who ably orchestrates the rich garden plantings throughout the property. **2006**

Hours: 10 a.m. to 3 p.m.

From Merritt Parkway/Route 15, take Exit 38 and follow Route 123 north through New Canaan to New York state line. Town of Lewisboro and village of Vista are first signs encountered. Go past Vista Fire Department about 0.25 mile. Just after shingled Episcopal church on right, Route 123 bears left and Elmwood Road bears right. Go about another 0.25 mile just over a hill. At beginning of a gray stockade fence on right is driveway at #199.

Syracuse Area
Open Day
Sunday, September 16
ONONDAGA COUNTY

JAMESVILLE
McAuliffes' Garden
3289 Ransom Road

Our gardens rest in the rural landscape where meadow drifts to a dramatic backdrop known as Tory Hill. Open beds planted with an eye for texture and form ramble along a gentle slope. In September, graceful grasses, sturdy sylphium and nubby amaranths intermix with slender nicotianas and spikes of *Verbena bonariensis*. A tidy belvedere capped for shade and with a bench for two, captures a view of the fall garden and Tory Hill beyond. A rustic potting shed nestled in the hedgerow is worth a visit. The courtyard garden features arbors, raised beds and structures built and planted with loving care by the owners and by friends David and

Ellen Suarez of Global Landscapes and designer friend, Michael Brennan. **2004**

Hours: 10 a.m. to 4 p.m.

From the city of Syracuse take Route 81 south to Route 481. Go east (sign says north) on Route 481 to the Jamesville Exit. Turn right at bottom of ramp onto Jamesville-DeWitt Road. Follow to end at a "T". Turn left onto Route 173 then right onto Route 91 south. Proceed 3 miles to Ransom Road. Turn right onto Ransom Road (watch for deer and critters) and continue 2 miles enjoying the vineyards along the way. Our mailbox, #3289 is on the left and the driveway is on the right. Visitors may park on Ransom Road or along the designated parking area in the field.

LAFAYETTE
Pagoda Hill—Michael Brennan & Robert Moss
1697 Berwyn Road

Pagoda Hill is named for the *Cornus alternifolia* (pagoda dogwood) that proliferate on our eighteen-acre hilltop. Mown paths allow access through the varied terrain of meadow, woodland, hillside, and pond. Close to the house is a sixty-foot locust pergola for growing roses and clematis, bordered by peonies and iris. The brick-lined gravel path continues into a formal perennial garden backed by a thirty-foot hot-colored border. The path ends with a locust arbor surrounded by twenty-seven raised beds for vegetables and cut flowers. Connected to the house is a shade shrub border featuring chartreuse foliage and blue and white flowers. **2004**

Hours: 10 a.m. to 4 p.m.

Take I-81 south to Lafayette. Turn right onto Route 20. Go through Lafayette and continue to Pompey. Just past sign marked "Hamlet of Pompey Hill", turn right onto Berwyn Road and go 3.3 miles. House is on right and #1697 is on mailbox. Coming west on Route 20, just past Citgo gas station in Pompey, turn left onto Berwyn Road. Park along road.

SOLVAY
Dr. & Mrs. Charles Mango
515 North Orchard Road

This is a collector's garden on a three-acre hillside with a picturesque view at all angles. Waterfalls and ponds create a serene atmosphere to relax in. The garden is accented with many unusual bulbs, perennials, ornamental shrubs, trees, and conifers. Many rocks accent the plants. Hundreds of colorful spring flowers awaken from a winter rest from April to May, while various flowering shrubs, perennials, and trees bring cheer to summer. More than 150 Japanese maples splash color in the fall months. Evergreens and sculptured plants add dimension to the winter snows. This is truly a garden for all seasons. **2006**

Hours: 10 a.m. to 4 p.m.

From Syracuse, take I-690 west to Route 5/West Genessee Street/Fairmont. Turn left and go through 2 traffic lights, about 0.25 mile on left is North Orchard Road. There will be a Village of Solvay sign in a triangle area. Westcott Reservoir is on right of Route 5. Turn left onto North Orchard Road and go about 0.25 mile to Mango Garden on right at #515. You will see a large stone wall with house set on a hillside.

WESTVALE
Tortuga—Ellen & David Suarez
2701 West Genesee Street

The yard around our ninety-year-old house on a busy thoroughfare was almost a blank slate when we moved in Thanksgiving of 2001. Without disturbing the towering black walnut trees, the dominating weeping willow tree, and a well-established little leaf lilac, we went to work turning this old suburban half-acre lot into the visually stimulating and functional garden it is today. The long, curving public brick walk down Cherry Road catches everyone's eye, while the dry-laid stone pillars, paths, and other brick walks draw the passerby into the gardens. Different kinds of stone are used throughout the gardens to elevate and frame extensive non-formal plantings that include apple, beech, boxwood, callicarpa,

cypress, dogwood, ginkgo, hemlock, pine, rose, viburnum, and witch hazel for starters, along with many perennials, annuals, bulbs, vegetables, vines, containers, and twelve-foot tall ornamental grasses. We have kept a little lawn that we like to mow with our old-fashioned reel-type mower. **NEW** ♿

Hours: 10 a.m. to 4 p.m.

From Syracuse take I-690 West to Exit 6/Route 695 to Route 5. Follow signs for Route 5 east to Fairmount. The highway ends at a traffic light at West Genesee Street; turn left. Go straight through 3 lights. The next street after the third light is Cherry Road. Turn right and park on west side (our side) of street only.

Westchester County Open Day
Sunday, September 16
WESTCHESTER COUNTY

BEDFORD
Penelope & John Maynard
210 Hook Road

We created a garden among rock ledges and oak woods on the steep shoulder of Mount Aspetong. The site is fragmented; thus, the garden areas are designed to flow from one to another, linked together by a ribbon of stone walls. The greatest challenge has been to create some flat, restful spaces. The wide variety of plants must meet one criterion—to prove themselves in dry woodland conditions. **2006**

Hours: 10 a.m. to 6 p.m.

From I-684, take Exit 4. Turn east onto Route 172. Go 1.5 miles to Route 22. Turn left and drive through Bedford. Just beyond Bedford Oak Tree, 2.1 miles from Routes 172 and 22, turn right onto Hook Road. Garden (#210) is almost at top of hill. Park along road.

NORTH SALEM
Dick Button—Ice Pond Farm
June Road

Ice Pond Farm has some interesting topography. It has a valley with an ice pond that sometimes gets black ice and a stone wall that pretends it's a rollercoaster. It has an icehouse, smokehouse, springhouse, and an outhouse with a view. It has a pair of perennial borders and a bocce court, a mini-orchard, gazebo, wildflower walk, and stone bridge. If we can get our act together, there will be a better vegetable garden than last year, some interesting plants in the borders, a new orangerie (or something that passes for one), and a more developed hillside woodland garden. **2004** ♿

Hours: 10 a.m. to 4 p.m.

From I-684 south, take Exit 8/Hardscrabble Road. Turn right onto Hardscrabble Road and go east about 5 miles to June Road/Old Route 124. Turn right onto June Road and go 0.75 mile to #115.

From I-684 south, take Exit 7/Purdys. Take Route 116 east for about 3 miles to North Salem. Turn left onto June Road/Old Route 124. Go 0.5 mile to #115. Please park in the field as directed.

POUND RIDGE
John & Melanie Danza
50 Upper Shad Road

The garden is entered through a grove of cedars and cypresses. A path to a stone staircase leads down to a moon gate set in a vine-covered wall. Composed in the circular frame are specimen trees and a pond with reflections of the distant hills. A long, gently curving boxwood hedge mimics the pond's flowing shoreline and defines the pathways and planting beds. The garden takes inspiration from a one-acre river-fed pond. Bordering water conservation land, the three-and-one-half-acre property appears limitless. Water is the dominate feature in the garden hence there are many native water plants, shrubs, sedges and a large number of taxodium. There is also a collection of *Cryptomeria japonica* and a bamboo allée. **NEW**

Hours: 10 a.m. to 4 p.m.

From the Merritt Parkway, take Exit 35. Take Route 137/Highridge Road north about 6 miles to Upper Shad Road. Turn right and go to third driveway on right.

From I-684, take Exit 4/Bedford/Mt. Kisco. Follow signs to Bedford. Pass Fox Lane High

School and come to a stop sign at a Shell gas station. Turn left onto Route 172 and bear right at second traffic light toward Pound Ridge. At intersection of Route 137, turn right (Pound Ridge Nursery is on right) and continue past fork to left. Go south and at bottom of hill turn left onto Upper Shad Road to third driveway on left.

WACCABUC
James & Susan Henry
36 Mead Street

A nineteenth-century farm is the setting for perennial gardens, specimen trees, a walled garden, cordoned apple trees, a vegetable garden, berries and fruits, a pond in a meadow, and a vineyard producing red and white wines. **2006** ♿

Hours: 10 a.m. to 4 p.m.

From I-684, take Exit 6/Route 35/Cross River/Katonah. Follow Route 35 east for 5 miles. After a long hill, look for Mead Street on left. Go 0.25 mile to #36 on left. Turn into driveway, then left into parking area.

From Connecticut, Mead Street is 4 miles from traffic light at Routes 35 and 123. Please park in field behind vineyard.

Public Gardens
BRONX COUNTY

BRONX
The New York Botanical Garden
200 Street & Kazimiroff Boulevard,
(718) 817-8700, www.nybg.org

The New York Botanical Garden is one of the foremost public gardens in America, with some of the most beautiful natural terrain of any botanical garden in the world. Within this grand 250-acre setting, forty-eight gardens and plant collections offer stunning seasonal displays, from rainbows of tulips and azaleas in the spring to the rich tapestries of fall foliage.

Hours: April through October, Tuesday through Sunday, and Monday holidays, 10 a.m. to 6 p.m.; November through March, 10 a.m. to 4 p.m.; closed Thanksgiving and Christmas.

Admission: Please call for rates or check the website

From Westchester County, take Cross County Parkway/I-287 to Bronx River Parkway south. Take Exit 7W/Fordham Road and continue on Kazimiroff Boulevard to Conservatory Gate on right.

From Connecticut, take I-95 to Pelham Parkway west. Take Exit 8C/Pelham Parkway west to Kazimiroff Boulevard and continue to Conservatory Gate on right.

From New Jersey, take George Washington Bridge to Henry Hudson Parkway north to Exit 24/Mosholu Parkway. Continue to Kazimiroff Boulevard, turn right, and continue to Conservatory Gate on right.

Wave Hill
679 West 252nd Street, (718) 549-3200,
www.wavehill.org

Often called "the most beautiful place in New York," Wave Hill is a twenty-eight-acre public garden in a spectacular setting overlooking the Hudson River and Palisades. Formerly a private estate, Wave Hill features several gardens, greenhouses, historic buildings, lawns, and woodlands, and also offers programs in horticulture, environmental education, woodland management, and the visual and performing arts. All programs focus on fostering relationships between people and nature.

Hours: October 15 through April 14, Tuesday through Sunday, 9 a.m. to 4:30 p.m. April 15 through October 14, Tuesday through Sunday, 9 a.m. to 5:30 p.m. Open until 9 p.m. on Wednesdays in June and July.

Admission: Free all day Tuesday and Saturday until 12 p.m., otherwise, $4 adults, $2 seniors/students, children under 6 free. Free December, January, February.

From West Side and New Jersey, take Henry Hudson Parkway to Exit 21/246-250th Street. Continue north to 252nd Street. Turn left at overpass and left again. Turn right at 249th Street to Wave Hill gate.

From Westchester, take Henry Hudson Parkway south to Exit 22/254th Street. Turn left at stop sign and left again at traffic light. Turn right onto 249th Street to Wave Hill Gate.

BROOKLYN COUNTY

Brooklyn
Brooklyn Botanic Garden
900 Washington Avenue, (718) 623-7200,
www.bbg.org

Celebrate the seasons at Brooklyn Botanic Garden, a living museum of plants, called the "premier horticulture attraction in the region," by The New York Times. Discover the many specialty gardens within this fifty-two-acre natural wonder in the midst of New York City, including the Japanese Hill-and-Pond Garden, Lily Pool Terrace, Cranford Rose Garden, Fragrance Garden designed for the visually impaired, Children's Garden, C.V. Starr Bonsai Museum, and Steinhardt Conservatory displaying tropical, desert, and temperate plants.

Hours: April though September, Tuesday through Friday, 8 a.m. to 6 p.m. Weekends and holidays, 10 a.m. to 6 p.m. October through March, Tuesday through Friday, 8 a.m. to 4:30 p.m. Closed Monday (except holidays), Thanksgiving, Christmas, and New Year's Day.

Admission: $5 adults, $3 seniors and students with I.D., children under 16, members, school groups, and Frequent Visitor Pass holders are free. The garden is free on Tuesday, Saturday until 12 p.m. Free for seniors every Friday.

From Brooklyn-Queens Expressway, take Kent Avenue exit. Follow service road (Park Avenue) along and then under expressway for 5 blocks. Turn left onto Washington Avenue and continue 1.75 miles to BBG. Fee parking at 900 Washington Avenue.

By subway, take Q local or Q express train to Prospect Park station; B train to Prospect Park station weekdays only; or, 2 or 3 train to Eastern Parkway. By bus, take B16, B41, B43, B48, or B71.

ბ indicates parts of garden are handicapped accessible

HUDSON

Olana State Historic Site

5720 Route 9G, (518) 828-0135,
www.olana.org; www.nyparks.com

The flower garden at Olana was designed in the nineteen-century "mingled garden" style. It is a 165-foot-long and twenty-foot-wide garden curving along the base of a rustic stone wall supporting one of the carriage drives to the main house. It was designed as a mini-vista of flowers to punctuate the visitor's experience as their carriage approached the house. It has a center path and ornamental gates at each end. The flowers are a mix of annuals, perennials, vines, and shrubs laid out in an irregular pattern to create a riot of color. The garden is at its height mid- to late summer, but carries on well into the fall foliage season. Landscape and garden tours are available in season. Self-guided tours of the garden and grounds are welcome any time the grounds are open.

Hours: Grounds open 8 a.m. to sunset; house and tours 10 a.m. to 5 p.m., Tuesday through Sunday and Monday holidays; weekends, December through March.

Admission: Grounds free Monday through Friday; $5 per car weekends and holidays (fee refund on price of house or garden tour). Guided tours: $7 adults, 5 seniors/students, children 12 and under free. Landscape/garden tour (first Saturday of every month) $5 per person.

From New York State Thruway/I-87, take Exit 21/Catskill. Follow Route 23 east to Rip Van Winkle Bridge, cross bridge, and go south on Route 9G for 1 mile. Entrance is on left.

From Taconic State Parkway, take Route 82/Ancram/Hudson exit. Follow signs for Hudson and Rip Van Winkle Bridge (Route 82 to Route 23 west). At bridge intersection, do not cross bridge; take Route 9G south. Entrance is 1 mile on left.

LIVINGSTON

The Climbery

201 Buckwheat Bridge Road
(518) 537-4141

The Climbery is the second largest clematis garden in the world, with nearly 6,000 vines. It was designed and created by Barbara Packer over a sixteen-year period. More than 600 feet on the Rocliff-Jeress Kill as well as seven acres of gardens border and surround the 1820 eyebrow Colonial house originally part of the Livingston estate, which is the home of the owner. In addition to the clematis, there is a continual rotation of bulbs and perennials, including massive plantings of tree and herbaceous peonies, irises (German, Siberian, and Japanese), *Aquilegia*, lilies, daylilies, and hardy gladiolas. There are separate English rose gardens and lotus ponds.

Hours: May 15 through Labor Day, Monday through Thursday, 1 p.m. to 5 p.m., by appointment

Admission: Free

From Taconic State Parkway, take Red Hook exit. Follow Route 199 west to Town of Red Hook. At second traffic light, turn right onto Route 9 north. Go about 7.25 miles and turn right onto Buckwheat Bridge Road. Go 1 mile over small bridge to first house on right.

AMENIA

Wethersfield

214 Pugsley Hill Road, (845) 373-8037

Ten acres of formal classical-style and outer gardens surround Chauncey D. Stillman's Georgian-style brick house. The original garden around the perimeter of the house was created in 1940 by Bryan J. Lynch. Evelyn N. Poehler oversaw the maintenance of the garden from 1952 on and designed the formal gardens over a twenty-year period.

Hours: June through September, Wednesday, Friday, and Saturday, 12 p.m. to 5 p.m.

Admission: Free

From Route 44 east of Millbrook, take Route 86 and turn right onto Pugsley Hill

Road. Follow signs for 1.3 miles to estate entrance on left.

ANNANDALE-ON-HUDSON
Montgomery Place
River Road, (845) 758-5461,
www.hudsonvalley.org
This 200-year-old estate enjoys a picturesque landscape, as extolled by Andrew Jackson Downing. Included are ancient trees and vistas of the Hudson River and Catskill Mountains. The early twentieth-century garden includes a wide variety of plants, many unusual. There are also walking trails, splendid waterfalls, and an audio grounds and landscape guide.

Hours: May through October, weekends only, 10 a.m. to 5 p.m.

Admission: $5 grounds only

From New York State Thruway/I-87, take Exit 19/Kingston onto Route 209/199 east across Kingston-Rhinecliff Bridge. Turn left onto Route 9G and proceed 3 miles, then turn left onto Annandale Road, bearing left onto River Road to estate entrance.

HYDE PARK
Beatrix Farrand Garden at Bellefield
Route 9, (845) 229-9115,
www.beatrixfarrandgarden.org
The enclosed formal garden and surrounding wild garden were designed in 1912 by the acclaimed landscape gardener Beatrix Farrand. Thought to be her earliest surviving residential project, it has been restored and is maintained by a small, nonprofit organization in partnership with the National Park Service. Adjacent to a magnificent eighteenth-century house that was remodeled by the architects McKim, Mead & White in 1911, the garden evidences Colonial American, Arts and Crafts, and formal European influences. Typical of Farrand's work, the subtle elegance of the plan and built elements is set off by lush borders in sophisticated color schemes.

Hours: Year round, daily, dawn to dusk
Admission: Free

Bellefield is part of Roosevelt-Vanderbilt National Historic Sites and located on a public campus along Route 9 that includes Franklin Delano Roosevelt Home and Presidential Library. Park at Wallace Visitor Center and follow signs to garden.

Vanderbilt National Historic Site: Italian Gardens
511 Albany Post Road/Route 9,
(845) 229-6432, www.vanderbiltgarden.org
This three-level formal garden covers three acres. The rose garden has more than 1,200 plants. The perennial garden, along the cherry walk, includes several hundred perennials. Thousands of annuals are planted each year in the upper beds.

Hours: Year round, daily, dawn to dusk. Group tours available by appointment
Admission: Free
Located on Route 9 North, on left, just north of Hyde Park Post Office.

MILLBROOK
Innisfree Garden
362 Tyrrel Road, (845) 677-5268
Innisfree reflects an Eastern design technique called a cup garden, which draws attention to something rare or beautiful by establishing the suggestion of enclosure around it. It may be an enclosed meadow, a lotus pool, waterfall, or single dramatic rock covered with lichens. Visitors to Innisfree stroll from one three-dimensional garden picture to another.

Hours: May 7 through October 20, Wednesday through Friday, 10 a.m. to 4 p.m., weekends and holidays, 11 a.m. to 5 p.m.; closed Monday and Tuesday, except holidays

Admission: $4 weekdays, $5 weekends and holidays, children under 4 free

Innisfree is on Tyrrel Road, 1 mile from Route 44 and 1.75 miles from Taconic State Parkway overpass at Route 44.

ₕ indicates parts of garden are handicapped accessible

Institute of Ecosystem Studies
Route 44A, (845) 677-5359,
www.ecostudies.org

Located on the site of the Mary Cary Flagler Arboretum, the Institute of Ecosystem Studies (IES) is dedicated to understanding the natural world. Several public attractions at IES provide visitors with a unique opportunity to interact with botanical diversity. The three-acre Gifford Perennial Garden features ecological demonstration beds. The fern glen is a two-acre display of native plants in natural communities. The tropical greenhouse, open year round, holds more than 1,200 species of plants (including staghorn ferns and orchids).

Hours: The gardens, grounds, and roadways are open from April through October, Monday through Saturday, 9 a.m. to 6 p.m.; Sunday, 11 a.m. to 6 p.m. The greenhouse is open year round, 9 a.m. to 3:30 p.m.

Admission: Free

From the Taconic State Parkway take Route 44 east for 2 miles. Turn left onto Route 44A. The Gifford House is 1 mile along Route 44A on left.

From Massachusetts and Connecticut, take Route 22 to Route 44. Where Route 44 takes a sharp left to the village of Millbrook, continue straight on Sharon Turnpike/Route 44A. The Gifford House is on right, just before Route 44A rejoins Route 44.

POUGHKEEPSIE
Springside Landscape Restoration
Academy Street, (845) 454-2060

Springside is the only unaltered documented work of Andrew Jackson Downing, one of the most influential landscape architects in American history. Once the summer home of Matthew Vassar (founder of Vassar College), the site was an "ornamental farm." Although unrestored, the landscape bears Downing's undeniable influence, illustrating the principles of the beautiful and the picturesque.

Hours: Year round, daily, dawn to dusk

Admission: Free

From Taconic State Parkway, take Poughkeepsie/Route 44 exit and proceed west on Route 44 through Poughkeepsie until just before Mid-Hudson Bridge. Stay in right lane for Route 9 south/Wappingers Falls and proceed on Route 9 for 1 mile to Academy Street exit. At bottom of exit ramp, turn left. Proceed to first entrance on right at bottom of hill.

Vassar College Arboretum & Shakespeare Garden
124 Raymond Avenue, (845) 437-5686,
www.vassar.edu

First planted in 1918, the Shakespeare Garden has brick walks, statuary, knot beds, rose beds, heath and heather beds, and twelve raised brick beds containing herbs and cottage garden plantings. A hemlock hedge encloses the garden. There is also an arboretum with 220 species of native and non-native trees and shrubs.

Hours: Year round, daily, dawn to dusk

Admission: Free

From Route 44/55 in Poughkeepsie, turn onto Raymond Avenue to Main Gate, about 3 blocks.

MADISON COUNTY

CAZENOVIA
Lorenzo State Historic Site
17 Rippleton Road, (315) 655-3200,
www.lorenzony.org

Lorenzo is the 1808 neo-classical home of John Lincklaen, founder of Cazenovia, and lived in continuously by five generations of the Lincklaen/Ledyard family. In 1914, Helen Lincklaen Fairchild hired garden designer Ellen Biddle Shipman to enhance the layout of the formal garden bed. Mrs. Shipman's plan was used to restore the garden in 1983.

Hours: Year round, daily, dawn to dusk

Admission: grounds are free

Lorenzo is located in village of Cazenovia, New York, 0.25 mile south of intersection of Route 20 and Route 13 on Rippleton Road.

NASSAU COUNTY

MILL NECK
The John P. Humes
Japanese Stroll Garden
Oyster Bay Road & Dogwood Lane,
www.humesjapanesestrollgarden.org,
(516) 676-4486

 A four-acre gem of landscape design, the garden provides a retreat for passive recreation and contemplation. The views, textures, and balance of elements in the garden follow Japanese aesthetic principles, encouraging a contemplative experience. The garden suggests a mountain setting beside a sea, where gravel paths represent streams forming pools and cascades, eventually flowing into the ocean, represented by a pond.

A PROJECT OF
THE GARDEN
CONSERVANCY

Hours: April 21 through October 21, weekends, 11:30 a.m. to 4:30 p.m. Private tours and tea ceremony demonstrations by appointment on Thursday and Friday. Public tours on designated Saturdays. Call for dates and reservations.

Admission: $7 adults, children under 12 free, $12 per person for guided tour. Admission free to Garden Conservancy members; $5 for guided tour with tea ceremony.

From Long Island Expressway/I-495 east, take Exit 39/Glen Cove Road north to Route 25A/Northern Boulevard, turn right onto Route 25A, pass C.W. Post University. At next traffic light, turn left onto Route 107/Wolver Hollow Road. Go to end and turn right onto Chicken Valley Road. Go past Planting Fields Arboretum, continue straight through blinking traffic light, and garden is 0.5 mile on right. You will see a terra-cotta colored wall. Turn right at end of wall onto Dogwood Lane to parking lot on immediate right.

From Long Island Expressway/I-495 west, take Exit 41N. Take Route 106 to Route 25A/Northern Boulevard west. Turn right at second light onto Wolver Hollow Road, and proceed as directed above.

OLD WESTBURY
Old Westbury Gardens
71 Old Westbury Road, (516) 333-0048,
www.oldwestburygardens.org

North America's most beautiful English-style country estate, its 200+ acres include a walled garden, a sunken parterre rose garden, boxwood garden, thatched cottage garden, woodlands, ponds, lawns, statuary, and follies. A magnificent 1906 mansion contains fine antiques and decorative arts. Old Westbury Gardens is listed on the National Register of Historic Places.

Hours: Late April through October, Wednesday through Monday, 10 a.m. to 5 p.m.; November, Sunday only, 10 a.m. to 5 p.m.; Holiday Celebration, December 1 to 16, 10 a.m. to 4 p.m.

Admission: $10 adults, $8 seniors, $5 children 7 to 12

From Long Island Expressway/I-495, take Exit 39/Glen Cove Road. Continue east on service road. At third traffic light, turn right onto Old Westbury Road. Entrance is 0.4 mile on left.

ONONDAGA COUNTY

SYRACUSE
E. M. Mills
Memorial Rose Garden
Thorden Park, Ostrom Avenue &
University Place, (315) 682-9688,
www.syracuserosesociety.org

This garden draws more than 30,000 local, national, and international visitors annually. Featuring approximately 4,000 roses, it is one of 122 American gardens accredited by the American Rose Society and the All American Rose Selections for advance display of award-winning roses. Established in 1922, owned by the City of Syracuse and maintained by the Syracuse Rose Society, it is one of the oldest municipal rose gardens in the country.

Hours: Year round, daily, dawn to dusk

Admission: Free

From I-90 eastm take Exit 36. Merge onto I-81 South toward Binghampton. Take Exit 18/Harrison Street towards Adams Street. Turn left onto East Adams Street. Turn right onto Ostrom Avenue.

From I-90 west, merge onto I-481 south at Exit 34A toward Syracuse/Cortland. Merge onto I-81 north. Exit at Adams Street. Turn right onto Adams Street. Turn right onto Ostrom Avenue.

From I-81 north, exit at Adams Street and turn right onto Adams Street. Turn right onto Ostrom Avenue.

ORANGE COUNTY

WEST POINT
Anna B. Warner Memorial Garden
Constitution Island at the U.S. Military Academy, (914) 446-8676, www.constitutionisland.org

This is an old-fashioned perennial and annual border garden lining a fifty-yard path, planted in nineteenth-century style with flowers described by Anna Warner in her book *Gardening by Myself* written in 1872. Cared for by dedicated volunteers, this garden received the Burlington House Award.

Hours: Mid-June through October. Tours to Constitution Island are available on Wednesday and Thursday, mid-June through September. Reservations required.

Admission: $10 adults, $9 seniors, children 6 and under free; present this book and admission will be reduced to $5.

From the south, take Route 9W or Palisades Interstate Parkway to Bear Mountain Bridge Circle. Go 2 miles north on Route 9W, then take Route 218 through Highland Falls to West Point. After Hotel Thayer, take first right (Williams Road) downhill. Cross railroad tracks. Park north of South Dock.

From the north, take Route 9W south. Take first sign to West Point. Drive through West Point on Thayer Road. After road goes under stone bridge, take first left (Williams Road) downhill. Proceed as directed above.

PUTNAM COUNTY

COLD SPRING
Stonecrop Gardens
81 Stonecrop Lane (845) 265-2000, www.stonecrop.org

Stonecrop Gardens, originally the home of Frank and Anne Cabot, became a public garden in 1992 under the direction of Caroline Burgess. Frank Cabot is also the founder of the Garden Conservancy. At its windswept elevation of 1,100 feet in the Hudson Highlands, Stonecrop enjoys a Zone 5 climate. The display gardens cover an area of about twelve acres and incorporate a diverse collection of gardens and plants including woodland and water gardens, a grass garden, raised alpine stone beds, a cliff rock garden, perennial beds, and an enclosed English-style flower garden. Additional features include a conservatory, display alpine house, pit house with an extensive collection of choice dwarf bulbs, and systematic order beds representing over fifty plant families.

Hours: Special Garden Conservancy Open Days, April 29, May 13, June 10, July 15, August 12, September 23, 10 a.m. to 5 p.m. Also open, April through October, Monday through Friday, and first and third Saturday of each month, 10 a.m. to 5 p.m.

Admission: $5

From Taconic State Parkway, take Route 301/Cold Spring exit. Travel 3.5 miles to Stonecrop's entrance on right. A street sign reading "Stonecrop Gardens" marks driveway.

From Route 9, take Route 301 east 2.7 miles. Proceed as directed above.

GARRISON
Boscobel
1601 Route 9D, Garrison, (845) 265-3638, www.boscobel.org

The gardens at Boscobel include a formal rose garden with more than 600 individual plants and 150 varieties of roses on display. Nearby, off an apple orchard, is an herb garden and orangery. A large lawn in front of the Federal period-style mansion offers a dramatic vista of the Hudson River.

A plant enthusiast's garden ...

STONECROP GARDENS
81 Stonecrop Lane, Cold Spring, New York
845.265.2000 www.stonecrop.org

Stonecrop Gardens consists of 12 acres of gardens at a windswept elevation of 1,100 feet in the Hudson Highlands in Cold Spring, New York.

Come see our diverse collection of gardens and plants
• Conservatory • Enclosed Flower Garden • Woodland Garden
• Mediterranean Garden • Alpine Rock Ledge • Systematic Order Beds

❋ Plants for sale / Memberships available ❋

....

Our mission is to uphold and demonstrate the highest standards of horticultural practice and to promote the use of such standards among amateur and professional gardeners through aesthetic displays and educational programs.

....

 Stonecrop is open Monday - Friday
and the first and third Saturday of each month
April - October, 10am to 5pm
Admission $5

Guided group tours (10 or more people) available by appointment

❋ **2007 Garden Conservancy Open Days** ❋
April 29, May 13, June 10, July 15, August 12, September 23

Hours: April through December, Wednesday through Monday, 10 a.m. to 5 p.m. (last tour of mansion is at 4:15 p.m.)

Admission: $10 adults, $9 seniors 62 and older, $7 children 6-14, children under 6 free. Special rates available for groups of 12 or more and for school groups.

From the New York Thruway/I-87, take I-84 over Newburgh-Beacon Bridge to Route 9D south to Boscobel.

From Taconic State Parkway, take Route 301/Cold Spring exit. Take Route 301 west to traffic light in center of Cold Spring. Turn left on Route 9D south.

From New Jersey, take upper level of George Washington Bridge to Palisades Parkway north to Bear Mountain and over Bear Mountain Bridge to Route 9D north to Boscobel.

Boscobel can be reached via train using Metro-North's Hudson division from Grand Central Station to Cold Spring. Upon arrival in Cold Spring, one can either walk about 1.5 miles to Boscobel or take a taxi from the train station. Call 845-265-8294 in advance to arrange a car to meet you and bring you to Boscobel. A shuttle trolley runs from April through December.

Manitoga/The Russel Wright Design Center
584 Route 9D, (845) 424-3812,
www.russelwrightcenter.org

A premier example of carefully designed naturalistic landscaping, industrial designer Russel Wright's woodland garden invites active participation in the two and one half miles of trails. This landscape abounds with native trees, ferns, mosses, and wildflowers and is meant not just to be seen but to be experienced. The seventy-five-acre site, including Wright's house, is listed on the National Register of Historic Places. Please note that Dragon Rock, Wright's house, may be visited only through a once-a-day scheduled tour, admission to which is separate from the Open Day. Reservations for the Open Day are required.

Hours: Special Garden Conservancy Open Day, June 10, 10 a.m. to 12 p.m. House tours

from April through October only, reservations required. Hiking permitted during daylight hours.

Admission: $5

Located at 584 Route 9D, 2.5 miles north of Bear Mountain Bridge and 2 miles south of intersection of Routes 403 and 9D.

BAYPORT
Meadow Croft, The John E. Roosevelt Estate
Middle Road, (631) 472-9395

This nature preserve of seventy-five acres of woods and tidal wetlands was the summer home of John E. Roosevelt, a first cousin of President Theodore Roosevelt. The privet-and- lattice-enclosed kitchen garden adjacent to the Colonial Revival home contains plant material that would have been available in 1910, the year to which the house is restored. Included are twenty-four varieties of heirloom roses, heirloom vegetables, annuals, and perennials.

Hours: First Sunday in June through last Sunday in October, Sunday, 12 p.m. to 5 p.m., with tours at 1 p.m. and 3 p.m.; no tours weekends of July 4th, Labor Day, and Columbus Day

Admission: Free

From Sunrise Highway/Route 27, take Lakeland-Ocean Avenue/CR 93 exit south about 2 miles to Main Street. Turn left and immediately bear right onto South Main Street/Middle Road. Continue 0.5 mile and turn left at estate entrance.

BRIDGEHAMPTON
Bridge Gardens Trust
36 Mitchell Lane, (631) 537-7440,
www.bridgegardens.org

The gardens on these five acres include a formal knot surrounded by herbal beds, perennial mounds, topiary, specimen trees, expansive lawns, aquatic plantings, woodland walks, a bamboo "room," lavender parterre, and hundreds of roses. A 750-foot-long double row of privet hedge encloses a pavilion-like garden house (not open to the public).

Hours: Late May through late September, Wednesday and Saturday, 2 p.m. to 4:30 p.m.

Admission: $15

From Montauk Highway/Route 27, go to Bridgehampton. At traffic light at western edge of village, turn left onto Butter Lane. Go 0.25 mile and under railroad bridge; turn left immediately onto Mitchell Lane. Bridge Gardens, #36, is first driveway on left. Please park along Mitchell Lane with flow of traffic.

EAST HAMPTON
LongHouse Reserve
133 Hands Creek Road, (631) 329-3568, www.longhouse.org

By far, the sixteen acres of LongHouse Reserve are the most exciting gardens in The Hamptons. From the moment you enter through the impressive allée of statuesque cryptomeria, you know you are in for a rarefied experience. The varied and fascinating landscape includes a gigantic lotus pond, numerous walks, a dune garden and a modern amphitheater. Collections of bamboo, conifers, broadleaf evergreens, and grasses are a compendium of each genus and the springtime entices with more than 200 varieties of daffodils and 1,000 times as many blooms, at least. Aside from the fantastic gardens and arboretum, there is a museum-worthy (in fact, Longhouse has museum status) collection of contemporary sculpture to intrigue you at every turn of every path. This is the one East End garden that is not to be missed. The large new house (not open to the public) was inspired by the seventh-century Shinto shrine at Ise, Japan.

Hours: Late April through September, Wednesday and Saturday, 2 p.m. to 5 p.m.

Admission: $10 adults, $8 seniors.

From East Hampton Village, turn onto Newtown Lane from intersection at Main Street. Go to Cooper Street, turn right, and go to end. Turn left onto Cedar Street and bear right at fork onto Hands Creek Road. Go 0.7 mile to #133, which is on left.

SAGAPONACK
Madoo Conservancy
618 Main Street, (631) 537-8200, www.madoo.org

This two-acre garden is a virtual compendium of major garden styles, including an Oriental bridge, a potager, renaissance-perspective rose walk, knot garden, laburnum arbor, hermit's hut, grass garden, and an exedra, as well as an Italianate courtyard, a user-friendly maze and a 120-foot rill. It is noted for its innovative pruning techniques and striking colors. The quincunx beds are notable. Rare trees and plants abound.

Hours: May through September, Wednesday and Saturday, 1 p.m. to 5 p.m. Tours of ten or more may be arranged at other times.

Admission: $10

From Long Island Expressway/I-495, take Exit 70 and follow signs to Montauk. Sagaponack is on Route 27, 1 mile east of Bridgehampton. Turn right at traffic light (first light east of Bridgehampton on Route 27). Madoo Conservancy is a little over 1 mile from highway and 3 driveways after post office on right.

TOMPKINS COUNTY

ITHACA
Cornell Plantations
One Plantations Road, (607) 255-2400, www.plantations.cornell.edu

Cornell Plantations is an area of great natural beauty and serenity; part of one of America's most renowned university campuses. The botanical garden features a famous herb garden, a decorative arts garden, a winter garden, collections of rhododendrons and ground covers, a peony and heritage vegetable garden, and a potted plant display. The arboretum features 150 acres of beautiful trees, shrubs, grasses, as well as ponds and streamside gardens.

Hours: Year round, daily, dawn to dusk. Closed to vehicle traffic in the winter. Information available at Garden Gift Shop year round, Monday through Friday, 9 a.m. to 4 p.m.; Spring and Summer, weekends, 11:15

♿ indicates parts of garden are handicapped accessible

a.m. to 4 p.m. Group tours are available by appointment.

Admission: Free

From downtown Ithaca take Route 79 East toward Cornell. Turn left onto Route 366/Ithaca Road. At the second light, turn left onto Judd Falls Road. Pass two stop signs and turn right onto ramp. At bottom of ramp, turn right onto Plantations Road. Follow signs to right turn into Plantations entrance.

Hospicare
172 East King Road, (607) 272-0212, www.hospicare.org

These gardens have been designed to provide hospice residents and their families with a space for reflection and healing. The entrance garden features beautiful stonework and a goldfish pond surrounded by contrasting grasses, flowering perennials, ornamental shrubs and trees. A stone memorial walkway weaves through a hillside rock garden and a children's circle garden. Bordered by a collection of hummingbird and butterfly plantings, a vine-covered arbor leads to a two-acre pond and surrounding trails. In addition, a rustic fence encloses an organic vegetable, fruit, and herb garden. Please respect the privacy of Hospicare's residents and their families by limiting photography to the gardens only.

Hours: Special Garden Conservancy Open Day, Saturday, June 9, 10 a.m. to 4 p.m.

Admission: $5

From downtown Ithaca, go south on Route 96B/Danby Road. At first light (1 mile past Ithaca College), turn left onto East King Road (by Sam Peter Furniture). Go 0.8 mile to top of hill. Entrance is on left, #172.

WESTCHESTER COUNTY

CROTON-ON-HUDSON
Van Cortlandt Manor
South Riverside Avenue, (914) 271-8981, www.hudsonvalley.org

This restored Federal period manor complex includes a border of period ornamentals of interest throughout the growing season, a large tulip display, a vegetable garden, an orchard, and narcissi naturalized at the woodland's edge. An extensive culinary and medicinal herb garden is also noteworthy.

Hours: April through October, daily except Tuesday, 10 a.m. to 5 p.m.; November and December, weekends only

Admission: $5 grounds only

Take Route 9 to Croton Point Avenue and go east to first traffic light. Turn right onto South Riverside Avenue. Van Cortlandt Manor is at end of road, past ShopRite shopping center.

KATONAH
Caramoor Gardens
Girdle Ridge Road, (914) 232-1253, www.caramoor.com

Located throughout the 100 acres are the Sunken Garden, Spanish Courtyard, Butterfly Garden, Marjorie Carr Adams Sense Circle for the visually impaired, Cutting Garden, Medieval Mount, Woodland Garden, Cedar Walk, the Renaissance Herb Garden, and numerous antique containers planted in creative ways.

Hours: May through October, Wednesday through Sunday. Group tours by appointment; call to reserve.

Admission: $9

Girdle Ridge Road is off Route 22. Enter through Main Gate.

John Jay Homestead State Historic Site
400 Route 22/Jay Street, (914) 232-5651, www.johnjayhomestead.org

Four garden sites are beautifully maintained by volunteer community garden groups on the grounds of the retirement home of the first chief justice of the U. S. Supreme Court. Jay was also the second governor of New York. The Bedford and Rusticus Garden Clubs use plants popular in the 1920s and 1930s in the formal and terrace gardens, following the plans of the last Jays to live on the site. The New York Unit of the Herb Society of America maintains a medieval-style herb garden on the site of the former greenhouses. The Hopp Ground Garden Club has established a charming courtyard garden using historic plantings not accessible to all patrons in other garden areas. A 700-foot-long lilac hedge blooms in early May. A self-guided walking tour is available for the gardens and other areas of interest on the sixty-two-acre site.

Hours: Gardens and grounds open year round, daily, dawn to dusk

Admission: Grounds are free, house as posted

From I-684, take Exit 6/Route 35/Cross River/Katonah. Take Route 35 east towards Cross River 0.25 mile to next traffic light. Turn right onto Route 22. Continue south 1.5 miles. Entrance to site on left.

Lasdon Park & Arboretum & Veterans Memorials
458 Croton Lane Road, (914) 864-7268, www.westchestergov.com/parks

A 234-acre property consisting of a twenty-two-acre arboretum and formal azalea garden, the park has woodlands with paths and open grass meadows. Focal points are the Azalea Garden, Historic Tree Trail, Lilac Collection, Magnolia Grove, Dwarf Conifer Collection, a collection of more than sixty varieties of dogwood from around the world, and the Chinese Culture Garden. A one-acre addition, the William and Mildred Lasdon Memorial Garden, is composed of fragrance, format, and synoptic gardens.

Hours: Year round, daily, 8 a.m. to 4 p.m.

Admission: Free

Entrance is on Route 35, 2.5 miles west of intersection of Routes 100 and 35.

Muscoot Farm
Route 100, (914) 864-7282

Muscoot is a Westchester country gentleman's farm circa 1880-1950. The herb garden on the property is cared for by the Muscoot Naturalist. The garden displays beds with tea, dye, fragrance, and cooking herbs to be used for programs and workshops.

Hours: Year round, daily, 10 a.m. to 4 p.m.

Admission: Free

From I-684, take Exit 6/Route 35/Katonah and go west on Route 35 for 2 miles. Turn left (south) onto Route 100. Muscoot Farm is on right after 1.5 miles.

NORTH SALEM
Hammond Museum & Japanese Stroll Garden
28 Deveau Road, (914) 669-5033, www.hammondmuseum.org

A three-and-one-half-acre garden with thirteen different landscapes, the Japanese Garden is a living collection. The stroll garden contains a pond and waterfall, a garden of the Rakan, a red maple terrace, Zen garden, and many species of trees and flowers, including cherry, katsura, quince, azalea, and iris. The café serves lunch on the terrace.

Hours: April through mid-November, Wednesday through Saturday, 12 p.m. to 4 p.m.

Admission: $5 adults, $4 seniors/students, children under 12 free. Group tours available.

From I-684, take Exit 8/Hardscrabble Road. Turn right off exit ramp and continue 4 miles to end. Turn right onto June Road. Take second left onto Deveau Road. Garden and museum are at top of Deveau.

OSSINING
The Wildflower Island at Teatown Lake Reservation
1600 Spring Valley Road, (914) 762-2912, www.teatown.org

The island is a woodland garden of more than 200 species of native flowers. Several hundred pink lady's slippers make a spectacular display in May. In late summer, the sunny shores of the island are ablaze with cardinal flowers, lobelia, ironweed, and other bright, moisture-loving flowers. Visitors are guided along narrow paths by experienced volunteers.

Hours: Special Garden Conservancy Open Day, May 20, 11 a.m. to 3 p.m.; otherwise, April through September. Reservations required. Guided tours available in April, weekends at 2 p.m.; May, Saturday, 10 a.m. and 2 p.m.,

Sunday, 2 p.m., Wednesday, 7 p.m.; June, weekends, 2 p.m.; July through September, Saturday, 10 a.m.

Admission: $6

Take Major Deegan Expressway to I-87 north to Exit 9/Tarrytown (last exit before Tappan Zee Bridge). Take Route 9 north to Ossining. Watch for Route 133 on right. At third traffic light after Route 133, turn right onto Cedar Lane, which becomes Spring Valley Road. Teatown is on left, 3.8 miles from Route 9.

POCANTICO HILLS
Kykuit, the Rockefeller Estate
Route 9, (914) 631-9491,
www.hudsonvalley.org

The extraordinary early twentieth-century gardens at Kykuit, The Rockefeller Estate, were designed by William Welles Bosworth. Included are a formal walled garden, woodland gardens, a rose garden, fountains, and spectacular Hudson River views. Important twentieth-century sculptures were added by Governor Nelson Rockefeller, including works by Alexander Calder, Henry Moore, Pablo Picasso, Louise Nevelson, David Smith, and many others.

Hours: Mid-May through October, daily except Tuesdays, 10 a.m. to 3 p.m. Weekends, 10 a.m. to 4 p.m. No reservations needed.

Admission: $22 adults, $20 senior, $17 children.

All tours begin at historic Philipsburg Manor, located on Route 9 in village of Sleepy Hollow.

PURCHASE
The Donald M. Kendall Sculpture Gardens at PepsiCo
700 Anderson Hill Road, (914) 253-2000

One hundred and sixty-eight acres of landscape designed by Russell Page surround the world headquarters of PepsiCo, Inc. Spacious lawns and shrubs, plantings of trees, and small gardens provide settings for forty-five sculptures by renowned twentieth-century artists.

Hours: Year round, daily, dawn to dusk

Admission: Free

From I-84, take I-684 south to Westchester Airport exit. Take Route 120 south to Anderson Hill Road to PepsiCo on right.

From Merritt Parkway/Route 15 south (which becomes Hutchinson River Parkway), take Exit 28/Lincoln Avenue/Port Chester. Turn left onto Lincoln Avenue and proceed 1 mile to PepsiCo on right.

TARRYTOWN
Lyndhurst
635 South Broadway, (914) 631-4481,
www.lyndhurst.org

The grounds at Lyndhurst are an outstanding example of nineteenth-century landscape design. Elements include a sweeping lawn accented with shrubs and specimen trees, a curving entrance drive revealing "surprise" views, and the angular repetition of the Gothic roof line in the evergreens. The rose garden and fernery are later Victorian additions.

Hours: Mid-April through October, Tuesday through Sunday, 10 a.m. to 4:15 p.m.; November through mid-April, weekends only, 10 a.m. to 3:30 p.m.

Admission: $4 grounds only

From New York State Thruway/I-87 north, take Exit 9/Tarrytown/Route 9. Turn left at end of exit ramp onto Route 119, continue to traffic light at Route 9/Broadway, and turn left. Proceed 0.5 mile to Lyndhurst gates on right side.

VALHALLA
The Lady Bird Johnson and the Stone Cottage Demonstration Gardens— The Native Plant Center
75 Grasslands Road, (914) 785-7870,
www.nativeplantcenter.org

This two-acre garden on the campus of Westchester Community College contains only native American plants indigenous to the northeastern United States. The perennial and shrub beds are designed to show how these genera can be used in the home landscape.

The garden is designed for summer and fall color but is interesting all year. No pesticides or fertilizers are used.

Hours: Special Garden Conservancy Open Day, July 15, 12 p.m. to 4 p.m., guided tours will be available; otherwise year round, daily, dawn to dusk

Admission: Free

From northern Westchester, take Taconic State Parkway south to Sprain Brook Parkway, to Eastview Exit. Turn left onto Route 100. Enter Westchester Community College at East Grasslands Gate and bear right at fork. Follow to parking lot 1 on right. Path through woods on far right of lot leads to garden.

From southern Westchester, take Sprain Brook Parkway to Eastview Exit. Turn right onto Route 100. Proceed as directed above.

From I-287, take Exit 4/Route 100A and go north 0.5 mile to entrance to Westchester Community College on right. At end of entrance road, turn right and follow to parking lot 1. Proceed as directed above.

♿ indicates parts of garden are handicapped accessible

NORTH CAROLINA

Edenton Open Day
Saturday, April 21

CHOWAN COUNTY

EDENTON
Beverly Hall Gardens

114 West King Street

The garden at Beverly Hall was laid out by Dr. Richard Dillard and by 1928 was one of the most highly developed Victorian gardens in North Carolina. The gardens have been restored during the last ten years. The gardens are divided into four principal sections. The formal garden at street side features a large late-nineteenth-century fountain surrounded by an enclosure of old fashioned spirea and English boxwood. A walkway and pergola covered by Confederate and Carolina jasmine, and Lady Banks roses leads to the back garden. The focus of the back garden is a round fountain filled with lotus and featuring a nineteenth-century lead water figure. Recently planted is a scent garden enclosed by an allée of beech hedges with peonies and gardenias. A small orchard of espaliered pear trees underplanted with hundreds of narcissus has also been added. The house and garden have remained in the same family for more than 150 years. Today, the sixth generation of this family can be found playing among camellia bushes and boxwood. **2004** ♿

Hours: 10 a.m. to 4 p.m.

From Route 17, take Edenton/Route 32 exit. Go about 1 mile towards town and continue through 2 traffic lights. At Chowan Crossing Shopping Center go 1 block to next light, where Route 32 dead-ends into North Broad Street. Turn right and continue through Main Street shopping district. At intersection of King and Broad Streets, turn right onto West King Street. Beverly Hall is fourth house on right.

Homestead Garden

101 East Water Street

The main axis of this garden runs from north to south from Water Street Gate through the 1773 house to King Street Gate and features 1843 'Louis Phillipe' roses at its south gate. Perennial beds border the north walk. There is a serpentine privacy wall as well as heritage roses, iris, candytuft, and Clusiana tulips from 1920. Elizabeth Lawrence was professionally retained by the owner's mother in the 1960s and some of the plants in the garden originated from her direction or were gifts. **2006** ♿

Hours: 10 a.m. to 4 p.m.

From Route 17, take Edenton/Route 32 exit. Go about 1 mile towards town and continue through 2 traffic lights. At Chowan Crossing Shopping Center go 1 block to next light, where Route 32 dead-ends into North Broad Street. Turn right and continue through Broad Street shopping district to East Water Street, last street before Edenton Bay. Turn left. The Homestead is first house on left.

Mary's Garden at the Brown-Elliott House

209 East Water Street

The Brown-Elliott House at 209 East Water Street is surrounded by a white picket fence. This small, semi-formal, enclosed garden is accented with three climbing rose arbors and antique planters. Designed by the owners, Roland and Peggy Anne Vaughan, plantings include hybrid tea roses, ferns, hydrangeas, boxwoods, and perennials with a patio and curved walkway paved with bricks taken from inside the house during restoration in 2002. **NEW**

Hours: 10 a.m. to 4 p.m.

From Route 17, take Edenton/Route 32 exit. Go about 1 mile towards town and through 2 traffic lights at Chowan Crossing Shopping Center. Go 1 block to next light, where Route 32 ends at North Broad Street. Turn right and go through Broad Street shopping district to East Water Street, last street before Edenton Bay. Turn left. Brown-Elliott house is in middle of second block on Water Street.

The Paine House Garden
100 South Granville Street

Hurricane Isabel in 2003 presented new gardening opportunities at the 1844 Paine House Garden. The loss of old trees in the yard inspired a transition from shady to sunny borders that is still in progress. The experimental southeastern border contains azaleas that were root propagated from existing specimens, and an infant vitex from its mother plant in the Cupola House Garden. There are also a variety of annuals, perennials, and specimen shrubs, including globe amaranth, rudbeckia and others chosen to complement one another in color, texture, and scent. Elsewhere along the streetscape is an "Edenton Tree Walk" with American holly, a cherry tree, a robust collection of hydrangea, a forsythia spray, and mature crape myrtle. The northwest privacy fence festooned with Confederate jasmine and Carolina jessamine complements the trellised 'Lady Banks' rose. Within the white picket fence are opposing informal borders full of pass-along plants and gifts from other Edenton gardens, relocated specimens from the North Carolina Piedmont, and established trees and shrubs planted by previous owners. Rich scents arise in every season from fragrant bulbs like *Ornithagalium nutans*, paper whites, roses, gardenia, garden phlox, ginger lilies, artemesia, rosemary, and osmanthus. Near the children's playhouse, look for a Florida anise collected from the owner's grandmother's Mississippi family farm. **NEW**

Hours: 10 a.m. to 4 p.m.

From Route 17, take Exit 227 onto Route 32 South/Virginia Road. Turn right at third traffic light onto Granville Street. Garden is on the southwest corner of Granville Street and Church Street.

Rose Cottage
400 East Queen Street

Our garden reflects the style and age of our house, a restored mill village cottage. Trees are a major focal point of design. The garden is enclosed by a picket fence and has the charm of a Southern cottage garden, with an edge of sophistication and formality. The predominant plant materials are roses, hydrangeas, lilies, and evergreens. The garden was designed by the owner, Carol Becker. **2006** ♿

Hours: 10 a.m. to 4 p.m.

From the north or west on Highway 17, exit onto Highway 32. At traffic light where Highway 32 dead ends at North Broad Street, turn right. Go south to traffic light at Queen Street. Turn left, and go east for 3 blocks to Wood Avenue. The garden is on right. Please park in open area immediately west of garden on opposite corner.

Skinner-Paxton House
115 West King Street, Edenton

The Skinner-Paxton House was built in the 1830s. It has been called "the epitome of the stylish side hall plan Federal-style dwelling in Edenton" by Thomas Butchko, writer and architectural historian. Presently owned by James and Marina Farr, the house is surrounded by gardens recently planted and growing as a work in progress. More than 300 boxwood have been planted to create parterres on the extensive grounds at the rear of the dwelling. The box parterres surround a fountain, flanked by a croquet court and a square for bocce ball. Fig vines cover the large back gate. Two pavilions, each a terrace with pergola, are covered with Confederate jasmine. Yoshino cherries, familiar to the owner from his native Maryland, also enhance the gardens. All spaces provide a view of beautiful Edenton Bay. **NEW**

Hours: 10 a.m. to 4 p.m.

See directions to Beverly Hall Gardens at 114 West King Street. The Skinner-Paxton House is located directly across the street.

Raleigh Open Days
Saturday & Sunday
September 22 & 23

WAKE COUNTY

RALEIGH
The Bromhal Garden
2507 Lewis Farm Road

The owners of this French-influenced house renovated the house and garden to flow seamlessly from indoors to out. The brick walkways throughout the gardens allow visitors to stroll leisurely to view the pond, a stream, and a very private courtyard garden off the bedroom. Visitors will surely feel like they are visiting a quaint garden in Europe. **NEW** ♿

Hours: Saturday, 11 a.m. to 4 p.m.; Sunday, 1 p.m. to 4 p.m.

From I-40 east, take Exit 289/Wade Avenue Extension. The end of exit is Wade Avenue, go 10 blocks. Turn left onto Canterbury. Go 5 blocks and turn right onto Lewis Farm Road. The garden is next to last on right before York.

Proceeds shared with JC Raulston Arboretum

The Davies Garden
508 Hertford Street

The owners of this Southern-style house found a little bit of their native Wales with this English-designed garden. The house and gardens are designed for entertainment. Visitors can delight in the formal sitting areas out front and then stroll through the boxwood edged courtyard. The path then leads to the back gardens to stroll by the little creek and wonder where the charming footbridge must lead. Finally, afternoon tea can be enjoyed sitting out on the back porch overlooking the rose and perennial gardens. The quaint Potting Shed holds the secrets of the garden's necessities. **NEW** ♿

Hours: Saturday, 11 a.m. to 4 p.m.; Sunday, 1 p.m. to 4 p.m.

From I 440, take Exit 71 at Glenwood Avenue (Crabtree Valley Mall). Turn east onto Glenwood Avenue (going towards downtown). Turn left onto Pasquotank Drive (across from Raleigh Orthopedic Clinic). Pasquotank Drive will become Transylvania Avenue with Alleghany Drive on left. Turn left onto Hertford Street. Number 508 is third house on left.

Proceeds shared with JC Raulston Arboretum

The Hanson Garden
2419 Anderson Drive

The gardens of this beautiful house were updated in 2004 to open up lawns and bring in the sunlight. A number of walking paths were also established to highlight forgotten spaces. Visitors may appreciate the addition of numerous perennials and the care for the historical deciduous and evergreen trees and shrubs, including Japanese maples, English boxwoods, and a spectacular osmanthus. The garden features a grape arbor, a courtyard garden, a spring walkway, and an herb garden. There is also a game lawn. **NEW** ♿

Hours: Saturday, 11 a.m. to 4 p.m.; Sunday, 1 p.m. to 4 p.m.

Take I-440 to Glenwood Avenue Exit. Go east towards downtown. Turn left onto Anderson Drive. The garden is on left at corner of Anderson Drive and White Oak Drive.

Proceeds shared with JC Raulston Arboretum

A Plant Collector's Paradise
3218 Oak Grove Circle

Beneath a canopy of mature oak trees lies a plant collector's paradise. The design and choice of material offers an alternative to the traditional 'Southern' garden. This garden represents well a new genre of gardening being seen ever more frequently in Raleigh. Gone are the camellias, hollies, azaleas, and crape myrtles. Bright colors, unusual growth habits, and topiary, combine to provide a feast for the eye, all the while paying careful attention to color, texture, and form. While the collection emphasizes the breadth and depth of conifers available today, it is also sprinkled with many unusual deciduous trees including more than thirty different Japanese maple cultivars. Many dwarf and miniature forms of plant material are also well represented in this garden. A must see study for the garden and plant enthusiast. **NEW** ☧

Hours: Saturday 11 a.m. to 4 p.m.; Sunday 1 p.m. to 4 p.m.

From I-40 East, take Exit 289/Wade Avenue Extension. The end of exit will be Wade Avenue, travel Wade Avenue and turn left onto Ridge Road. Turn right onto Lewis Farm Road (park on Lewis Farm Road). Oak Grove Circle is second Street on the right.

Proceeds shared with JC Raulston Arboretum

Mrs. Alton B. Smith
2503 Wake Drive

This fantastic southern house is graced with abundant trees providing shade for the many different garden rooms. Various paths of stone, gravel, and grass, lead visitors to the garden beds of azaleas, ferns, hellebores, hostas, lamium, English laurels, and many more delights. The house is the central accent to the design with gardens bordering the house and designed to be enjoyed from inside and out. The fishpond and water garden are situated so a visitor may pause and reflect. The garden also has a wonderful sense of calm, with seating to encourage you to stay awhile and garden accents providing focal points and interest. A rose garden is presently a "work in progress" and should be beautiful in September. **NEW** ☧

Hours: Saturday 11 a.m. to 4 p.m.; Sunday 1 p.m. to 4 p.m.

Take I-440 to Glenwood Avenue Exit. Travel east on Glenwood/Route 70 towards downtown. Turn right onto St. Mary's Street. Make immediate right onto Wake Drive to second house on left.

Proceeds shared with JC Raulston Arboretum

Public Gardens
CHOWAN COUNTY

EDENTON
The Cupola House Gardens
Broad Street, (252) 482-2637,
www.cupolahouse.org

This is a Colonial Revival-style garden in the heart of downtown Edenton. Planted in 1975 according to plans by Donald Parker of Colonial Williamsburg, it follows a 1769 Sauthier map of Edenton with urban layouts. This pleasure garden contains plants that could have been grown before 1800. An herb garden was planted in 1990, the design based on door panels from the exterior of the house from 1758. This is the oldest successful preservation of a single house in North Carolina. The garden is entirely maintained by volunteers.

Hours: Year round, Monday through Saturday, 8 a.m. to 4:30 p.m.; Sundays, 2 p.m. to 4:30 p.m.

Admission: Free

Located on lower end of Broad Street in downtown Edenton.

ORANGE COUNTY

HILLSBOROUGH
Montrose
320 St. Mary's Road, (919) 732-7787

A PROJECT OF THE GARDEN CONSERVANCY

Montrose is a sixty-one-acre property listed on the National Register of Historic Places, with gardens begun in the nineteenth century. The grounds contain several nineteenth-century buildings, a rock garden, scree garden, several acres of woodland plantings, and large areas of sunny gardens with unique color and planting schemes. Mass plantings of bulbs, including rain lilies, cyclamen, *Galanthus*, and crocus species, bloom throughout the year. Unusual trees, shrubs, trellises, fences, and arbors provide structure in winter and large urns planted with spectacular color combinations brighten the summer gardens.

☧ indicates parts of garden are handicapped accessible

Hours: Year round, guided tours by appointment, Tuesday and Thursday, 10 a.m.; Saturday, 10 a.m. or 2 p.m. Tours for larger groups may be arranged at other times.

Admission: $10

From I-85, take Exit 164 and go north into Hillsborough. Turn right onto East King Street. At stop sign, bear left and go up hill onto St. Mary's Road (not a sharp left). Pass St. Matthew's Church on right and Cameron Park Elementary School. Montrose is just past school on right. There are large red brick gateposts with a plaque on right that reads "Montrose 320."

From I-40, take Exit 261. Go north towards Hillsborough and pass under I-85. Proceed as directed above.

WAKE COUNTY

RALEIGH

JC Raulston Arboretum at North Carolina State University
Beryl Road, (919) 515-3132, www.ncsu.edu/jcraulstonarboretum

Are you fascinated by plants? Then you will want to visit the JC Raulston Arboretum the next time you are in Raleigh. The Arboretum is a nationally acclaimed garden with the largest and most diverse collection of landscape plants in the southeast United States. The Arboretum features more than 8,000 taxa on display. Plants include diverse collections and one-of-a-kind trees, shrubs, vines, ground covers, herbaceous perennials, and annual bedding plants displayed in a beautiful garden setting. The Arboretum, is named in memory of its founder and one of the twentieth-century's most treasured plantsmen, the late J. C. Raulston. You are cordially invited to visit with us and explore the eight acres of beautiful gardens and unique plant collections.

Hours: April through October, daily, 8 a.m. to 8 p.m.; November through March, daily, 8 a.m. to 5 p.m.

Admission: Free

From I-440, take Exit 3/Hillsborough Street. Turn left onto Hillsborough and pro-ceed to Beryl Road. Turn right (you will see a restaurant called Waffle House). Cross railroad tracks and go straight. We are located on left of Beryl Road across from Capital City Lumber.

Juniper Level Botanic Garden at Plant Delights Nursery
9241 Sauls Road, (919) 772-4794, www.plantdelights.com

Juniper Level Botanic Garden is a six-acre display garden containing more than 17,000 different plants...some woody, some perennial, and some in-betweeners. The botanical garden not only functions as a display area, but doubles as a research and development facility. New plants from seed exchanges, our breeding program, and our expeditions are evaluated for their garden worthiness, their adaptability to the climate of the southeastern United States, and their ability to peacefully co-exist with our natives. We also strive to sort out some of the misinformation and nomenclature problems that unfortunately abound in this industry by assembling complete collections of specific plant groups.

Hours: Open eight weekends each year. Visit www.plantdelights.com for dates and times. Also open by appointment.

Admission: Free

From north or west of Wake County, take I-40 east to Exit 298/Highway 401 south. Take Highway 401 south to the intersection of Ten Ten Road at traffic light (McDonald's). Turn left, go 4 miles, then turn right onto Sauls Road. The nursery is 1 mile on left.

From south or east of Wake County, take I-40 west to Exit 312/Highway 42. At top of exit, turn left and go west 4.2 miles, then turn right onto Sauls Road at bottom of hill. The nursery is 3 miles on right.

From Raleigh, take Lake Wheeler Road 6.5 miles past I-40 to intersection of Ten Ten Road. Turn left and go 4.5 miles. Turn right onto Sauls Road, and nursery is 1 miles on left.

OREGON
Portland Open Day
Saturday, May 12
MULTNOMAH COUNTY

PORTLAND
Heims Garden
4309 S.W. Cullen Boulevard

A rare opportunity to view unusual collections of shade perennials and wildflowers, camellias, Japanese maples, conifers, and ephemera. This garden is situated on a third of an acre with a thirty-three-foot drop. A patio creates a large outdoor room set in pavers. A naturalistic waterfall and pond provide comforts to help forget that downtown Portland is only nine minutes away. Plants are tested here from Terra Nova Nurseries (Dan is president) including a few that are the only specimens in the world. A number of plants here have been collected world-wide. Come. Enjoy. **NEW**

Hours: 10 a.m. to 4 p.m.

From downtown Portland, go south on Front Avenue/Naito Parkway, which becomes 99 West, then merges onto Barbur Boulevard. Turn right onto Highway 10/Capitol Highway. Go through Hillsdale and continue towards the right onto Beaverton-Hillsdale Highway for 1 mile. Watch for a 76 gas station on right. Go about 1.5 blocks and turn left onto S.W. 42nd. Go up hill about 1 block and look for a brown house on right. Driveway is on 42nd, house is on Cullen Boulevard. Please park on Cullen Boulevard or 42nd.

Proceeds shared with The Hardy Plant Society of Oregon

June's Garden
7320 S.W. Newton Place

My one-acre garden evolved over thirty years, from firs, lawns, and rhododendrons, to accommodate the needs of this intensely passionate propagator. Ninety percent of the trees, shrubs, climbers, and perennials were propagated by me. Features include a redwood greenhouse, a rock garden, mixed borders, and a sixty-foot rose arbor. The copper structures throughout the garden were designed and created by me. Attracting birds and butterflies is a very important part of my gardening, as is sharing seeds, plants, and knowledge with other gardeners. **2002**

Hours: 10 a.m. to 4 p.m.

From downtown Portland, follow Highway 26 west approximately 2 miles. Take next exit (Sylvan), turning left over freeway, and follow signs toward Raleigh Hills. At bottom of hill with Parr Lumber Yard on right, take an abrupt right at west end of lumberyard before large intersection, onto S.W. Dogwood Lane. Take first left onto Newton Place and garden is near end on left. Our house is a two-story gray colonial with white and charcoal trim. Please park on street only.

Proceeds shared with The Hardy Plant Society of Oregon

The Narizny Garden
5637 S.W. Cheltenham Drive

Our half-acre garden is interesting in its variety of plants, many unusual, and its collections of some species. Hardy fuchsias, ceanothus, hebes, and many trees abound. It is also notable for its low maintenance and organic culture. I am a collector, so the garden has evolved into an assemblage of whatever I like, matching appropriate living conditions to the plants. I don't amend the soil—except in the vegetable garden—but the garden is a testament to what will grow in the clay soil conditions that exist here. Our *Quercus garryana* is a seedling of our neighbor's huge Portland Heritage Tree, also open for viewing in conjunction with our garden. **NEW** ♿

Hours: 10 a.m. to 4 p.m.

From downtown Portland, take S.W. Naito Parkway/Front Street south. This becomes S.W. Barbur Boulevard. Take turnoff on right, after traffic light at S.W. Hamilton Street, before next light at S.W. Third Avenue. The turnoff is labeled "Highway 10, Beaverton, Hillsdale". It is about 1 mile from Ross Island Bridge to this turnoff. You are now on S.W.

Capitol Highway, going west uphill. After passing light at S.W. Terwilliger Boulevard, take first right turn onto S.W. Cheltenham Street, 1 very short block before light at crest of hill. Go 2 blocks to a multi-street intersection. Veer left, straight uphill, on S.W. Cheltenham Drive, clearly marked "Dead End". We are last house on left.

Proceeds shared with The Hardy Plant Society of Oregon

The Jane Platt Garden
4550 S.W. Humphrey Boulevard

Many specimens in this sixty-year-old garden are among the oldest and largest to be seen outside their native ranges. Designed with a painter's eye, the plantings feature trees and shrubs whose bark and foliage provide interest in all seasons. The two-and-one-half-acre garden surrounds a house designed in 1940 by Pietro Belluschi and a large rock garden filled with treasures from around the world. In 1984, the Garden Club of America awarded Jane Platt the Mrs. Oakleigh Thorne Medal "for the establishment of an exquisite garden incorporating rare and difficult botanic material into a design of incredible harmony, beauty, and distinction." **2004** ⚬

Hours: 10 a.m. to 4 p.m.

Heading west out of Portland on Highway 26, take Sylvan exit and turn left over highway. Go through traffic light and onto Scholls Ferry Road, and then take an immediate left onto S.W. Humphrey Boulevard. Continue 0.8 mile, then turn right into drive across from 4 black mailboxes. Follow signs to parking in field on right below hedge.

Proceeds shared with The Hardy Plant Society of Oregon

WASHINGTON COUNTY

PORTLAND
Barbara Blossom Ashmun
8560 SW Fairway Drive

Twenty years of passionate plant collecting and experiments in plant marriages (and divorces) is an ongoing source of pleasure. Mixed borders

screen the property while providing bird habitat. Island beds, a grape arbor, a greenhouse, meditation hut, fruit trees, an idesia grove, as well as many roses, viburnums, and willows mingle in a peaceful atmosphere. **NEW**

Hours: 10 a.m. to 4 p.m.

From downtown Portland, take Highway 26 West to Sylvan exit. Turn left, crossing back over the freeway, and descend Scholl's Ferry Road. After passing Safeway on left, turn right onto Beaverton-Hillsdale Highway. Turn right at next traffic light, S.W. 78. Go through one stop sign and turn left at second stop sign onto S.W. Fairway Drive (school is on right). Garden is 1.5 blocks along Fairway Drive, on left, at small blue house. Please park across street or around corner to avoid blocking garden and driveway.

Proceeds shared with The Hardy Plant Society of Oregon

Clackamas County Open Day
Saturday, June 16

We suggest you visit the gardens in this order or reverse order:
Walt Hodges, Mike & Linda Darcy, Bonnie's Garden, Foxglove Point, Y. Sherry Sheng Garden, Smith's Solitude,
Sharon McCauley & Dean Dikeman.
Maps will be available at all gardens and parking volunteers will be on hand.

CLACKAMAS COUNTY

LAKE OSWEGO
Mike & Linda Darcy
2311 Prestwick Road

This garden was started in 1974 when the house was built. It was a clean slate and what you see has been planted since that time. This garden is a collection of plants, not any particular genus or species, just plants in general, with new ones constantly being added. There is art scattered throughout the garden. Note the large steel screens at the bottom of the driveway. In the front courtyard, note the espaliered *Feijoa sellowiana* (pineapple guava) on the wall and the *Acacia pravissima* with its gray green, triangular leaves. As you walk through the garden entrance, note the *Schizophragma hydrangeoides* 'Moonlight' on the trellis to your left. Several new features this year include a Thai Spirit House and the two glass windows used as a screen which were taken from a local house before it was demolished. There is also a new water feature in a large pot at the end of the lawn. Our pathways are filbert shells and wind around the area so you do not see everything at once. The cement patio area in the back part of the garden was originally a basketball pad for our boys. You can now walk through the copper arbor leading into the garden of Steve & Peggy Penberthy.

Steve and Peggy have graciously opened their garden as a gateway between the Darcy and Hodges Garden. Stroll through the back area and notice the outdoor living space as an extension of the house. A stream flows into the pond with garden art and shade-loving plants all around. You can't miss the beautiful mature oak trees. They are a real treasure. As you leave this garden you will be on Prestwick Road. Turn right and walk the short distance to Wembley Park Road. You'll see Prestwick Park which for many years was an 'eyesore' in the neighborhood with heavy growth of blackberries and ivy. Three years ago, Mike Darcy and Walt Hodge co-chaired a committee and worked with the City of Lake Oswego and neighbors to create this space. Stroll through the Park to Wembley Park Road. A short distance later you'll come to the Hodges' garden on the left at the corner of Glen Eagles and Wembley Park. **NEW**

Hours: 10 a.m. to 4 p.m.

Due to parking constraints, please park at the Hodges Garden, walk 2 blocks east on Wembley Park Road and turn right onto Prestwick Road. Proceed to the Darcy Garden.

Proceeds shared with The Aloha Garden Club

Walt Hodges
2656 Wembley Park Road

When Walt moved into this house in 2000, it was a clean slate with respect to the garden.

He has created and planted everything you see. With three large dogs, having a garden could be quite challenging, and so before making paths, Walt observed the dogs to determine what areas they would generally be using. He then built the pathways reflecting this. 'Random and evolving' is how Walt describes his garden with a wide assortment of plants and garden art scattered throughout. Notice the large pot in the inner circle of the front garden with a Japanese maple. This is a good example of how the same container can be something different in another garden. This same pot is a water feature in the Darcy garden. A focal point in the back garden is the huge gunnera. There are three water features including a dog water bowl by the front entryway. The arbors and archways have all been designed and hand crafted by Walt. Scattered throughout the garden are many large containers and a deck made from mahogany. There are extensive plantings in front and back, be sure to walk up the back stairs to the upper deck to get an overview of the entire back garden. Along the driveway, you'll see pots of blooming annuals providing color all summer. **NEW**

Hours: 10 a.m. to 4 p.m.

From I-5, take Highway 217 exit and go east on Kruse Way (Highway 217 becomes Kruse Way at the interchange) to end, 1.4 miles. Turn left onto Boones Ferry Road. Go 0.3 mile and turn right onto Twin Fir Road. Go 0.1 mile and turn left onto Fir Ridge Road. Go 0.1 mile and turn left onto Wembley Park Road to the Hodges Garden.

Proceeds shared with The Aloha Garden Club

OREGON CITY
Sharon McCauley & Dean Dikeman
15836 South Beaverglen Drive

Nestled into a large clearing in a four-acre Douglas fir forest lies our two-acre garden. Over the past twenty years we have amassed an extensive collection of trees, shrubs, and perennials including *Pinus patula*, *Tetracentron sinense*, and *Cornus controversa* 'variegata' as well as more than forty Japanese maples, 200 conifers of all sizes, and much more. This is definitely a collector's garden, but with emphasis on gardening as a creative activity of blending this collection of more than 1,000 individual plants into a harmonious tapestry of color and texture. Stroll through the arboretum and around the many large planting beds and then relax for a while at one of the many seating areas, including the rock patio with its rebar trellis, or the sunken patio under the canopy of two large Japanese maples. Other areas of interest include scree beds, a small pond, a fruit orchard, a large screened berry patch, and a raised vegetable garden. **NEW** ♿

Hours: 10 a.m. to 4 p.m.

From I-205, take Exit 10. Go south on Highway 213/Trail's End Highway for about 3 miles and turn left onto Beavercreek Road. Travel about 4 miles to the town of Beavercreek. Continue straight onto Kamrath Road for about 0.5 mile to Beaverglen Drive and turn right. Go about 0.2 mile to #15836 on left.

Proceeds shared with The Aloha Garden Club

Smith's Solitude
17200 South Holly Lane

Follow an inviting wooded lane to Smith's Solitude. The three-acre garden reveals itself in a series of whimsical scenes punctuated by rusty found objects and sculpture by local artists. Meditation benches, patios, and a moon gate encourage contemplation of harmonious groupings of perennials, vines, shrubs, grasses, and trees. The tree house folly provides an overall view. Cobalt blue, the garden's signature color, repeats throughout in unexpected ways—glistening bottle sculptures, a spindle fence, a collection of glass, and surprising artifacts nestled among island beds. A pleasant meander will reveal new delights…a tribute to agriculture: the round hay bale topped by a rusty tractor seat and a fountain of dried grasses, the "Bingo-Bongo-Boogie-Woogie", a Scandinavian-inspired round wood pile. Those with sharp eyes and a sense of wry humor will note the bedspring trellis (salvaged from a nineteenth-century brothel) entwined by a passion vine! **NEW** ♿

Hours: 10 a.m. to 4 p.m.

Take Exit 10 off I-205. Drive south on Highway 213/Trail's End Highway to second stop sign at Redland Road. Turn left. Follow Redland Road 1 mile to Holly Lane. Turn right onto Holly Lane and go about one block to a red school bus shelter and gravel drive on left. Smith's Solitude is 0.6 mile from start of Holly Lane.

Proceeds shared with The Aloha Garden Club

WEST LINN
Bonnie's Garden
5505 River Street

Our house is a charming 1927 English Tudor-style cottage on three-quarters of an acre overlooking the Willamette River. We have transformed our yard into several garden rooms that complement our English cottage. Along one side of our house a cottage garden was formed from curved brick pathways, trellises, and garden art. Lilies and dahlias poke out from behind neatly trimmed scrubs that line the pathway. Be sure to check out the two koi ponds. The upper pond flows to the lower pond filled with koi. Continuing along the path by the river you will come to a screened gazebo with a plush sitting area—perfect for viewing the river activity. Falcons fly overhead and sit in the tall trees to keep watch over the Willamette. **NEW**

Hours: 10 a.m. to 4 p.m.

From I-205, take Exit 8 and go toward Lake Oswego for 0.1 mile. Turn right onto Holly Street. Go 2 blocks to end and turn left onto River Street. Number 5505 is on right just after turn.

From Lake Oswego, go south on Highway 43 about 4.6 miles. Turn left onto Burns Street. Go 0.2 miles and turn right onto River Street. All three West Linn Gardens are on River Street. within walking distance of each other.

Proceeds shared with Friends of McLean House and Park

Foxglove Point
5597 River Street

Our garden focuses on colorful native perennials to complement the craftsman-style house. A water feature and large hanging baskets are a focal point with native trees providing a backdrop. Establishing foxgloves and ferns on the riverbank is an ongoing effort and you will find a pathway and sitting area to pause and enjoy river wildlife and the progress of the garden. The vegetable garden on the lower riverbank changes from year to year but always provides an ample amount of produce to share with our friends and neighbors. **NEW** ♿

> Hours: 10 a.m. to 4 p.m.
>
> See directions under Bonnie's garden.
>
> *Proceeds shared with The Aloha Garden Club*

Y. Sherry Sheng Garden
5725 River Street

Feast your eyes and rejuvenate your spirit in this lush and colorful garden on the Willamette River. Discover views of the garden and river from three decks—over the river, on the second-story, and at ground level. Deck designs were inspired by visits to the Amalfi Coast of Italy. Two dozen trees frame the sunny lot where flowers abound year-round and shrubs and perennials offer structure, texture, and fragrance. Dotting the beds are two water features designed and installed by the owners. A stroll through the garden promises close encounters with small songbirds, hummingbirds, and butterflies. Look above to spot soaring red-tailed hawks, ospreys, great blue herons, and turkey vultures partaking in the river's bounty. **NEW** ♿

> Hours: 10 a.m. to 4 p.m.
>
> See directions under Bonnie's garden.
>
> *Proceeds shared with The Aloha Garden Club*

Eugene Open Day
Sunday, July 8
LANE COUNTY

EUGENE
The Alba Garden
3902 Monroe Street

This large, one-plus-acre wooded garden is planted with deer-friendly shrubs and perennials. Much of the lot is wetlands, so the garden area is close to the house. A path, steps, and circular seating area provide a focal point for a colorful and exuberant display of grasses, rhododendrons, perennials, and evergreens. Farther away from the house the open woodland invites you and the deer to wander at will. **NEW** ♿

> Hours: 10 a.m. to 4 p.m.
>
> From the Steelman/Sams garden, return to Jefferson Street, turning right, and continue to the end of Jefferson. At the stop sign, turn left onto West 28th Avenue, then one block later, turn right onto Washington Street. After one block, turn left onto West 29th Street. At Willamette Street (major intersection with gas station) turn right onto Willamette. Continue south on Willamette Street to 39th Avenue. Turn right onto West 39th Avenue Go 0.3 mile, turn right onto Monroe Street. Take first right onto Deertrail. The next intersection is with Monroe Street. (Again!). The Alba Garden at #3902 on right.
>
> *Proceeds shared with Willamette Valley Hardy Plant Group*

Circles in Thyme
415 Brae Burn Drive

The Kirk's garden is a study in time and stone. It began with rock terraces and pathways in the sloping side yards. Over time, rock gardens were sculpted into the front yard, including a newly refurbished crevice garden, a small water feature in natural stone, and footpaths threaded between plantings. Where natural stone could not be managed, Gary has hand-built larger "stone" structures from concrete that has been shaped, carved, and painted to resemble native rock. **NEW** ♿

Hours: 10 a.m. to 4 p.m.

From the Steelman/Sams garden, return to Jefferson Street, turning right (south), and continue to the end of Jefferson. At the stop sign, turn left onto West 28th Avenue, then one block later, turn right onto Washington Street. After 1 block, turn left (east) onto West 29th Street. At Willamette Street (major intersection with gas station) turn right onto Willamette. Continue south on Willamette Street to 39th Avenue. Turn right onto West 39th Avenue. Go 0.3 mile, turn right onto Monroe Street. Turn left onto Deertrail then left again at the first stop sign onto Monroe. At the next stop sign turn right onto Brae Burn Drive and go 0.4 mile to #415. Continuing on Brae Burn will bring you back to Willamette Street.

Proceeds shared with Willamette Valley Hardy Plant Group

The Hewitt Garden
3811 Monroe Street

This tranquil, woodland garden is located on a shaded hillside where the front garden is an informal mix of deer-proof plantings. The back garden, enclosed by a deer fence, is a shade garden with plantings ranging from mature twenty-five-year-old rhododendrons to newer plantings including many hostas, ferns, and dwarf conifers representing the changing interests of the resident gardeners. A newer garden area added four years ago contains mixed shrub, and perennial borders with a large "Bobby James" rose climbing an old tree, an herb garden, and a greenhouse. Arbors, pathways, and rock terracing complete the garden. **NEW**

Hours: 10 a.m. to 4 p.m.

From the Steelman/Sams garden, return to Jefferson Street, turn right and continue to the end of Jefferson. At the stop sign, turn left onto West 28th Avenue, then one block later, turn right onto Washington Street. After one block turn left onto West 29th Street. At Willamette Street (major intersection with gas

station) turn right onto Willamette. Continue to 39th Avenue. Turn right onto West 39th Avenue Go 0.3 mile, turn right onto Monroe Street. Take first right onto Deertrail. The next intersection is with Monroe Street. (Again!). Turn right onto Monroe and go 0.2 mile to #3811, on the downhill side of street.

Proceeds shared with Willamette Valley Hardy Plant Group

The Bernard Levine Garden
939 Polk Street

Enter the secret gate beside the front door. Pass through the courtyard with its "metropolis bed" of chimney thimbles, then the four-season pavilion. The main garden features a proscenium-style grape arbor, a raised shade rockery, and a pond with a site-built fountain. Plantings center on a slab/crevice rockery, flanked by tall perennials, shrubs, and trees chosen for form and foliage. **NEW**

Hours: 10 a.m. to 4 p.m.

From I-5, take Exit 194B. Take I-105 west to its end. Continue straight on Jefferson Street. Turn right onto 11th Avenue. Turn right at the second light onto Polk Street. The garden is on right between West 10th Avenue and West Broadway.

Proceeds shared with Willamette Valley Hardy Plant Group

Buell Steelman & Rebecca Sams
662 West 25th Place

You may have seen Rebecca Sams and Buell Steelman's space in this year's *Fine Gardening's Great Gardens* special issue. Their tiny garden unites contrast of color, form and texture with a healthy disregard for convention. A corrugated metal fence provides the perfect foil for bold plantings, and meticulously crafted stone borders, and retaining walls create a geometric foundation for the boisterous and colorful garden. This space has also been featured in *Sunset, Pacific Horticulture* and *Garden Design*. Rebecca and Buell own MOSAIC, a garden design and construction company in Eugene, Oregon. **2006** ♿

Hours: 10 a.m. to 4 p.m.

From I-5 exit 194B take I-105 west to its end. Continue straight ahead on Jefferson Street to the light at 13th Avenue. Following the sign for Jefferson Street, use the center lane, turn left onto 13th Avenue and immediately right onto Jefferson again. Continue south on Jefferson, past 25th Avenue and turn right onto 25th Place. The garden is half way down the hill on the left.

Proceeds shared with Willamette Valley Hardy Plant Group

The Garden of Monica Tallerday & Gene Humphreys
2035 Alder Street

This is a garden in which the owners have worked with relationships–plant to plant, plants to people, garden to neighborhood. They have created a "real time" garden, a space for relaxation, learning, dancing, and play. Look for the willow tunnel, children's garden house, wall fountain, and outdoor bath. **NEW**

Hours: 10 a.m. to 4 p.m.

From I-5, take Exit 194B. Take I-105 west to end. Continue straight on Jefferson Street to traffic light at 13th Avenue. Turn left and continue through downtown about eight blocks to Pearl Street. Turn right onto Pearl Street and go 6 blocks to 19th Avenue. Turn left and go east through two traffic lights. Kinkaid Street is the second street after light at Hilyard Street. Turn right. Go one block; turn right onto 20th Avenue and left in one block onto Alder Street. The garden is on east side of street.

Proceeds shared with Willamette Valley Hardy Plant Group

Public Gardens
LANE COUNTY

EUGENE
Hendricks Park & Rhododendron Garden
1800 Skyline Boulevard, (541) 682-5324

Hendricks Park's seventy-eight acres include a mature forest, a world-renowned rhododendron garden, and a new native plant garden. Visitors can walk among 200-year-old Douglas firs, ferns, and wildflowers, such as trillium and irises, and over 6,000 varieties of ornamental plants.

Hours: Year round, daily, dawn to dusk

Admission: Free

From Franklin Boulevard (which runs adjacent to University of Oregon), head south on Agate Street. Turn left onto 19th Street. Turn right onto Fairmount Boulevard. Then left onto Summit Avenue. At top of hill park in Forest Parking lot on right.

Owen Rose Garden
300 Jefferson Street, (541) 682-4915

Nestled next to the Willamette River near the Washington-Jefferson Street Bridge is the Owen Memorial Rose Garden. It is part of a riverfront park stretching from the Ferry Street Bridge to the Greenway Bike Bridge near Valley River Center.

Hours: Year round, daily, dawn to dusk

Admission: Free

Follow Washington Street north, go past entrance to I-105. Turn left onto 5th Avenue, and right, one block later, onto Jefferson Street. Drive to #300.

MULTNOMAH COUNTY

PORTLAND
The Berry Botanic Garden
11505 S.W. Summerville Avenue, (503) 636-4112, www.berrybot.org

Guide yourself through this six-acre historic garden, created by renowned plantswoman Rae Selling Berry. Explore the curving herb

---

♿ indicates parts of garden are handicapped accessible

lawn, 150-tree rhododendron forest, a secluded and shady fern garden, our water garden, a native plant trail, the sunny quarter-acre rock garden, and moist border areas featuring species primroses.

Hours: By appointment only

Admission: $5

From I-5, take Exit 297/Terwilliger Boulevard, taking the right turn lane and following signs for Lewis & Clark. Turn right onto Terwilliger Boulevard and cross over freeway. Drive through small business district. Go straight at intersection with Boones Ferry; at Terwilliger Boulevard, go around traffic circle onto Palater Road. This immediately becomes Palatine Hill Road. Go past the college and turn right on Military Road. Summerville Avenue is about 0.5 mile on left. Follow Summerville to end and follow sign down the left driveway.

Crystal Springs Rhododendron Garden

S.E. 28th Avenue, (503) 771-8386

This is a unique seven-acre garden with 2,000 rhododendrons and azaleas, 141 varieties and 121 species, three waterfalls, a fountain, and numerous companion plants. The rhododendrons bloom February through June. Winter trees add color and structural interest. A lake surrounds the garden, attracting waterfowl to nest.

Hours: Year round, daily, 10 a.m. to 6 p.m.

Admission: Labor Day through February, free; March through Labor Day, $3, children under 12 free

A 10-minute drive from city center, nearly surrounded by Eastmoreland Golf Course and across street from Reed College. One block north of Woodstock Boulevard.

Elk Rock, The Garden at the Bishop's Close

11800 S.W. Military Lane, (503) 636-5613

Begun in 1916 by an avid plantsman, this six-and-one-half-acre English-style garden is a treasure trove of rare and unusual plants. A

delightful rock garden, woodland garden, fishpond, and cascade garden are all features of this garden, which was innovative in its blending of new plant introductions from around the world with Northwest natives. A renowned collection of magnolia species provides spectacular interest March through June.

Hours: Year round, daily, 8 a.m. to 5 p.m. Closed some holidays.

Admission: Free

Take Route 43 south from downtown Portland to S.W. Military Road (traffic light) about 1.5 miles south of Sellwood Bridge. Turn left, then immediately right onto S.W. Military Lane. The garden is at end of lane. Parking is limited and guests are asked to park in upper lot only on weekdays. There are no restroom facilities and no food or drink is permitted. Children must be accompanied by adults and should be reminded that this is not a playground or a park. The garden is not wheelchair accessible. No buses.

Hoyt Arboretum

4000 S.W. Fairview Boulevard, (503) 865-8733, www.hoytarboretum.org

Hoyt Arboretum is a treasured living museum with a collection of over 1,500 species and varieties of trees and shrubs from around the world. The Arboretum's plantings and programs promote the understanding, appreciation, and scientific study of woody plants and nature. This tranquil setting in Portland's urban environment is available for everyone to enjoy.

Hours: Year round, daily, 6 a.m. to 10 p.m. Visitor Center open Monday through Friday, 9 a.m. to 4 p.m.; Saturday, 9 a.m. to 3 p.m.

Admission: Free, donations encouraged to help support the Arboretum's collections.

From downtown Portland, take Route 26 to Washington Park/Oregon Zoo exit and follow signs to Hoyt Arboretum. TriMet bus #63 stops directly in front of visitor center and Max Light Rail station is nearby at zoo.

International Rose Test Gardens

400 S.W. Kingston Street, (503) 823-3636

Portland is home to one of the world's most famous rose gardens, the International Rose Test Gardens in Washington Park. Each year hundreds of thousands of visitors from around the world visit this garden. This popular tourist site, with spectacular views and nearly 8,000 roses, is one of Portland's most notable signature landmarks.

Hours: Year round, daily, 6 a.m. to 9 p.m.

Admission: Free

From West Burnside, travel west and turn left onto Tichner Avenue. At stop sign, turn right. Park is about three blocks ahead. The Japanese Garden parking lot is on right, tennis courts on left. Park there or go to next stop sign, turn left and go into garden parking lot.

Japanese Garden Society of Oregon

611 S.W. Kingston, (503) 223-1321, www.japanesegarden.com

Nestled in the scenic west hills of Portland, the Japanese Garden is a haven of tranquil beauty. The garden includes a formal Japanese Tea House, meandering streams, intimate walkways, and an unsurpassed view of Mt. Hood. The five-and-one-half-acre Japanese Garden is composed of five separate garden styles: a Strolling Pond Garden, a Tea Garden, a Natural Garden, a Flat Garden, and a Sand and Stone Garden.

Hours: April 1 through September 30, Tuesday through Sunday, 10 a.m. to 7 p.m.; Monday, 12 p.m. to 7 p.m.; October 1 through March 31, Tuesday through Sunday, 10 a.m. to 4 p.m., Monday, 12 p.m. to 4 p.m.

Admission: $8 adults, $6.25 seniors (62 & over), $6.25 students with ID, $5.25 students 6-17, children under 5 free

From Route 26 west, take zoo exit and follow road past the zoo, Forestry Center, and Vietnam Memorial. Turn right onto Kingston, follow 1.6 miles, and continue left on Kingston to garden's parking lot on left across from The Rose Garden Tennis Courts. Shuttle bus takes visitors to main entrance or there is a walking path.

Ladd's Addition Rose Gardens

Between S.E. Hawthorne & S.E.Division, (503) 823-3636

Ladd's Addition Rose Gardens, the smallest and most intimate gardens, are located in a historic southeast residential area just across the river from downtown. The four rose gardens display many varieties popular earlier in this century. This garden contains about 3,200 roses.

Hours: Year round, daily, 6 a.m. to 9 p.m.

Admission: Free

Located between S.E. Hawthorne and S.E. Division, S.E. 12th Avenue, and S.E. 20th Avenue. Like a spoke on a wheel are the four separate gardens around a large landscaped center circle.

Leach Botanical Garden

6704 S.E. 122nd Avenue, (503) 823-9503, www.leachgarden.org

The fifteen-acre public garden with four and one-half acres in cultivation is located in a riparian drainage with a dense overhead canopy of evergreen and deciduous specimens. As a result, the major plant collections are adapted to shade. The garden's focus is on Pacific Northwest native species and historic collections displayed with like genera, showcasing an extensive collection of non-native plants such as viburnums, witch hazel, camellias, woody groundcovers, and azaleas from southwestern United States, as well as diverse members of plant families such as barberry, rhododendron, woodland lily, and fern. The collection also includes North American alpines, cacti and succulents, vines and tropicals.

Hours: Year round, Tuesday through Saturday, 9 a.m. to 4 p.m.; Sunday, 1 p.m. to 4 p.m.

Tours: February through November, Saturday, 10 a.m. December through January, first Saturday of the month.

Admission: Free, donations welcome.

Located four blocks south of 122nd Avenue and Foster Road. We are 3 miles east of the I-205 Foster Road exit.

ら indicates parts of garden are handicapped accessible

Lewis & Clark College

0615 S.W. Palatine Hill Road,
(503) 768-7000, www.lclark.edu

The sixty-five-acre Lloyd Frank estate, once maintained by twenty-eight gardeners, is now a bustling college campus. Expanses of lawn, pools, and watercourses built in the 1920s still lead the eye down the formal terraces to a large hidden rose garden. Splendid Japanese lace-leaf maples and stately Atlas cedars accent these terraces. From the first terrace, Mount Hood is framed by the trees. On the rest of the campus are spring-flowering shrubs, native dogwoods, and unusual trees such as sassafras, Spanish fir, Mexican umbrella pine, and dawn redwood.

Hours: Year round, daily, dawn to dusk

Admission: Free

Take I-5 to Exit 297/Terwilliger Boulevard. Follow signs to Lewis & Clark College.

Peninsula Park Rose Garden

North Ainsworth Street & Albina Avenue,
(503) 823-3636

Peninsula Park Rose Garden is a treasure located just a few minutes from the city center. More than 6,000 fragrant roses engulf the visitors of this sunken garden of distinct early twentieth-century design.

Hours: Year round, daily, 6 a.m. to 9 p.m.

Admission: Frees

From I-5, take Portland Boulevard exit. Go east to Albina and turn right. The garden is at south end of Peninsula Park.

Portland Classical Chinese Garden

239 N.W. Everett Street, (503) 228-8131,
www.portlandchinesegarden.org

The Portland Classical Chinese Garden is a friendship collaboration between Portland and its sister city, Suzhou, located on the southeastern coast of China. A year-round wonder, Lan Su Yuan Garden of Awakening Orchids is an authentic Ming Dynasty-style garden. Covered walkways, bridges, open colonnades, pavilions, and richly planted landscapes frame Zither Lake, creating views that are never twice the same.

Hours: November 1 through March 31, daily, 10 a.m. to 5 p.m.; April 1 through October 31, daily, 9 a.m. to 6 p.m.

Admission: $7 adults, $6 seniors, $5.50 students, children under 5 free

From I-405, take Everett Street exit east. Travel to Third and Everett. We are located on corner of N.W. Third and Everett.

WASHINGTON COUNTY

ALOHA

Jenkins Estate

8005 S.W. Grabhorn Road,
(503) 629-6355, www.thprd.org

Tualatin Hills Park and Recreation District welcomes you to this tranquil setting in the wooded niche crowning Cooper Mountain. Listed in the National Registry of Historic Places, this sixty-eight-acre estate includes historic buildings suitable for corporate meetings or social events.

Hours: Year round, daily, dawn to dusk

Admission: Free

From Portland Airport/downtown Portland, take I-205 south/I-84 west to I-5 south. Continue to I-405 north to Highway 26 west to Exit 64/185th Avenue/Rock Creek. Turn left onto 185th Avenue and go to S.W. Farmington Road (approximately 5 miles) and turn right. Turn left onto S.W. Grabhorn Road.

From downtown Hillsboro, take Tualatin Valley Highway/Highway 8 east toward Beaverton. Turn right onto 209th Avenue. Cross S.W. Farmington Road at light and turn onto S.W. Grabhorn Road.

From Salem, take I-5 north to Highway 217 north. Take Exit 2A/Beaverton/Canyon Road. Take first left onto Highway 10 west /S.W. Farmington Road. Turn left onto S.W. Grabhorn Road.

PENNSYLVANIA

Bucks County Open Days
Friday & Saturday
April 20 & 21

BUCKS COUNTY

DOYLESTOWN

Heronswood Nursery
Comes to Fordhook Farm of
W. Atlee Burpee & Co.
105 New Britain Road

You will have the opportunity to take a "behind the scenes" tour of the Burpee and Heronswood's famed trials and testing operations. In 1888, W. Atlee Burpee acquired several hundred acres of farmland in bucolic Bucks County. Today at Fordhook Farm, as before, hundreds of new vegetables, annuals, and perennials are grown, tested and evaluated on a sixty-acre test farm and network of gardens to guarantee Burpee's high standards of quality. Once home to the Burpee family, the eighteenth-century manor has been designated a National Historic Site. The house features the richly paneled study where W. Atlee Burpee compiled and edited the first Burpee catalogs. Burpee Hall, located in an adjoining stone barn, has been fully renovated as a conference center. It features a 360° hand-painted mural of Fordhook Farm during the late nineteenth century. Once the hub for seed processing at Fordhook, the one-of-a-kind Seed House is located across the drive from the manor. Be sure to visit the many trial gardens—birthplace of culinary favorites such as Golden Bantam, the first yellow sweet corn, Big Boy tomato, Iceberg lettuce, Fordhook lima bean, and ornamental innovations such as the double-flowered rudbeckia daisy, 'Gloriosa', and the many generations of pure white marigolds. See the ad on page 243 for information on speakers and the opporturnity to purchase plants from Burpee's Heronswood collection. **2006**

Hours: 10 a.m. to 4 p.m.

From Philadelphia, take I-95 north to Route 332 west towards Newtown. Take Route 332 for 3.7 miles to Route 413 north. Take Route 413 for 10.4 miles to Route 202 south. Take Route 202 for 3.5 miles to State Street. Follow State Street south past the hospital and over Route 611, then go 0.25 mile and turn left onto New Britain Road (the first road on the left next to Delaware Valley College). The entrance to Fordhook Farm is 0.25 mile on the left through two stone pillars.

From New York and points north, take I-287 south to Route 202 across the Delaware River to Doylestown (about 45 miles from Somerville). Proceed as directed above.

From Baltimore/Washington, D.C., take I-95 north. At Chester, Pennsylvania, exit onto I-476, towards Plymouth Meeting. Stay on I-476, then exit onto I-276 east. Take I-276 to Exit 343 (Willow Grove). Follow Route 611 north (follow bypass route not business route through Doylestown)11 miles to Route 202 south—Norristown exit. Bear right off of exit onto 202 South for 0.25 mile, turn left on New Britain Road (first road on left next to Delaware Valley College). Entrance to Fordhook is 0.25 mile on left through two stone pillars.

Bucks County Open Days
Friday & Saturday
May 18 & 19

BUCKS COUNTY

DOYLESTOWN

Heronswood Nursery
Comes to Fordhook Farm of
W. Atlee Burpee & Co.
105 New Britain Road

You will have the opportunity to take a "behind the scenes" tour of the Burpee and Heronswood's famed trials and testing operations. In 1888, W. Atlee Burpee acquired several hundred acres of farmland in bucolic Bucks County. Today at Fordhook Farm, as before, hundreds of new vegetables, annuals, and perennials are grown, tested and evaluated on a sixty-acre test farm and network of gardens to guarantee

Burpee's high standards of quality. Once home to the Burpee family, the eighteenth-century manor has been designated a National Historic Site. The house features the richly paneled study where W. Atlee Burpee compiled and edited the first Burpee catalogs. Burpee Hall, located in an adjoining stone barn, has been fully renovated as a conference center. It features a 360° hand-painted mural of Fordhook Farm during the late nineteenth century. Once the hub for seed processing at Fordhook, the one-of-a-kind Seed House is located across the drive from the manor. Be sure to visit the many trial gardens—birthplace of culinary favorites such as Golden Bantam, the first yellow sweet corn, Big Boy tomato, Iceberg lettuce, Fordhook lima bean, and ornamental innovations such as the double-flowered rudbeckia daisy, 'Gloriosa', and the many generations of pure white marigolds. See the ad on page 243 for information on speakers and the opporturnity to purchase plants from Burpee's Heronswood collection. **2006**

Hours: 10 a.m. to 4 p.m..

From Philadelphia, take I-95 north to Route 332 west towards Newtown. Take Route 332 for 3.7 miles to Route 413 north. Take Route 413 for 10.4 miles to Route 202 south. Take Route 202 for 3.5 miles to State Street. Follow State Street south past the hospital and over Route 611, then go 0.25 mile and turn left onto New Britain Road (the first road on the left next to Delaware Valley College). The entrance to Fordhook Farm is 0.25 mile on the left through two stone pillars.

From New York and points north, take I-287 south to Route 202 across the Delaware River to Doylestown (about 45 miles from Somerville). Proceed as directed above.

From Baltimore/Washington, D.C., take I-95 north. At Chester, Pennsylvania, exit onto I-476, towards Plymouth Meeting. Stay on I-476, then exit onto I-276 east. Take I-276 to Exit 343 (Willow Grove). Follow Route 611 north (follow bypass route not business route through Doylestown)11 miles to Route 202 south—Norristown exit. Bear right off of exit onto 202 South for 0.25 mile, turn left on New Britain Road (first road on left next to Dela-

ware Valley College). Entrance to Fordhook is 0.25 mile on left through two stone pillars.

Bucks County Open Day
Saturday, May 19
BUCKS COUNTY

van Dyke/Reynolds Garden
330 Linden Avenue

This garden, designed by landscape architect Carter van Dyke, was begun in 1992 when the historic Dolington Library was moved to the site to prevent its destruction. The yard is divided into several distinct "rooms" dictated by the unusual shape of the yard. Two formal axes give structure to the design. A kitchen garden contains raised beds, while a warm hue garden surrounding a small pond is largely hidden from the house. Between the library and side yard are spring flowering perennials. This is an all season garden. **NEW**

Hours: 10 a.m. to 4 p.m.

Take Route 202 south to Doylestown. After crossing Route 113, Route 202 veers left to become a 4-lane bypass. Continue straight up hill into center of Doylestown. Near top of hill turn right at intersection of Spruce Street. Continue to end of block, then turn right onto Linden Avenue. #330 Linden Avenue is second house on right. There is a white picket fence and privet hedge in front.

Take Route 611 North from Pennsylvania Turnpike. Upon nearing Doylestown, avoid bypass and take Doylestown exit onto South Main Street. At second traffic light turn right onto Oakland Avenue. Continue until fourth intersection and turn left onto Spruce Street. Proceed as directed above. Please park on street or in church parking lot on left.

WRIGHTSTOWN
Hortulus Farm
60 Thompson Mill Road

Our garden appears as an integral part of the Pennsylvania landscape, as befits an eighteenth-century farmstead with barns and a healthy population of animals. We are lucky

enough to be nestled in our own little valley, quite far off the road and unusual for a house of this age. Our 100 acres try to respect the integrity of the farm's historical significance and the natural landscape, with the occasional whimsical or formal statement thrown in. There are lots of woods and pasture, lots of shrubs and naturalized perennial plantings in the stream and woodland gardens, yet also formal borders, follies, gazebos, and sizeable herb and vegetable gardens. All are anchored by the formal simplicity of classic Bucks County architecture. In the past years, we have been fortunate enough to have had the gardens featured in *House & Garden*, *House Beautiful*, *Horticulture*, *Garden Design*, *Organic Gardening*, *Country Living*, *Quest*, and *Food & Wine* magazines, as well as on HGTV's "Secret Gardens of Philadelphia" and "The Travel Channel". **2006**

Hours: 10 a.m. to 4 p.m.

From New Hope, take Windy Bush Road/Route 232 south about 5 miles. At "Wrightstown Township" sign on right, turn immediately left onto Pineville Road. Go about 1 mile to right onto Thompson Mill Road. Continue over bridge through series of steep, winding, up-hill turns and up into a clearing and straightaway. Proceed to #60 for parking.

From Philadelphia, take I-95 north towards Trenton about 40 miles to Exit 31/New Hope. Turn left at end of exit ramp onto Taylorsville Road. Go north 3 miles to Wood Hill Road and turn left. Go about 2.7 miles to first stop sign. Turn right onto Eagle Road, go 0.3 mile, and make first left onto Pineville Road. Proceed as directed above.

Philadelphia Area Open Day
Sunday, June 10

There is a garden open in nearby New Castle County, Delaware. See their listing on page 117.

CHESTER COUNTY

WEST CHESTER
Inta Krombolz
1660 Fox Crossing

The thee-and-one-half-acre everchanging wonderland that is Inta Krombolz's garden began twenty-five years ago when she and her husband Skip built their home in West Chester. The garden is planted with not only her collection of choice plants, but also her elegant iron sculptures, most of which are rarely permanent and are often up for grabs to her clientele. With the help of her husband and son, Inta hand digs the pond, stream, and channels that meander through mature oak, ash, and beech trees in a natural runoff area fed by underground springs. A tour of this garden leads to discovery of treasure after treasure, an experience that lead the Garden Writers of America to bestow their own award up the garden during their tour last summer. **NEW**

Hours: 11 a.m. to 5 p.m.

From Blue Route/Route 476, take the Route 3 Exit toward West Chester. Turn right onto Duttong Mill Road. Turn left onto Manley. Turn right onto Wyllpen Drive. Turn left onto Fox Crossing and go to #1660 on left.

DELAWARE COUNTY

CHADDS FORD
WynEden
10 Lafayette Place

Set between two hills with two ponds fed by three small streams and thus blessed with abundant natural moisture and high shade, this garden resembles a small, private park carved out of the Brandywine Woods. The six and one-half acres of the main garden contain three distinct sections: the first section is dominated by thousands of hosta of three varieties that sweep down the north hillside in large waves of color. This area is bordered on each side by large shade gardens containing hardy, woodland orchids, wood anemones, large patches of spring blooming phlox, trilliums, hellebores, dozens of different types of ferns and numerous epimediums, asarum, arisaema, hepaticas and of course more hosta (more than 350 different cultivars at last count). The natural setting of this garden is spectacular and great care has been taken in designing the gardens to ensure that they enhance the many vistas and contribute to the sense of serenity that reigns in this place. **NEW**

Hours: 11 a.m. to 5 p.m.

From Route 202 south, pass Route 926/Street Road. Turn right at Volvo dealership and follow signs for Dilworthtown Inn. Pass the Inn. At the "five corners" intersection, take the street at "11 o'clock", Oakland Street. Turn right onto Webb Road at first stop sign. Go about 0.75 mile, and turn right onto Lafayette Place. If you get to Route 1, you have gone too far. Number 10 is the last and only house on the cul-de-sac.

From Route 52, turn onto Route 1 going north. Pass Creek Road/Old 100 North and the Chadds Ford Inn. Take the next left onto Webb Road. If you get to the battlefield you have gone too far. Follow Webb for about 1 mile and turn left onto Lafayette Place. If you get to Oakland Road, you have gone too far. Number 10 is the last and only house on the cul-de-sac From the intersection of Route 1, 322 and 202, follow the sign for combined Route 322 west and Route 202 north. Turn left at 2nd traffic light after Garnett Ford, onto Oakland Road. At 2nd stop sign, turn left onto Webb Road. Go about 0.75 mile and turn right onto Lafayette Place. If you get to Oakland Road, you have gone too far. Number 10 is the last and only house on the cul-de-sac.

DOWNINGTOWN
David Culp
1158 Osborne Road

David has created a mixed border for sun and shade that combines native and exotic plants in a naturalistic design. There are rock, woodland, and vegetable gardens, the latter enclosed with a charming picket fence and beautifully design by plants that form an artful structure. The ruins of an old carriage house allow for a walled garden featuring many troughs and containers full of unusual plants. David breeds hellebores and there are bound to be some of the beauties he favors still lingering. **NEW**

Hours: 11 a.m. to 5 p.m.

From Route 202, take Route 30 West/Route 30 Bypass to the Thorndale Exit. Turn right from the ramp to the second road on right, Osborne Road. Turn right and cross one-lane

bridge. Go up hill to the house on the right behind a stockade fence.

GLEN MILLS
Jim & Conny Parsons
1206 Holly Lane

Appropriate names for the property would have been "Briar Patch" or "Thornberry," giving you an idea of what we faced when making room for lawn, gardens, and deer fence. A center lawn sweeps back through an odd, pie-shaped lot bordered by trees and under-planted with long borders and beds on all sides. The stones in the pond and borders were salvaged from large piles of rock from an old farm house that previously occupied the land. The two-tiered pond is designed to maintain a natural balance using water hyacinths in the upper tier to filter the water for the larger, lower pond. The developer contributed several large pieces of farm equipment which have been incorporated into the landscape. There are nearly 500 hosta cultivars throughout the garden. Views from the shady borders look out to a sunny rose and perennial garden and other beds that show a passion for bright colorful foliage in shrubs and trees. Paths and stopping points with benches create intimate spaces in this large garden. There is a secret garden in the back of the property that has a gazebo with rockers where you can sit and pretend that all the world is a garden. The gardens are maintained solely by Jim, Conny, and John Deere. **NEW**

Hours: 11 a.m. to 5 p.m.

From south, take I-95 south, past airport, to I-476 North towards Plymouth Meeting. Take Exit #5 South/Route 1/Lima. Go 3.7 miles to Route 352. Exit onto Route 352 and go 2.9 miles, turn left onto Sycamore Mills Road (the sign is hard to see, look for Locus Crest Tavern and Red Bud Native Nursery). Go 0.6 mile, over a narrow bridge, up a hill and turn right onto Holly Lane. We are a white house with green window trim at #1206.

From north, take I-76 West to I-476 South towards Chester. Take Broomall/Newtown Square/West Chester Exit onto Route 3/West Chester Pike. Drive through Newtown Square

on Route 252, go past light at Providence Road (there is a Dairy Queen on left), to the next light, turn left onto Delchester Road. Delchester Road ends at Gradyville Road, turn right. Go a short distance to light at Gradyville Road and Route 352, turn left and go 0.5 mile and turn right onto Sycamore Mill Road at Red Bud Native Nursery. Drive 0.6 mile, over a narrow bridge, up hill and turn right onto Holly Lane. Number 1206 is the white house with green window trim.

Bucks County Open Days
Friday & Saturday
August 3 & 4
BUCKS COUNTY

DOYLESTOWN
Heronswood Nursery
Comes to Fordhook Farm of
W. Atlee Burpee & Co.
105 New Britain Road

You will have the opportunity to take a "behind the scenes" tour of the Burpee and Heronswood's famed trials and testing operations. In 1888, W. Atlee Burpee acquired several hundred acres of farmland in bucolic Bucks County. Today at Fordhook Farm, as before, hundreds of new vegetables, annuals, and perennials are grown, tested and evaluated on a sixty-acre test farm and network of gardens to guarantee Burpee's high standards of quality. Once home to the Burpee family, the eighteenth-century manor has been designated a National Historic Site. The house features the richly paneled study where W. Atlee Burpee compiled and edited the first Burpee catalogs. Burpee Hall, located in an adjoining stone barn, has been fully renovated as a conference center. It features a 360º hand-painted mural of Fordhook Farm during the late nineteenth century. Once the hub for seed processing at Fordhook, the one-of-a-kind Seed House is located across the drive from the manor. Be sure to visit the many trial gardens—birthplace of culinary favorites such as Golden Bantam, the first yellow sweet corn, Big Boy tomato, Iceberg lettuce, Fordhook lima bean, and ornamental innovations such as the double-flowered rudbeckia daisy, 'Gloriosa', and the many generations of pure white marigolds. See the ad on page 243 for information on speakers and the opporturnity to purchase plants from Burpee's Heronswood collection. **2006**

Hours: 10 a.m. to 4 p.m.

From Philadelphia, take I-95 north to Route 332 west towards Newtown. Take Route 332 for 3.7 miles to Route 413 north. Take Route 413 for 10.4 miles to Route 202 south. Take Route 202 for 3.5 miles to State Street. Follow State Street south past the hospital and over Route 611, then go 0.25 mile and turn left onto New Britain Road (the first road on the left next to Delaware Valley College). The entrance to Fordhook Farm is 0.25 mile on the left through two stone pillars.

From New York and points north, take I-287 south to Route 202 across the Delaware River to Doylestown (about 45 miles from Somerville). Proceed as directed above.

From Baltimore/Washington, D.C., take I-95 north. At Chester, Pennsylvania, exit onto I-476, towards Plymouth Meeting. Stay on I-476, then exit onto I-276 east. Take I-276 to Exit 343 (Willow Grove). Follow Route 611 north (follow bypass route not business route through Doylestown)11 miles to Route 202 south—Norristown exit. Bear right off of exit onto 202 South for 0.25 mile, turn left on New Britain Road (first road on left next to Delaware Valley College). Entrance to Fordhook is 0.25 mile on left through two stone pillars.

Bucks County Open Day
Saturday, August 4

PERKASIE

Carol A. Pierce
839 Callowhill Road

Located five minutes from Peace Valley Park, the gardens within this tranquil setting have won twelve first place awards in the Bucks Beautiful Garden competitions. This is a series of vignette gardens designed to flow from one to another. There are many elements of interest,

great fragrances, a private area, a peaceful feeling, and a little bit of playfulness. Featured is a beach theme garden packed with ornamental grasses, boulders and perennials for a burst of color and surprise. This imaginative garden prepares the visitor for the interesting gardens and beautifully decorated deck located in the back yard. To add to the property's tranquility, there are two water gardens–the first, of traditional style, was designed to be viewed from the house's breakfast room. The second water garden is of very contemporary design and uniquely built into the house's entranceway deck. Perennials and flowering shrubs, punctuated with the use of unusual garden ornaments and elements, combine to attract birds and butterflies. The use of strong color is an important element and very harmonious as all of the annuals, perennials, and flowering shrubs were specifically selected to coordinate with the house's unique exterior color scheme. **2006**

Hours: 11 a.m. to 5 p.m.

From I-276, take Fort Washington exit. Take Route 309 north to Route 113 exit. Turn right. At sixth traffic light, turn right onto Callowhill Road; #839 is 1 mile on left.

From Doylestown, go north on Route 313 through Dublin. Turn left onto Route 113. Travel to first light and turn left onto Callowhill Road; #839 is 1 mile on left. Please park on right, next to detached garage. Additional parking is available directly across the street.

Go northwest on New Britain Road toward Route 202 West/State Street. Turn left onto East Butler Avenue/Route 202. Go 1.4 miles and turn right onto Keeley Avenue which quickly becomes Ironhill Road. Ironhill Road then becomes Old Ironhill Road. At the traffic light, turn left onto Ferry Road. At the 'T' intersection, turn right onto Callowhill Road. At the light, continue on Callowhill Road. At the 'T' intersection, turn left and then quickly turn right back onto Callowhill Road. Number 839 is located 0.4 mile on right.

POINT PLEASANT
The Gardens at Mill Fleurs
27 Cafferty Road

The gardens at Mill Fleurs, a 1742 grist mill on the often-raging Tohickon Creek, are set into massive rock outcroppings and steep woodland slopes. We have drama and drainage. Everything else is pure challenge. I am a hopeless collector of any plant family that thrives in shade; anything with a green or black flower, any plant we haven't seen before in Zone 6. Creating a landscape that will appeal to people who might be casual gardeners out of all these collections is a challenge I enjoy. The gardens are organized by color: all the plants in a given area will have either foliage or flowers of the same color family. This subtle arrangement is demanding because it makes you look closely, which visitors seem to like doing. **2005**

Hours: Guided tours at 10 a.m., 12 p.m., & 2 p.m.

Mill Fleurs is 100 yards off River Road/Route 32, 9 miles north of New Hope and 7 miles south of the bridge over the Delaware River at Frenchtown, NJ. The Point Pleasant Baptist Church is in the fork where Cafferty Road branches off Route 32. Please park in the church parking lot, entering it from River Road on the north side of the church. Walk around the split rail fence at the back of the church and cross Cafferty Road. Walk down the driveway across from the back door of the church and enter the garden.

Bucks County Open Days
Friday & Saturday
September 21 & 22

BUCKS COUNTY

DOYLESTOWN
Heronswood Nursery
Comes to Fordhook Farm of
W. Atlee Burpee & Co.
105 New Britain Road

You will have the opportunity to take a "behind the scenes" tour of the Burpee and Heronswood's famed trials and testing operations. In 1888, W. Atlee Burpee acquired several hundred acres of farmland in bucolic Bucks County. Today at Fordhook Farm, as before, hundreds of new vegetables, annuals, and perennials are grown, tested and evaluated on a sixty-acre test farm and network of gardens to guarantee Burpee's high standards of quality. Once home to the Burpee family, the eighteenth-century manor has been designated a National Historic Site. The house features the richly paneled study where W. Atlee Burpee compiled and edited the first Burpee catalogs. Burpee Hall, located in an adjoining stone barn, has been fully renovated as a conference center. It features a 360º hand-painted mural of Fordhook Farm during the late nineteenth century. Once the hub for seed processing at Fordhook, the one-of-a-kind Seed House is located across the drive from the manor. Be sure to visit the many trial gardens—birthplace of culinary favorites such as Golden Bantam, the first yellow sweet corn, Big Boy tomato, Iceberg lettuce, Fordhook lima bean, and ornamental innovations such as the double-flowered rudbeckia daisy, 'Gloriosa', and the many generations of pure white marigolds. See the ad on page 243 for information on speakers and the opportunity to purchase plants from Burpee's Heronswood collection. **2006**

Hours: 10 a.m. to 4 p.m.

From Philadelphia, take I-95 north to Route 332 west towards Newtown. Take Route 332 for 3.7 miles to Route 413 north. Take Route 413 for 10.4 miles to Route 202 south. Take Route 202 for 3.5 miles to State Street. Follow State Street south past the hospital and over Route 611, then go 0.25 mile and turn left onto New Britain Road (the first road on the left next to Delaware Valley College). The entrance to Fordhook Farm is 0.25 mile on the left through two stone pillars.

From New York and points north, take I-287 south to Route 202 across the Delaware River to Doylestown (about 45 miles from Somerville). Proceed as directed above.

From Baltimore/Washington, D.C., take I-95 north. At Chester, Pennsylvania, exit onto I-476, towards Plymouth Meeting. Stay on I-476, then exit onto I-276 east. Take I-276 to Exit 343 (Willow Grove). Follow Route 611 north (follow bypass route not business route through Doylestown)11 miles to Route 202 south—Norristown exit. Bear right off of exit onto 202 South for 0.25 mile, turn left on New Britain Road (first road on left next to Delaware Valley College). Entrance to Fordhook is 0.25 mile on left through two stone pillars.

Public Gardens

BUCKS COUNTY

LANGHORN

The Healing Gardens at St. Mary Medical Center

*1201 Langhorne-Newtown Road
(Route 413),
www.healinggardens-stmary.org*

This is one of the few Japanese gardens within the Delaware Valley. The garden includes a Japanese walk, koi pond, woodland glade, bamboo grove, and a dining terrace. The garden is filled with Japanese plantings and ornamental structures. The gardens were designed by Carter van Dyke, Landscape Architect.

Hours: Year round, daily, dawn to dusk

Admission: Free

The garden is located in the center of the St. Mary Medical Center building campus. The hospital is located on Route 413 midway between Newtown Borough and Langhorne Borough in Bucks County, Pennsylvania.

MORRISVILLE

Pennsbury Manor

*400 Pennsbury Memorial Road,
(215) 946-0400, www.pennsburymanor.org*

Pennsbury Manor is the recreated summer home of William Penn, founder of the state of Pennsylvania. The forty-four-acre site sits along the Delaware River, north of Philadelphia. Guests can visit a seventeenth-century-style kitchen garden, formal garden, and tour historic buildings.

Hours: Year round, Tuesday through Saturday, 9 a.m. to 5 p.m.; Sunday, 12 p.m. to 5 p.m. Closed Mondays. Please call for tour times.

Admission: $5 adults, $4.50 seniors, $3 children 6 to 17, children under 5 free.

From Pennsylvania Turnpike, take Exit 358 to Route 13N. Turn right onto Green Lane at first traffic light. Turn left onto Radcliffe Street at dead end. Continue 4.6 miles (road changes names to Main Street and Bordentown Road). Pass pair of lakes, and turn right onto Pennsbury Memorial Road.

From 1-95 north, take Exit 40/Bristol to Route 413S to Route 13N. Go 2 miles to turnpike. Turn right onto Green Lane at next traffic light; then follow directions noted above.

From I-95 south, take Exit 51A/Yardley onto Taylorsville Road south (Main Street in Yardley, becomes Route 13S, south of Yardley). Continue on Route 13S to Tyburn Road east. Turn right at first traffic light onto New Ford Mill Road. Turn right at dead end and then first left onto Pennsbury Memorial Road.

From Route 1, take Route 13S to Tyburn Road east. Go about 2 miles to first traffic light and turn right onto New Ford Mill Road. Turn right at dead end and then first left onto Pennsbury Memorial Road.

CHESTER COUNTY

CHADDS FORD

Brandywine River Museum Wildflower & Native Plant Gardens

*Route 1, (610) 388-2700,
www.brandywinemuseum.org*

Begun in 1974, the gardens feature indigenous and some naturalized plants of the greater Brandywine region displayed in natural settings. The gardens use wildflowers, trees, and shrubs in landscaped areas. Plants are selected to provide a succession of bloom from early spring through the first killing frost.

Hours: Year round, daily, dawn to dusk

Admission: Free

From I-95 north, take Route 141 north exit to Route 52 north. Follow Route 52 until it intersects with Route 1. Turn right and travel 2 miles to museum.

🕭 indicates parts of garden are handicapped accessible

KENNETT SQUARE
Longwood Gardens
Route 1, (610) 388-1000,
www.longwoodgardens.org

One of the world's premier horticultural displays, Longwood offers 1,050 acres of gardens, woodlands, and meadows; twenty outdoor gardens; twenty indoor gardens within four acres of greenhouses; 11,000 types of plants; spectacular fountains; extensive educational programs; and 800 events each year.

Hours: Year round, daily, 9 a.m. to 5 p.m. Frequently open late for seasonal display.

Admission: $12 to $15 adults (varies by season), $6 students 16 to 20, $2 children 6 to 15, children under 6 free.

Located on Route 1, 3 miles northeast of Kennett Square, Pennsylvania, and 12 miles north of Wilmington, Delaware.

DELAWARE COUNTY

SWARTHMORE
Scott Arboretum
of Swarthmore College
500 College Avenue, (610) 328-8025,
www.scottarboretum.org

The Scott Arboretum is a green oasis uniquely situated on the Swarthmore College campus. More than 300 acres comprise the college landscape and provide a display of the best ornamental plants recommended for Delaware Valley gardens. There are more than 3,000 different kinds of plants grown on the campus. Major plant collections include flowering cherries, crabapples, hydrangeas, lilacs, magnolias, rhododendrons, tree peonies, viburnums, wisteria, and witch hazels. Special gardens include the Rose Garden, Fragrance Garden, Teaching Garden, Entrance Garden, and Winter Garden.

Hours: Year round, daily, dawn to dusk

Admission: Free

From I-95, take Exit 7/I-476 North/Plymouth Meeting. Take I-476 to Exit 3/Media/Swarthmore. Turn right onto Baltimore Pike and follow signs for Swarthmore. Stay in right lane 0.25 mile and turn right onto Route

320 south. Go to second traffic light; turn right onto College Avenue.

WAYNE
Chanticleer
786 Church Road, (610) 687-4163,
www.chanticleergarden.org

This thirty-five-acre pleasure garden was formerly the home of the Rosengarten family. Emphasis is on ornamental plants, particularly herbaceous perennials. The garden is a dynamic mix of formal and naturalistic areas, collections of flowering trees and shrubs, ponds, meadows, wildflower gardens, a ruin garden, and a garden of shade-loving Asian herbaceous plants.

Hours: April through October, Wednesday through Sunday, 10 a.m. to 5 p.m.; May through August, extended hours to 8 p.m. on Fridays.

Admission: $5, children under 16 free.

Take I-76 west to I-476 south. Take Exit 13 toward Villanova. Turn right at intersection of Routes 30 and 320 south. Turn right at next traffic light onto Conestoga Road. Turn left at second light onto Church Road. Go 0.5 mile to Chanticleer.

MONTGOMERY COUNTY

MEADOWBROOK
Meadowbrook Farm
& Greenhouse
1633 Washington Lane, (215) 887-5900,
www.meadowbrook-farm.com

This beautiful garden is the life's work of J. Liddon Pennock. Designed as a series of outdoor rooms, each garden is unique and comfortable, with the emphasis on design. The public display garden leads to the greenhouse, where plants and garden gifts are available.

Hours: Year round, Monday through Saturday, 10 a.m. to 5 p.m. Tours for groups of fifteen to forty people by appointment only; call for reservations and fee.

Admission: Free

From I-76, take Route 611 south and turn left onto Route 63. After about 1.5 miles, turn right onto Washington Lane. Meadowbrook Farm sign is located about 0.75 mile on left.

PHILADELPHIA

Bartram's Garden
54th Street & Lindbergh Boulevard,
(215) 729-5281, www.bartramsgarden.org

Bartram's Garden is America's oldest living botanic garden, founded in 1728 by John Bartram, America's first great botanist, naturalist, and plant explorer. The forty-five-acre site on the banks of the Schuylkill River includes the National Historic Landmark Bartram house and other unique eighteenth-century farm buildings, a botanic garden, historic trees, a fifteen-acre wildflower meadow, a water garden, a wetland, a parkland, and a museum shop.

Hours: March through December, Tuesday through Sunday, 12 p.m. to 4 p.m.; January and February, group tours by reservation.

Admission: Grounds free, call for tour fee.

Less than 15 minutes from Center City Philadelphia and convenient to I-76 and I-95. Please visit website or call for directions.

Fairmount Park Horticulture Center & Arboretum
Belmont Avenue & North Horticultural Drive, (215) 685-0096

The arboretum covers twenty-two acres and boasts an assortment of trees, many of which have been labeled with both common and botanical names. The display house is the first greenhouse you enter from the lobby. Its permanent display includes palm and fig trees, oleander, and bougainvillea. The next greenhouse contains a magnificent collection of cacti and succulents. There are also many statues and perennial gardens.

Hours: Year round, daily, 9 a.m. to 3 p.m.

Admission: Free

From I-76/I-276, take Exit 341/Montgomery Drive. Turn left at traffic light onto Montgomery Drive and go 1 block. Turn left onto Horticultural Drive. Proceed to #100.

Morris Arboretum of the University of Pennsylvania
100 Northwestern Avenue,
(215) 247-5777,
www.morrisarboretum.org

Morris Arboretum is an historic Victorian garden and educational institution dedicated to understanding the relationships between people and plants. Its living collection contains about 2,550 taxa and more than 14,000 accessioned and labeled plants from the temperate northern hemisphere, parts of Asia, Europe, and North America.

Hours: April through October, weekdays, 10 a.m. to 4 p.m.; weekends, 10 a.m. to 5 p.m.; November through March, daily, 10 a.m. to 4 p.m.

Admission: $10 adults, $8 seniors, $5 children 3 to 18 and students with valid ID, children under 3 free.

Take I-76/Schuylkill Expressway to Blue Route/I-476 north. Take Plymouth Meeting exit and follow signs for Germantown Pike east. Continue on Germantown Pike 4 miles and turn left onto Northwestern Avenue. Arboretum entrance is 0.25 mile on right.

TENNESSEE
Knoxville Open Days
Saturday & Sunday
May 19 & 20

KNOX COUNTY

KNOXVILLE
Bush Garden
4084 Kingston Pike

Nine years ago, when Condon and Betsey Bush began renovating the 1927 house built by Ben A. Morton, they found evidence of the original garden, designed by Alma Alison in 1934, buried under eight to forty inches of soil. That soil was removed and features of the original garden were incorporated into the current design. The garden entrance is a beautiful wrought-iron gate set in a magnificent brick wall. An herb garden bordered by boxwood is the first of many beds to be found throughout the property. Ivy-covered brick pillars set into a fence separate the main garden from the side entry. Walnut, hackberry, and white oak trees in the main garden are from the original garden. Stone paths accented with mill stones lead from the back of the house to a series of terraces with stone walls planted with perennials, bulbs, and shrubs. One terrace is used exclusively for roses, another for dahlias of exceptional size and beauty. The four ponds on the grounds have incorporated sculpture for added interest. An informal, meandering path leads the visitor through well-planted perennial gardens. The sunny portion of the path is home to daylilies, iris, and other sun-loving perennials. Dappled shade is filled with trillium, Jacob's ladder, Jack-in-the-pulpit, hostas, astilbes, ferns, and Lenten roses. Visitors will have the opportunity to see the "before" pictures from nine years ago to compare with the amazing renewal of this old garden. **NEW**

Hours: Saturday, 10 a.m. to 5 p.m.; Sunday, 1 p.m. to 5 p.m.

From I-40, take Exit 386B south/Alcoa Highway. Take first exit (Kingston Pike). Go about 1.9 miles and turn left onto Kingston Park Drive at Saint George Greek Orthodox Church. Park on right in church parking lot and follow signs to garden's entrance.

Proceeds shared with Knoxville Botanical Garden & Arboretum

GATOP
2705 Riverside Drive

Atop a hillside overlooking the Tennessee River and the Great Smoky Mountains exists an estate of great historical and botanical interest called GATOP (God's Answer to Our Prayers). Among the many hundreds of botanical specimens are deciduous and coniferous trees, as well as hollies, shrubs, perennials, and groundcovers. Large millstones, used two centuries ago to grind corn at nearby Williams Creek Mill, have been used as pathways. Many stone walls, walkways, and steps have been built using indigenous limestone. Waterfalls, ponds, and meandering streams have been constructed. Extensive collections of native wildflowers and ferns have been planted. Many unusual and rare specimens have been intermixed with large native trees including American elm, walnut, hackberry, mulberry, pines, cedars, and various species of oaks, hickories, and magnolias. These are complemented by prominently sited stainless steel, iron, bronze, and stone sculptures. **NEW**

Hours: Saturday, 10 a.m. to 5 p.m.; Sunday, 1 p.m. to 5 p.m.

From I-40, exit at Alcoa Highway and take Neyland Drive exit; continue east to Riverside Drive exits. Continue east on Riverside Drive for 1.5 miles, bear right at Vulcan Materials and continue 0.4 miles to #2705. There is a black mailbox on the left. Proceed up driveway to parking area.

Proceeds shared with Knoxville Botanical Garden & Arboretum

Hill Top Farm
5617 Lyons View Pike

Hill Top Garden sits on an elevated site with a spectacular view of the Tennessee River and the Great Smoky Mountains. Master garden designer and internationally acclaimed champion of gardens, Ryan Gainey, together with architect Marc Mosley, have created this one-of-a-kind garden. Distinctive architectural elements of the Arts and Crafts-style 1916 house have been combined with considerations of lifestyle and favorite vistas create an environment of elegance and gracious living. A pergola of stone and wood nearly 100-feet-long dominates the center of the design and echoes that of Hestercombe Gardens in the Cotswolds. Planted with wisteria, roses, asters, and many other annuals, perennials, and shrubs, this main axis gives way to stone stairs through lushly planted beds to a lower demilune terrace with a Dumbarton Oaks-inspired semi-circular allée of meticulously pruned hornbeam trees centered by a baptistery fountain. **NEW**

Hours: Saturday, 10 a.m. to 5 p.m.; Sunday, 1 p.m. to 5 p.m.

From I-40/I-75, take Papermill Road Exit. Then take Northshore Drive south to Kingston Pike. Go 0.7 miles south on Northshore and turn left at second light onto Lyons View Pike. Go 0.6 mile and turn left into the driveway of Hill Top Farm (second driveway past Cherokee at West Cliff Condominiums).

Proceeds shared with Knoxville Botanical Garden & Arboretum

Public Gardens
KNOX COUNTY

KNOXVILLE
Blount Mansion Garden
200 West Hill Avenue, (865) 525-2375, www.blountmansion.org

The Knoxville Garden Club has been responsible for maintaining the Blount Mansion Garden since 1934. The present garden was designed by Alden Hopkins, former head of landscape for Colonial Williamsburg, to create an eighteenth-century garden with respect for historical detail. The style and plantings are authentically eighteenth century and is a perfect example of a colonial revival-style garden.

Hours: March through December, Tuesday through Saturday, 9:30 a.m. to 5 p.m.; Sunday,

1 p.m. to 5 p.m. Closed January through February, except for scheduled group tours.

Admission: Free to garden. Mansion, $4.95 adults. $2.50 children 6-17, under 6 free.

From I-40, take Exit 389 to Hill Avenue. (Turn left from I-40 West or right from I-40 East). Go on Hall of Fame Drive to end and turn right onto Hill Avenue. Cross the viaduct, turn left into the visitor parking area behind the mansion.

Ivan Racheff House & Gardens
1943 Tennessee Avenue, (865) 522-6210, www.disoveret.org/racheff

The property consists of three acres surrounding the house. Plantings include flowering shrubs, wildflowers, ferns, bulbs, perennials, and annuals. There is a freshwater pond, a memorial fountain, and a Blue Star Memorial Marker in the gardens. Construction of a children's garden is under way.

Hours: February 15 through December 15, Monday through Friday. Monday through Sunday during Knoxville's Dogwood Arts Festival in April. The house is open by appointment.

Admission: Free. Donation for house.

From I-40 west, exit onto I-640 West and go to Exit 1. Turn east onto Highway 62 and go about 1 mile to Tennessee Avenue on left. Entrance to garden is on left.

From I-75 South, exit onto I-640 and take Exit 1. Proceed as directed above.

Knoxville Botanical Garden & Arboretum
2743 Wimpole Avenue, (865) 540-8690, www.knoxgarden.org

In 2001, a group of interested Knoxvillians formed a nonprofit organization for the purpose of creating a botanical garden and arboretum at the site of the Joe N. Howell and C. B. Howell Nurseries. The C. B. Nursery was established in 1786 on property the first Mr. Howell received through a land grant from the state of North Carolina in 1784 and was the oldest, continually operating business in the state of Tennessee until it was purchased by the Knoxville Botanical Garden and Arboretum in 2004. The site

ら indicates parts of garden are handicapped accessible

sits on a ridge-top five minutes from downtown Knoxville. The gardens are a magical place with whimsical round-stone buildings, stone-sided greenhouses, and secret garden paths and alleys. Today, mature specimens of rare and unusual trees and shrubs remain surrounded by thousands of feet of beautiful stone walls.

Hours: Special Garden Conservancy Open Days, May 19 & 20, 10 a.m. to 5 p.m. Otherwise Monday through Friday, 8 a.m. to 4 p.m.

Admission: Free

Take I-40, Exit 389/Hall of Fame Drive. From the I-40 E, turn right onto Hall of Fame and go to fourth traffic light and turn left onto Summit Hill Avenue. From I-40 W, turn left onto Hall of Fame Drive. Go to the fifth traffic light and turn left onto Summit Hill Drive. Continue on Summit Hill. At next light at Martin Luther King Avenue, street becomes Dandridge Avenue, go to five-way stop, go straight but to left at a convenience store. Road becomes Brooks Road. Go up a hill and down a steeper grade. At bottom of grade, turn left onto Biddle Street. Go to three-way stop and turn right onto Boyd's Bridge Pike. Go 0.25 mile there will be stone walls on left. Follow wall which then turns left at Wimpole Avenue. Proceed on Wimpole to parking area across from the garden office.

University of Tennessee Gardens
E. J. Chapman Drive, (865) 974-7324, www.utgardens.tennessee.edu

These gardens are an outdoor laboratory and classroom used to evaluate the performance and demonstrate the landscape use of every type of plant including trees and shrubs, annuals and perennials, ornamental grasses, and herbs. These mid-South test gardens are important proving grounds for leading commercial seed and plant companies around the world to ultimately determine what plants reach the commercial market. Established in 1983 by the Department of Plant Sciences, the gardens are one of the thirty-seven official All-America Selections test sites in the country. The perennial collection contains more than 500 varieties while the herb garden features more than 350 varieties. The tree and shrub collection has

more than 500 different selections with an emphasis on dwarf conifers.

Hours: Year round daily, dawn to dusk

Admission: Free

Take I-40 to Exit 386B/Airport/Alcoa/Highway 129/Smoky Mountains. Next take Neyland Drive/University of Tennessee/Highway 158 exit. Turn left at light. Go to second light and turn left into Campus main entrance/Joe Johnson Drive. Go to traffic light and turn right onto E. J. Chapman Drive. This takes you into parking lot #66. Go to right end far corner of parking lot where you will see signs for the UT Gardens and parking.

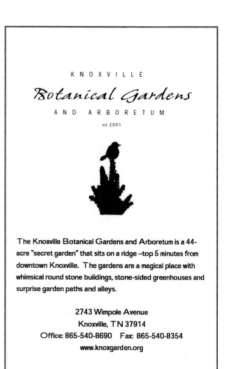

KNOXVILLE
Botanical Gardens
AND ARBORETUM
est 2001

The Knoxville Botanical Gardens and Arboretum is a 44-acre "secret garden" that sits on a ridge –top 5 minutes from downtown Knoxville. The gardens are a magical place with whimsical round stone buildings, stone-sided greenhouses and surprise garden paths and alleys.

2743 Wimpole Avenue
Knoxville, TN 37914
Office: 865-540-8690   Fax: 865-540-8354
www.knoxgarden.org

TEXAS
El Paso Open Days
Saturday & Sunday
May 5 & 6

EL PASO COUNTY

EL PASO
Azar Garden
5014 Vista del Monte

Enter through the old wooden door to the right of the garage. You'll step through a hidden garden and a gate to the back. To the left is a flagstone patio that leads into a garden room, then the patio at the center of our house. This is a subtropical world, ready to be experienced. Our goal in the back garden was "green", to be enjoyed from all facing windows, and some whimsy to delight. Front plantings reflect the owners' love of color…lots of color. You're most welcome and we hope you enjoy. **NEW**

Hours: 10 a.m. to 4 p.m.

From I-10 take North Mesa Street west over railroad tracks onto Country Club Road. Go 1 mile from tracks to Vista del Monte Street on left. Our house is fifth on left. Please park on street; do not block driveways.

Proceeds shared with El Dedon Verde Garden Club and Master Gardeners Association

Beltran Family Garden
750 Linda Avenue

The garden sits between a pecan orchard and alfalfa field, giving it a rural, pastoral feeling. Surrounding a casual mission revival -style house built in 1949, the landscape completes this rustic setting. Meander through some twenty fifty-year-old trees (mulberries, live oaks, pecans and sycamores). Access the back through a recycled lumber arbor to a small old orchard (pears, pomegranates, apples, and plums) and the garden tea room "Amparo." The back yard features include an artificial pond and waterfall, a vegetable box garden, a wintering shed, a covered porch, a 1950s lap pool, and a sun-drenched patio. Bradford

pears, purple plums, and crape myrtles have been added to the landscape in recent years. **NEW** 🌿

Hours: 10 a.m. to 4 p.m.

Two miles from I-10/Exit 11/Mesa Street. Take Mesa west, cross Doniphan Drive and railroad tracks onto Country Club Road. Turn left onto Montoya (second traffic light) and right onto Linda. There will be signs for parking.

Proceeds shared with El Dedon Verde Garden Club and Master Gardeners Association

Brandt Garden
913 Vista Mia Court

We are located in the country atmosphere of the upper valley. Our garden is designed for privacy and lushness with heat-tolerant trees and plants. The aim is to have "hidden rooms" where the sounds of splashing water and birds can be enjoyed. To accomplish this we planted 100 trees and 900 plants for foliage and flowers interspersed for seasonal color. Our special tree, a sapling from the Treaty Oak in Austin, Texas; and our special plant is the Texas River Fern. Discover serenity and surprises around every corner. **NEW** 🌿

Hours: 10 a.m. to 4 p.m.

From I-10, take Exit 11/Mesa Street, turn west toward upper valley. At Doniphan Drive, Mesa Street becomes Country Club Road. Follow this through two traffic lights (Doniphan Drive and Country Club Place) to Vista del Monte Street, turn left and follow to Vista Mia Court (a gated cul-de-sac). Number 913 is at the end. Please do not block driveways or park on lawns.

Proceeds shared with El Dedon Verde Garden Club and Master Gardeners Association

Dodd Garden
5101 Memory Drive

The Dodd garden is one of the few nationally registered Backyard Habitats in the El Paso area. All plants offer food, water, shelter, and safe haven for the young wildlife. All animals and insects are welcome in this organic garden. The area has two large koi ponds each with a large waterfall on both and about sixty koi that

---

🌿 indicates parts of garden are handicapped accessible

can be hand fed. Both ponds have large seating areas with lots of trees, flowers, shrubs, and aquatic plants that help to maintain a natural and healthy environment for fish, frogs and all other water friends. There is also a flagstone walkway connecting both ponds to the pool area where a large mulberry tree and many succulent plants provide a nesting area and haven for forty to fifty hummingbirds along with robins and other nesting birds. **NEW**

Hours: 10 a.m. to 4 p.m.

From I-10 take North Mesa Street west over the railroad tracks onto Country Club Road. Turn right at the light onto Memory Drive. Number 5101 is the first house on the left with large palm trees.

Proceeds shared with El Dedon Verde Garden Club and Master Gardeners Association

Stewart Garden
801 Cervantes Court

This is a very open space with a variety of trees plus seating areas within several smaller venues of flowers, a bird bath, and a rose garden. The other side of this large space is a fish pond, two waterfalls, and a pavilion to sit and enjoy the view. There are several flower gardens throughout the property beginning at the entry gate. **NEW**

Hours: 10 a.m. to 4 p.m.

From I-10 take Mesa Street exit and go north, away from mountains. Continue into valley where the street name will change to Country Club Road. Turn left onto Montoya Drive. Go 0.7 miles and turn right onto Meadowlark Drive. Go 0.1 miles and turn right onto Cervantes Court to #801.

Proceeds shared with El Dedon Verde Garden Club and Master Gardeners Association

Fort Worth Open Day
Sunday, October 14
TARRANT COUNTY

ARLINGTON
Debbie Duncan & Randy Jordan
2316 Starlight Court

The homeowner wanted to preserve the native trees on the property and have a compatible, low-maintenance landscape. The design by Cliff Mycoskie of Site Planning, Site Development uses native and well-adapted plants to accent the open and spacious lawn. The hardscape is exceptional with effective use of native stone. **NEW** ♿

Hours: 10 a.m. to 4 p.m.

Drive east from Fort Worth or west from Dallas on I-30 to Exit 24/Eastchase Parkway. Turn south onto Eastchase Parkway which becomes Dottie Lynn Parkway, then Green Oak Boulevard. After about 4 miles, turn left onto Arkansas Lane. Go 1.2 miles, cross a bridge and on right is a gated community. The gate will be open and you will be on Panorama Court. Take first left to top of hill and #2316 is first house on right. Please park in the cul-de-sac.

Proceeds shared with Tarrant County Master Gardeners Association

Mary Nell's Garden
1305 Cochise Drive

Gracious, welcoming, charming—the old fashioned, magical gardens of former Miss Texas Mary Nell (Hendricks) Hubbard bring beauty and national attention to North Texas. A lifetime lover of flowers and wildlife, Mrs. Hubbard, an accomplished watercolorist, was inspired to create her garden when she needed subjects for her paintings. Her lovely garden is a feast for the senses combining found objects, garden art, line, and color. She has incorporated fragrant scents, peaceful water features, and visual movement into her creation. Distant church bells even cooperate. Sea glass scattered among colorful stepping stones, a bevy of stone angels resting on a low wall, an old wheelbarrow tipped on end, an arroyo, an antique fire hydrant, iron bedsteads, carved wooden animals and more form a background for an abundance of native and adapted Texas plants. Historic roofing tiles and an antique door and window lend character to a whimsical, memory-laden greenhouse partially covered with an old blush rose. Under the dappled shade of huge post oaks are lovely antique roses, spring- and fall-blooming wisteria, oakleaf hydrangea, kerria, salvia, and ornamental oreganos. This organically maintained garden is certified as a Texas Wildscape Backyard Wildlife Habitat. Mary Nell is a Master Gardener and with the help of her husband, Bill, has created a charming, fun-filled garden of happy surprises that is a must-see treasure. **NEW**

Hours: 10 a.m. to 4 p.m.

Mary Nell's Garden is located in north Arlington, Texas between Fort Worth and Dallas near I-30. From I-30 exit at North Fielder Road. Travel south 0.2 mile to traffic light. Turn left onto Cochise Drive. Go 0.4 mile to #1305. Please park on street. MAPSCO 68Y.

Proceeds shared with Tarrant County Master Gardeners Association

FORT WORTH
Mr. & Mrs. Fred Cauble
3860 Westcliff Road S.

When the Caubles purchased their 1930s three-story Tudor house in 1995, they wanted to create a classic landscape to showcase the front of their stone house and a woodland oasis for their private retreat in the back. Jennifer, an ardent fan of old-fashioned English cottage gardens partnered with Libby Villari to create a whimsical facsimile, but with native and adapted plants tough enough to thrive in the extreme climate of North Texas. The two-acre estate now features more than 175 plant varieties with more than 100 blooming in Jennifer's preferred palette of pinks, purples, blues, and whites. They are currently excited about the growing antique rose collection. Elizabeth's Gardens maintains the plants with a completely organic program and the landscape remains capricious, evolving, and changing as all true gardens do. **NEW** ♿

Hours: 10 a.m. to 4 p.m.

Take I-30 to Hulen. Go south on Hulen to Bellaire Drive South, and turn left. Go to the four-way stop at Bellaire Circle and turn right. Go 1 block to Westcliff Road South. Turn right and go to end of street on the right.

Take I-20 to Hulen. Go north on Hulen to Bellaire Drive. Turn right and go Bellaire Circle at four-way stop. Turn right and go to Westcliff Road South. Turn right and go to end of street on right.

Proceeds shared with Tarrant County Master Gardeners Association

Gardens of Little Castle— Bill & Donna Vance
2105 Indian Creek Drive

This eclectic shade garden is defined by the native limestone footpaths that wind among foliage, the stone embanked Indian Creek that meanders among the trees, and the overlooking "Little Castle" rock house that shelters this hidden green space. A forest of cedar elms shade multiple varieties of Japanese maples and crape myrtles while columbine, Turk's caps, and butterfly bushes thrive among fields of Asian jasmine, mondo, and liriope. Silver leaf, autumn, wood, and holly ferns line the creek and footpaths. A charming garden cottage, two graceful arched wooden bridges, and a unique water sculpture provide balance to this creek-side park. **NEW**

Hours: 10 a.m. to 4 p.m.

From I-30 West, take 9B/Horne Street/ Camp Bowie Boulevard exit. Turn right onto Horne Street/Roaring Springs Road and go to the first traffic light. Turn left onto Merrymount. Turn right onto Indian Creek Drive. Garden is at the fourth house on the right.

From I-30 East, take Exit 9B/Horne Street/ Camp Bowie Boulevard. Turn left at the traffic light and cross over the interstate. Travel north on Horne Street/Roaring Springs Road to Merrymount, turn left. Turn right onto Indian Creek Drive. The garden is at the fourth house on the right.

Proceeds shared with Tarrant County Master Gardeners Association

♿ indicates parts of garden are handicapped accessible

The Moncrief Garden

313 Rivercrest Drive

This is one of the oldest established gardens in the area. Begun in 1930 by Elizabeth Moncrief, it is essentially an experimental garden within the footprint of an English-style garden. The mix of exotic and native plants, shrubs, and trees represents successes in various stages of maturity. Younger growths represent plantings that have either run their natural course or that have not successfully faced the challenges of Texas gardening. The garden is still recovering from extensive damage caused by the tornado of 2000. Environmentally conscious care of the garden includes a large, four-part compost area hidden behind a tool shed, formerly a chicken coop. Unique plantings include paw paw trees (the only native North American fruit), a macrophyla magnolia, bald cypresses that are more than eighty years old and a stand of mature male and female gingko biloba trees. **NEW** ♿

Hours: 10 a.m. to 4 p.m.

Take I-30 west to Hulen exit. Turn right and follow to deadend on Crestline Road. Turn right and go to Hillcrest. Turn left and continue on Rivercrest Drive to #313.

Proceeds shared with Tarrant County Master Gardeners Association

Sherrod-Pool Garden

1870 Ederville Road South

When we bought this acre-and-a-half full of towering oaks, it had been neglected for years. Today its 100-year-old farmhouse is restored, and a greenhouse, a guesthouse, and our residence have been added. We have spent fifteen years creating the gardens: the bougainvillea-filled Chapel Garden which surrounds a "ruin" with ten-foot-tall Gothic windows salvaged from an old church; shade gardens with Japanese maples, hostas, ferns, and ginger; a garden with antique roses, lilies, spireas, and a weeping redbud; a woodland walk ringed with privet and filled with ancient oaks, winter honeysuckle, and viburnums; and a persimmon grove around a patio in the shape of a Canterbury Cross. **NEW** ♿

Hours: 10 a.m. to 4 p.m.

Take I-30 to the Oakland exit just east of downtown Fort Worth. Go south on Oakland just less than 1 mile to Normandy. Turn left. The next street is Ederville Road. Turn left, the garden is on the northwest corner of Ederville Road and Normandy. Come up the driveway and enter through the double gates.

Proceeds shared with Safe Haven of Tarrant County

Dallas County
Open Day
Saturday, October 20
DALLAS COUNTY

DALLAS

Angelica's Four Season Garden

4509 Wildwood Road

Situated in Bluffview, the "Little Hill Country of Dallas", this garden features an eclectic configuration of small outdoor rooms intended to blur the transition between the open indoors and the beauty and biodiversity of the outdoors. Hidden behind berms for intimacy, the garden provides pleasing vistas and a nurturing environment for those who linger—hummingbirds, butterflies, and humans. Structural evergreens serve as visual anchoring points and dividers between the garden rooms. On the east side you will find the square-shaped Azalea Courtyard, the White Garden with camellias and hydrangeas, and the Japanese Nook next to the entrance. On the south side is the formal, round-shaped Rose Garden, with mostly antique roses, as well as the English-style Perennial Garden with a collection of native and adapted plants. The west holds a shaded subtropical Poolside Garden with large architectural plants along ferns, ginger, bamboo, and Japanese maples. There are also some sunny spots with grasses, hardy hibiscus, and hardy tropicals as well as native, semi-evergreen plants. Potted tender tropicals are interspersed throughout, and a few modern sculptures complement the artistry of nature. Finally, for some culinary zest, the northwest corner features a small monastery-style Herb Garden with annual, perennial, and evergreen herbs. **NEW** Hours: 10 a.m. to 4 p.m.

From Midway and Northwest Highway, drive south on Midway across overpass and up the hill, passing two intersections, turn left into Wildwood. Go to next block, garden is on the left.

Chantilis Garden
8722 Daytonia Avenue

The garden is home to a 200-year-old Catalpa tree named Grace. She is thought to be one of the oldest in Texas. The front landscape features drought tolerant yuccas, a large variety of cactus, palms, cypress, rosemary and native grasses in crushed granite. The landscape is accented with slag glass, rocks, and vintage mosaics works; as well as mosaic installations created by the artist, resident, and gardener— Connie Chantilis. **NEW** Hours: 10 a.m. to 4 p.m.

From Interstate 30 East, exit Ferguson, go 1.9 miles to Lakeland. Turn left and then right onto Daytonia. The garden is in second block, on left. Please park on street.

Proceeds shared with Juliette Fowler Homes, Inc.

Newport Garden
6641 Desco Drive

This garden transformation started twelve years ago and is constantly evolving. Curving pathways of oversized flagstone are interplanted with fragrant herbs and groundcovers. Raised beds in brick and stone provide splashes of seasonal color, and perennial beds overflow with an assortment of irises, daylilies, salvias, native plants, and evergreens in a multitude of textures, form, and color. Cedar trellises and a pergola add architectural interest and privacy and host a variety of blooming, evergreen vines. A large greenhouse houses tropicals and a collection of orchids. This is truly a garden for all seasons. **NEW** ♿ Hours: 10 a.m. to 4 p.m.

From I-75/Central Expressway north, take Park Lane exit and go west approximately 1 mile to Hillcrest Road. Turn right and then first left onto Desco Drive.

From Dallas North Tollway, take Loop 12/Northwest Highway West Exit and go east to Preston Road about 0.375 mile. Turn left, go about 0.5 mile to Desco Drive and turn right.

Peter & Julie Schaar
3515 Haynie Avenue

The garden of Peter and Julie Schaar is an inner city garden on a small lot. It is a mixed planting of roses, trees, shrubs, palms, woody lilies, perennials, bulbs, and containers, and includes a wide variety of native and adapted plants. The Schaars maintain their garden organically, using no sprays, fungicides, or insecticides, and fertilize only with manure, compost, and other organic products. The garden is watered only occasionally, usually five to eight times per year. The front yard is an informal design inspired by cottage gardens in order to conform to the cottage house. The backyard is a paved subtropical Mexican courtyard exhibiting strong evergreen structure and exuberantly planted beds. Colorful pots line the courtyard, palms, cacti, yuccas, and other woody lilies, Southern magnolia, and crape myrtle make the small space appear larger and contribute dramatic form and texture. Cestrum, cassia, oleander, roses, callistemons, and camellias display bright color and heavy fragrance, as do several flowering vines. Mexican oregano, rosemary, lemon verbena, and shrub basil provide brushy herbs for cooking and fragrance, as do a number of long-blooming salvias. The garden is in bloom twelve months of the year, although the evergreen structure gives it a lively appearance even in the intervals of scant bloom. The Schaars welcome you to their garden and hope you have an enjoyable visit. They ask only that you refrain from smoking and please ask for starts of any plants that interest you. **2005** ♿ Hours: 10 a.m. to 4 p.m.

From intersection of Hillcrest and Lovers Lane, go south on Hillcrest to SMU campus (4 to 5 blocks). Turn right onto Haynie Avenue; Schaar garden is in second block, between

♿ indicates parts of garden are handicapped accessible

Dickens and Thackery, at #3515. Please park on street.

Sewell Garden
9508 Chiswell Road

Our yard has a unique shape—wide at the front, narrowing toward the back, with a narrow, finger-like extension going to our alley. Our gardens are fantastic. I have lived here for almost twenty-two years and I am impressed. If I could describe our yard in one word, it would be "variety" from front to back. There are numbers of different beds with fountains and walkways, each with a different appearance. With a myriad of native plants, this xeriscape award-winning yard was chosen by Dallas Water Utilities to kick off their 2002 water-conservation campaign. Come join us. Words can't describe what your eyes will see. **2003** ♿

Hours: 10 a.m. to 4 p.m.

From North Central Expressway/Highway 75, go east on Northwest Highway for 3.5 miles to Audelia Road. Turn left and go 0.4 mile to Chiswell Road. Turn left and go to #9508 on the corner of Chiswell Road and Parkford Lane. Please park on either street.

Waisanen
5105 Swiss Avenue

Visiting Swiss Avenue is a step back in time to a more genteel era of shady boulevards and graceful front lawns leading to unique homes. Our gardens surround an Italian renaissance-style house built in 1924. The gardens were extensively redesigned and put on an organic program in 1998. We purchased the house in 2003. Since then we have been getting to know our garden and gradually making changes and additions. The lot is almost one acre and includes a series of garden rooms, terraces, fountains, an outdoor kitchen, play area, and swimming pool. There is a great variety of plant material in the garden from vegetables, fruit trees, berry bushes, and herbs and flowers for all seasons. **NEW** ♿

Hours: 10 a.m. to 4 p.m.

The garden is just a few miles east of downtown Dallas in the Swiss Avenue Historic District. From Central Expressway/I-75, take the Knox-Henderson exit and follow Henderson southeast to Munger. Turn right and cross Live Oak. Turn right onto Swiss Avenue. Number 5105 is the third house of the right.

From I-30, take the Munger Exit N.W. Cross Gaston and turn left onto Swiss Avenue. Number 5105 is third house on right.

Public Gardens
COLLIN COUNTY

McKINNEY
The Heard Museum
Texas Native Plant Display Garden
One Nature Place, (972) 562-5566, www.heardmuseum.org

The two-acre Texas Native Plant Display Garden is home to more than 300 native species, including twenty-six trees, twenty-nine shrubs, fifteen vines, twenty grasses, and more than 100 varieties of perennial and annual wildflowers. The purpose of the garden is to educate the public about the beauty and diversity of our native plants and how they may be used in urban landscapes.

Hours: Year round, Monday through Saturday, 9 a.m. to 5 p.m., Sunday, 1 p.m. to 5 p.m.; closed major holidays

Admission: $8 adults, $5 children

From Route 75, take Exit 38A and follow brown-and-white highway signs. Heard Museum is located 1 mile east of Highway 5 on FM 1378, southeast of McKinney.

Texas Discovery Gardens at Fair Park
3601 Martin Luther King Jr. Boulevard, (214) 428-7476, www.texasdiscoverygardens.org

The first certified organic garden in the state, Texas Discovery Gardens is a seven-acre showcase of beautiful native and adapted plants grown using sustainable methods that conserve water and protect the environment. Special features include the butterfly habitat, scent garden, heirloom garden, shade garden,

Benny J. Simpson Texas Native Plant Collection, and a picturesque pond teeming with tadpoles, turtles, frogs, and dragonflies.

Hours: Year round, dates and hours vary seasonally

Admission: $3 adults, $2 seniors, $1.50 children ages 3 to 11, children under 3 free.

From I-30 east, take Exit 47/Fair Park/Second Avenue, curve to right, and turn left at second traffic light, which is Martin Luther King Jr. Boulevard.

From I-30 west, take Exit 47C/Fair Park/First Avenue, turn right at Exposition Avenue, and turn right onto Parry Avenue. Parry becomes Robert B. Cullum Avenue. Turn left at fourth light, which is Martin Luther King Jr. Boulevard.

From I-45 north, exit onto I-30 east, take Exit 47/Fair Park/Second Avenue, and proceed as directed above.

DALLAS COUNTY

DALLAS
Dallas Nature Center
(972) 296-1955,
www.dallasnaturecenter.org

The Dallas Nature Center is a 630-acre wilderness sanctuary that provides vital habitat for several endangered plants and animals, including the black-capped vireo. In addition to prairie wildflower areas, the Dallas Nature Center also features a butterfly garden landscaped with native plants.

Hours: Year round, Tuesday through Sunday, dawn to dusk

Admission: $3 suggested donation

From I-20, take Mountain Creek Parkway exit. Go south 2.5 miles. Nature Center entrance is just south of intersection with Wheatland Road.

PARKER COUNTY

WEATHERFORD
Chandor Gardens
711 West Lee Avenue, (817) 613-1700,
www.chandorgardens.com

Created from a limestone hilltop, this unique three-and-one-half-acre estate garden is the brilliant vision of famed portrait artist Douglas Chandor (1897-1953). His passion for art and beauty are expressed in the garden's ingenious layout, rich with water features, intricate stonework, timeless sculpture, and delightful surprises around every corner.

Hours: April through third weekend in November, Saturday, 9 a.m. to 3 p.m.; Sunday, 1 p.m. to 5 p.m. Private tours available year round, Tuesday through Sunday. Call for rates and reservations.

Admission: $5 adults, children 12 and under free (must be accompanied by an adult).

Located about 25 miles west of Fort Worth. From I-20 take Exit 409/Santa Fe Drive. Go North to Lee Avenue and turn left. Proceed west to Chandor Gardens Entrance.

TARRANT COUNTY

FORT WORTH
Fort Worth Botanic Garden
3220 Botanic Garden Boulevard,
(817) 871-7686, www.fwbg.org

The Fort Worth Botanic Garden is the oldest botanic garden in Texas. Covering an area of 109 acres, the botanic garden features a world-renowned Japanese Garden, an historic Rose Garden, one of the few floral clocks in the nation, a tropical conservatory, a restaurant, and meeting facilities.

Hours: Year round, daily, dawn to dusk. Garden Center hours, summer weekdays, 8 a.m. to 9 p.m.; Saturday, 8 a.m. to 7 p.m.; Sunday, 1 p.m. to 7 p.m.; winter weekdays, 8 a.m. to 9 p.m., Saturday, 8 a.m. to 5 p.m., Sunday, 1 p.m. to 5 p.m. Conservatory closes at 6 p.m. in summer, 4 p.m. in winter, opens at 10 a.m. Closed Christmas Day and Thanksgiving Day.

Admission: Conservatory $1, $.50 children; Japanese garden $3 weekdays for adults, $3.50 weekends for adults; $2 children; seniors $.50 less than adults

Located 1.5 miles west of downtown Fort Worth at the intersection of I-30 and University Drive. Turn north onto University Drive and turn left onto the first street north of I-30.

FORT WORTH
Weston Gardens In Bloom, Inc.
8101 Anglin Drive, Fort Worth,
(817) 572-0549, www.westongardens.com

Weston Gardens is one of the most fascinating and unique sites in Texas. The gardens are the result of a restoration of historical gardens that were originally built in the 1920s. The gardens include lily ponds, limestone and sandstone arbors, tons of stone retaining walls, multiple fountains and water features, and a 1920s barn complete with a bois d'arc brick floor. A special emphasis is given to using perennials and native Texas plants. The gardens have been featured in *Southern Living* and *Texas Highways* magazines.

Hours: February through October, Monday through Friday, 10 a.m. to 5 p.m.; Saturday, 9 a.m. to 5 p.m.; Sunday, 12 p.m. to 5 p.m.

Admission: Free

From I-20, take the Exit 441/Anglin Drive south for 2.3 miles to garden.

GRAPEVINE
Botanical Gardens at Heritage Park
411 Ball Street, (817) 410-3122,
www.gvpard.org

Welcome to a very special garden. Step into this quiet, ten-acre public garden located in historic downtown Grapevine. Special features include an herb garden, butterfly garden, numerous water features, annual color displays, perennials, trees, and shrubs. The garden also features a 200-year-old burr oak tree.

Hours: Year round, daily, dawn to dusk

Admission: Free

Take Highway 114 and exit at William D. Tate Avenue, and go north. After crossing rail-road tracks, street changes name to Ball Street. Botanical Gardens will be on right.

WEATHERFORD
Clark Gardens Botanical Park
567 Maddux Road, Weatherford,
(940) 6824856, www.clarkgardens.com

Clark Gardens Botanical Park is more than thirty-five acres of cultivated beds with an emphasis on north Texas adaptable plants. Large collections of azaleas, roses, iris, canna, and daylilies are the backbone of this garden. Overseen by Max and Billie Clark, the gardens have grown from a backyard herb and vegetable garden to a collection of well over 1,000 different adaptable plant varieties.

Hours: Year round, Monday through Saturday, 7:30 a.m. to 6 p.m.; Sunday, 10 a.m. to 5 p.m. Closed Christmas Day.

Admission: $7 adults, $5 seniors and children

Clark Gardens Botanical Park is located 3 miles east of Mineral Wells off of Highway 180. Turn north onto Maddux Road, gate is 1.5 miles down on right. Located about 45 minutes from Fort Worth. Please call for directions.

WALLER COUNTY

HEMPSTEAD
Peckerwood Garden
20571 FM 359, (979) 826-3232,
www.peckerwoodgarden.org

A PROJECT OF
THE GARDEN
CONSERVANCY

Peckerwood Garden is an artist's garden uniquely combining aesthetic experience and scientific exploration. It holds an unrivaled collection of plants from around the world with emphasis on plants collected in Mexico by its founder, John G. Fairey. The cultivated garden occupies about seven acres and includes a woodland garden along the banks of a creek, a higher dry garden, and a meadow garden that is being developed into an arboretum. More than 3,000 species and cultivars can be found here. Peckerwood is a Preservation Project of the Garden Conservancy.

Hours: March 31 & April 1, April 14 & 15, May 5 & 6, October 20 & 21, 1 p.m. to 4 p.m.

Admission: $10 for Open Days. Call for private tour rates.

From Houston, take Highway 290 west past Prairie View. Before reaching Hempstead, take Exit FM359 towards Brookshire. Proceed through traffic light at intersection with Business 290. Garden is located 1.7 miles past this intersection on right. Look for small sign. Park at Yucca Do Nursery located just south of garden.

Scotland's Gardens Scheme

Gardens open for charity

Created in 1931 Scotland's Gardens Scheme's objective was to raise funds for the Queen's Nurses; a charity that educated, promoted and supported community nurses in primary care, by opening country house gardens to the public for a nominal charge. Today Scotland's Gardens Scheme has a small management team and approximately two hundred volunteers in twenty-seven Scottish districts who organise the opening of three hundred and sixty gardens to the public, ranging from formal castle gardens to groups of small village gardens.

The Queens Nursing Institute (as it has become) remains one of the Scheme's principal beneficiaries; the other is the Gardens Fund of The National Trust for Scotland. Perennial (The Gardeners' Royal Benevolent Society) and the Royal Fund for Gardeners' Children also receive support annually. These four worthy charities receive 60% of the money raised from our gardens whilst 40% is allocated to charities of the garden owners' choice.

The privately owned gardens that open for us on a certain day or days are our backbone, very few of these gardens are accessible to the public at other times. The season begins with the snowdrop gardens followed by woodlands with daffodils and spring bulbs, rhododendrons and azaleas with early summer flowers, then a huge selection of summer gardens: moving then into magnificent autumn colours and finally winter gardens with wonderful bones!

Most garden openings provide home-baked teas and a plant stall. Children are welcome.

In February, our handbook, known as the 'Yellow Book', is published and distributed to leading bookshops and other appropriate retail and tourist outlets. This provides pertinent information on all the garden openings.

E-mail: sgsgardens@btconnect.com   Web: www.gardensofscotland.org

♿ indicates parts of garden are handicapped accessible

VERMONT
Upper Valley Open Day
Saturday, June 9

There are gardens open today in nearby New Hampshire. See listings on page 156.

WINDSOR COUNTY

BRIDGEWATER
The Shackleton Garden
Grandma'ams Hill Road

The Shackleton garden is a two-acre plus garden on a twenty-five acre site. There is a 100-foot-long herbaceous border, water garden and stream, with woodland walks. The house and garden is in a beautiful high setting with sixty-mile views to the east to Cardigan Mountain in New Hampshire. The garden surrounds an unaltered 1814 cape, original stone walls and terraces, at an elevation of 2,000 feet. The garden is still in an early phase of design. Miranda and Charles Shackleton are slowly planting trees, shrubs, and indigenous plants that compliment the wild elevation setting. Their intent is to create a "wild garden" reminiscent of an old Vermont rambling setting and using plants to accentuate this natural setting. They are opening up walks across their land so visitors can enjoy the fauna and different views. There is a wild orchard and meadow walk. **NEW** ♿

Hours: 10 a.m. to 4 p.m.

From Woodstock, take Route 12N toward Barnard and go about 3 miles. Turn left onto North Bridgewater Road (next left after Prosper Road). Continue for 3.25 miles to a dirt road. Turn right onto Grandma'ams Hill Road and go 1 mile. House is old white Cape-Cod style. Turn left onto Brown Road to get to driveway on immediate right.

WOODSTOCK
Indian Tree Hill—
The Highberg Garden
414 Randall Road

This is a dynamic garden that has evolved over the past thirty years. It combines an extensive collection of plants in a natural setting, giving it year-round interest, continuity of style, and an intimate appeal. The various garden areas are defined by the meandering paths and the creative use of native stone. Explore the alpine scree, woodland garden, sunny pool area, alpine wall, and more. Each place has its own unique feature: a sculptured steel archway and gates, an echoing waterfall, mossy stone benches, and a carved fountain. The vast variety of plant material and its arrangement will interest the seasoned collector, the student of design, as well as any garden enthusiast. Hundreds of alpines, dozens of dwarf conifers, countless bulbs, interesting ground covers, native and exotic woodland species, unusual trees, and many old favorites make this garden unique. A cutting garden of mixed perennials and annuals, a vegetable garden, and apple trees provide beauty and bounty. **2005** ♿

Hours: 10 a.m. to 2 p.m.

From "The Green" in Woodstock at the west end, go to the left of the stone Episcopal Church and take Church Hill Road for 1.5 miles. Turn left onto Randall Road, a dead end gravel road, and go another 1.5 miles. The driveway is on the left, directly across from a red steel field gate. The house is #414 at the end of the drive.

Proceeds shared with Planned Parenthood of Northern New England

The Garden of Fiona & Bob McElwain
27020 Church Hill Road

We chose our small 1850 Vermont farmhouse because of the gardening potential offered by its fields and woods. In particular, we fell in love with several vernal ponds in the overgrown woods near the house. We took a number of trees down, limbed up the rest and then cleared and dug out a lot of overgrown brambles and bracken. We created wood chip pathways and started mass plantings of moisture-tolerant shade and large leaf plants. There was no exact plan for the garden, it just grew larger every year. In June, one wanders by pink *Primula japonica* and mauve creeping phlox complemented by the interesting foliage of umbrella plants, hosta, and petasites. Later the color comes from astilbe, ligularia, etc. The house itself is surrounded by cottage-style perennial beds plus a shade garden of grays, whites, and blues. Another personal favorite is the more formal shrub garden, enclosed within an amsonia hedge, and creating a garden room of the stone terrace. Please come and enjoy these different areas. **NEW**

Hours: 10 a.m. to 4 p.m.

Woodstock is a pretty village in east central Vermont with Route 4 running through the village. From the east or west follow Route 4. From the south take I-91 to Exit 9/Hartland. Go about 10 miles north on Route 12, then left (west) onto Route 4 towards Woodstock. From the north, take I-89 south to Exit 1/Woodstock. Go west on Route 4 about 10 miles. Come through the village of Woodstock (25 m.p.h. zone) on Route 4. In the center of the village is an oval-shaped green. At the west end is a stone church—St. James. Keeping this church on right, take road directly beside the church (Prospect Street/Church Hill) up hill for 1.1 miles. Our house is on left—a cream colored farmhouse with light green shutters. Please park on house side of the street. Welcome!

Proceeds shared with Doctors without Borders

Public Gardens

BENNINGTON COUNTY

Manchester
Hildene,
The Lincoln Family Home
1005 Hildene Road, (802) 362-1788, www.hildene.org

Robert Todd Lincoln's Hildene was the home of Abraham Lincoln's descendants until 1975. The Georgian Revival-style mansion is

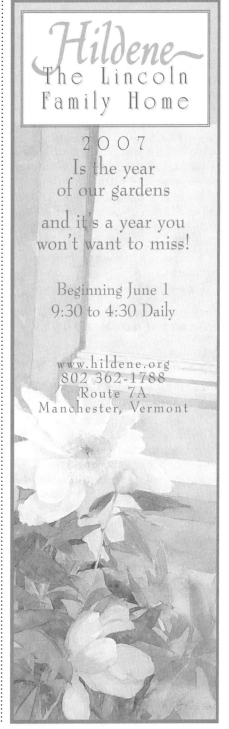

Hildene
The Lincoln
Family Home

2007
Is the year
of our gardens
and it's a year you
won't want to miss!

Beginning June 1
9:30 to 4:30 Daily

www.hildene.org
802 362-1788
Route 7A
Manchester, Vermont

♧ indicates parts of garden are handicapped accessible

situated among formal gardens that have been restored to their original beauty. Many of the original plantings remain and the location on a promontory provides breathtaking views of the surrounding mountains and the valley below. Each summer season begins with a garden party and garden market, "The Uncommon Garden" and finishes with a celebration of works created by "Artists in the Garden." The original Cutting and Kitchen Garden restoration began in 2003 and a new round of restoration there, as well as in the formal garden and adjacent meadow was completed in 2006.

Hours: June through October, daily, 9:30 a.m.to 4:30 p.m.; November through May, Thursday through Monday, 11 a.m. to 3 p.m. Closed Thanksgiving, Christmas, and Easter.

Admission: $10 house and grounds, $5 grounds only

Located just 2 miles south of junction of Routes 7A, 11, and 30.

CHITTENDEN COUNTY

SHELBURNE
Shelburne Farms
1611 Harbor Road, (802) 985-8498, www.shelburnefarms.org

The gardens at the Inn at Shelburne Farms, originally designed by Lila Vanderbilt Webb, feature lush perennial borders inspired by the English cottage style of Gertrude Jekyll. The peak of the gardens' bloom is early June, when the 'Queen Victoria' peonies are in their glory, through July, when delphiniums bloom in front of a backdrop of tall plume poppies. Low brick walls provide the formal architectural structure to define the rooms within the garden and create multiple levels for the rose garden, the lily pond surrounded by Dutch and Japanese iris, and an herb garden. Continuing Lila's tradition to welcome the community into her gardens, we invite you to visit. Shelburne Farms is a 1,400-acre working farm, a National Historic Landmark, and a nonprofit environmental education center whose mission is to cultivate a conservation ethic by teaching and demonstrating the stewardship of natural and agricultural resources.

Hours: Mid-May through mid-October, four property tours daily, 10 a.m. to 4 p.m.

Admission: Property tour is $10

From I-89, take Exit 13 to Route 7 and turn south. Proceed to traffic light in center of Shelburne. Turn right onto Harbor Road and drive 1.6 miles. Turn right into Welcome Center parking area before entering gates. Tickets may be purchased there.

VIRGINIA

Charlottesville Area Open Day Saturday, May 19

ALBEMARLE COUNTY

CHARLOTTESVILLE

Balge-Crozier Garden
624 Preston Place

Only a ten-minute walk from Thomas Jefferson's rotunda, this twenty-six-year-old shade garden is designed to provide a natural refuge for wildlife. Native shrubs such as witch hazel, lindera, and azaleas are underplanted with spring bulbs, hostas, ferns, and hellebores, while a variety of Japanese maples, tree peonies, and conifers add color and structure. Winding paths connect the front garden to a terraced back area that includes a studio behind which is a recently created secret garden. Local sculptor Caesar Morton's carved wooden snake guards this meditation space. Ceramic tiles, pots, and architectural elements also add interest to the garden. **NEW** ♿

Hours: 10 a.m. to 4 p.m.

From Washington, D.C., at intersection of Emmet Street/Highway 29/Barracks Road, turn left onto Barracks Road and go 6 miles to third traffic light and Rugby Road. Turn right onto Rugby Road and proceed 0.4 mile to first light at intersection of Rugby Road and Grady Avenue/University Circle. Turn left onto Grady; go past 2 fraternity houses and take first left onto Preston Place (marked on stone pillar). Preston Place is one-way and we are 5th house on left.

From Ivy Road/250 west, at intersection of Ivy & Emmet Street/Highway 29, stay on 250 Business east (which becomes University Avenue) and go approximately 0.3 mile to first light at intersection with Rugby Road. Turn left onto Rugby Road and go 0.3 mile to first light, which is intersection with Grady Avenue. Turn right and go short distance to Preston Place. On street parking allowed on Saturdays.

The Frierson Garden
602 Lyons Court

Boxwood dominates in the small "collector's garden" surrounding this 1939 Dutch Colonial-style house. More than fifteen cultivars of boxwood, some rare and unique, are used as hedges and single specimens. These are complemented by a wide array of perennials, bulbs, and annuals for seasonal interest. Experimentation is always ongoing. The zoysia lawn, planting beds, and patio are outlined by soapstone paths and local river rock edging, much of it work by Japanese stonemason and sculptor Toru Oba, who also created the stone basin at the foot of the back steps. **NEW**

Hours: 10 a.m. to 4 p.m.

From the U.S. 250 bypass, take Park Street exit and turn towards downtown (heading south). Drive 2 long blocks and Lyons Court is second left. Number 602 will be first house facing Lyons Court on right. Please park along Lyons Court or around corner on neighboring streets, being careful not to block driveways.

The Frischkorn Garden
936 Rugby Road

The Frischkorn garden is situated on a two-and-one-half acre site just one mile from Thomas Jefferson's Academical Village, the campus of the University of Virginia. Although the garden design offers gestures toward the traditional "brick and box," this garden extends beyond the conventional. Three enclosed garden rooms adjoin the house. A series of trails extends throughout the woodland, a forest of mature oaks with a rich understory of native ornamental trees, shrubs, and groundcovers. Made within the bones of an early twentieth-century garden, the current design is a renovation after more than twenty-five years of utter neglect. This garden dates to the spring of 2001. **NEW** ♿

Hours: 10 a.m. to 4 p.m.

From I-64, take Exit 118B toward Charlottesville. Follow Route 29 north following signs to the University of Virginia. Exit onto Route 250 Business, turn right and proceed to the University. At the Rotunda, turn left

♿ indicates parts of garden are handicapped accessible

onto Rugby Road. Go through one traffic light. Number 936 is the last house on right before second light, which is a T-intersection at Preston Avenue. Please park along Preston Avenue or on side road off Rugby Road; no on-site parking.

Howard Garden
627 Park Street

Although the Howard's garden is located on just one acre of land in the historic section of downtown Charlottesville, it has evolved over a twenty year period into a landscape of garden rooms: the nineteenth-century gazebo (moved from Augusta County) and the charming little pond behind and the shaded "secret garden" approached through an arbor, are particularly charming. There is a reproduction of the eighteenth-century dairy located at the Governor's Palace in Colonial Williamsburg which is used as the garden shed. One will also see a section of original brick walk discovered when the owners were hoping to plant in the area, it is now used to add architectural interest. Take special note of the variety of trees on the property: the ancient beech and the graceful surviving American elm, the Davidia (dove tree), the yellowwood with its wisteria-like flowers and distinctive bark, the flowering native stewartia trees as well as the huge slow-growing Japanese umbrella pine and the rapidly growing metasequoia, among others. There are areas to sit and enjoy the perspectives and "smell the flowers"! **NEW** ♿

Hours: 10 a.m. to 4 p.m.

Take Route 250 to Park Street exit. Go south on Park Street toward downtown for about 0.25 mile until the corner of Park Street and Northwood Avenue. The house and gardens are on the southwest corner. A low brick wall wraps the front of the property and there is a very large American beech on corner. The house is red-brick Georgian.

Tank Hut
700 Rugby Road

The sloping terrain around this European style house which dates from the early 1900s has been attractively terraced. The upper terrace

at the entrance of the house is landscaped with a wide variety of shrubs and spring bulbs. Shrubs include lilac, abelia, dwarf crape myrtle, boxwood, *Jasminum nudiflorum*, althea, and azalea. The focal point of another terrace is a lovely large fish pool in the shape of an irregular ellipse planted with yellow water iris and dwarf papyrus. A large perennial bed surrounds the fish pool. The lowest terrace has been developed into a vegetable and cutting garden. **NEW** ♿

Hours: 10 a.m. to 4 p.m.

From Route 29 north, turn left onto Barracks Road. Turn right at third traffic light (Rugby Road), third house on left in third block.

From Route 29 south, take Barracks Road exit and turn right off ramp. Two lights to intersection; go straight through and continue as above.

From I-64 west, take Exit 118B. Stay on 29 north/250 bypass to Barracks Road exit; continue as above.

From I-64 east, take first Charlottesville exit. Go 2.5 to 3 miles to Rugby Avenue exit. Turn left at second traffic light. Turn right at next traffic light at Rugby Road. There are 5 parking spaces on premises.

Charlottesville Area Open Days Saturday & Sunday May 19 & 20

ALBEMARLE COUNTY

FREE UNION
Bird Hill—C. Colston Burrell & D. Bruce Ellsworth
5685 Peavine Hollow Trail

Bird Hill is a ten-acre pleasure grounds, a pastiche of woodland, meadow, and garden inspired by the beauty of the regional landscape. I designed our collector's wonderland to be viewed from the house, as well as to be viewed with the house as the garden's centerpiece. I have emphasized plantings rich in texture, color, and scent to envelop comfortable circular spaces conceived for reverie. Circular elements repeat throughout, inspired by landscape architect Jens Jensen, who used them as I do to "add order to the randomness of nature." Though natives make up the heart of the palette, plants from around the world blend together within the natural framework. Shaded beds surround the house, filled to overflowing with sedges, ferns, bulbs, wildflowers, shrubs, and flowering trees. In sunny areas, temperate and tropical plants meld for a season-long feast of foliage and flowers that overwhelms the senses. Potted plants, small water features, and antique stone pieces abound. Rectilinear borders featuring tropicals and meadow wildflowers are under construction, so visitors can see garden expansion in progress during the tour. **2004** ♿

Hours: 10 a.m. to 4 p.m.

From Charlottesville, from Route 29/250 bypass, take Barracks Road exit. Take Barracks Road/Route 654 out of town to where it joins Garth Road/Route 601. Go straight for 4.6 miles to Free Union Road (Hunt Country Market on right). Turn right onto Free Union Road/Route 601 and go 4.1 miles to Free Union. Past gas station, road jogs left. Turn left onto Millington Road/Route 665 and go .4 miles. Turn right onto Wesley Chapel Road/Route 609. Go 2.4 miles then bear left onto Fox Mountain Road/668 (dirt road). Go .4 mile then turn right onto Peavine Hollow Road. Parking will be available on left after a short rise in road. Do not pull into paved driveway, but continue a short distance to enter sign. Attendants will be available to direct you. You will catch a shuttle bus here for short 1 mile drive to garden. Busses will run continuously throughout day.

Proceeds shared with the Virginia Native Plant Society

Galvin Garden
4196 Millington Road

We purchased our nearly two-acre property in 2003. Immediately we fenced the perimeter and began gardening. We plowed up vegetable gardens, pruned existing fruit trees and began planting all kinds of trees, shrubs, perennials, fruits, and vegetables. We have planted, planted, and planted. The driveway has been redefined with stone edging. The front walk has been recreated with bluestone and many fieldstone stepping stone paths have been added in various areas around the property. The garden is still a work in progress and is expected to mature over the next several years. We have tried to incorporate color, texture, and year round interest to keep the garden alive through the seasons. **NEW** ♿

Hours: 10 a.m. to 4 p.m.

Follow Garth Road out of town. Turn right onto Route 601 at Hunt Country Store (Free Union Road). Follow 601 through small town of Free Union. Turn left onto Route 665/Millington Road. We are 0.5 mile on right.

The Gardens at Waterperry Farm
4284 Ballards Mill Road

Begun sixteen years ago, and so named for the turn-of-the-century horticulture school in Waterperry, England, our garden is a passionate work of ongoing experiment. Enclosed by stone walls and hedges, and graced with old trees and glorious views of the Blue Ridge Mountains, it is both formal and welcoming in scale, with many inviting places to sit. Soft spectrum colors abound, as well as many plant collections and a variety of boxwoods and yews. The visitor is guided through several "rooms" which ultimately open out onto a large shrub border, potager, and woodland. A tucked-away shade walk loops around to the hornbeam-hedged tennis court and out to the pool, and a disappearing deer fence protects the garden on three sides. **NEW** ♿

Hours: 10 a.m. to 4 p.m.

From Route 64 west, take Charlottesville exit/Route 250. Turn right at bottom of ramp. Follow 250/Bypass to Barracks Road Exit. Turn right. Go about 4 miles past Foxfield Racetrack. Turn right at Hunt Country Store onto Free Union Road. Go about 4 miles into Free Union. As road winds to the left, look for and turn left onto Millington Road/Route 665. After red church on right, bear right onto

Wesley Chapel Road/Route 609. Go 1.4 miles and turn left onto Ballards Mill Road. Follow road for about a mile to the stone entrance on right.

Proceeds shared with The International Rescue Committee

Public Gardens

ALBEMARLE COUNTY

CHARLOTTESVILLE

Ash Lawn-Highland

1000 James Monroe Parkway,
(434) 293-9539,
www.ashlawnhighland.org

James Monroe's plantation home at Ash Lawn-Highland includes the original house and furnishings, service buildings, and 535 acres of fields, forests, and gardens. The ornamental gardens include a formal allée of English and American boxwood as well as borders of period flowers and an arbor of heirloom roses. The vegetable garden provides produce for period cooking demonstrations.

Hours: April through October, daily, 9 am. to 6 p.m.; November through March, 11 a.m. to 5 p.m.; closed New Year's Day, Thanksgiving, and Christmas.

Admission: $9 adults, $8 seniors and AAA members, $5 children from 6 to 11, $5 local residents, group rates available

From I-64 east, take Exit 121. From I-64 west, take Exit 121A. Turn left onto Route 53, pass Monticello, and turn right onto Route 795. Ash Lawn-Highland is 0.5 mile on right.

Thomas Jefferson Center for Historic Plants

Monticello, Tufton Farm, Route 732,
(434)984-9822, www.monticello.org/chp

Monticello's Center for Historic Plants, an educational program, collects, preserves, maintains, and sells plants documented in American gardens before 1900, especially those grown by Jefferson or developed in his lifetime. The center publishes an annual journal, Twinleaf.

Hours: November through February, daily, 9 a.m. to 4:30 p.m.; March through October, daily, 8 a.m. to 5 p.m. Nursery by appointment.

Admission: Free

From I-64 west, take Exit 121. Turn left onto Route 20 south. Past first traffic light, turn left onto Route 53/Thomas Jefferson Parkway. Go 1.75 miles, passing under stone arch (Saunders Bridge), and stay straight. Go 1 mile and bear left onto Route 732/Milton Road. Turn left at Tufton sign and follow road to Center for Historic Plants sign.

Thomas Jefferson's Gardens at Monticello

Route 53, (434)984-9822,
www.monticello.org

Thomas Jefferson delighted in gardening. Flower and vegetable gardens, orchards, vineyards, and an ornamental grove were included in his landscape plans for his home, Monticello. The gardens have been restored to their appearance during Jefferson's lifetime and many of the trees, vegetables, and flowers that Jefferson cultivated are grown here today.

Hours: November through February, daily, 9 a.m. to 4:30 p.m. March through October, daily, 8 a.m. to 5 p.m.

Admission: $15 adults; $7 children 6 to 11; children under 6 free

From I-64 west, take Exit 121. Turn left onto Route 20 south. Past first traffic light, turn left onto Route 53/Thomas Jefferson Parkway. Go 1.75 miles, passing under stone arch (Saunders Bridge); take immediate right, which goes over bridge to Monticello.

From I-64 east, take Exit 121A. Just after first light, turn left onto Route 53 and proceed as directed above.

WASHINGTON

Bainbridge Island
Open Day
Saturday, July 21

KITSAP COUNTY

BAINBRIDGE ISLAND
Little and Lewis
1940 Wing Point Way, N.E.

The garden/gallery of Little and Lewis is internationally known as one of the most photographed and published gardens in the United States and now with the release of their first book *A Garden Gallery: The Plants, Art, and Hardscape of Little and Lewis* (Timber Press), their unique and magical style has been aptly recognized. Sitting on a third of an acre in a small, quiet waterfront community, the garden is a paradise filled with exotic plants, wonderful concrete sculptures, and gently dripping water features. Little and Lewis have earned a reputation for creating beautiful, unique, and colorful concrete sculptures and water elements. Their work can be seen in private and public gardens all over the country. This is a rare opportunity to see this extraordinary garden gallery and meet these two creative gardening artists. To see a preview, visit www.littleandlewis.com. **2006** ♿

Hours: 10 a.m. to 3 p.m.

From Coleman Dock in Seattle, take Bainbridge Island Ferry (35-minute crossing). Once off ferry, turn right at first traffic light onto Winslow Way. Go to Ferncliff and turn left. Go 2 blocks to Wing Point Way. Turn right and go 0.5 mile to garden on left just after Park Avenue.

Take Highway 3 to Highway 305. Cross Agate Passage Bridge onto Bainbridge Island. Go down two-lane highway to High School Road (McDonald's and Chevron gas station are on corner). Turn left. Go to Ferncliff. Turn right. Go to Wing Point Way. Turn left. Go 0.5 mile to garden on left just after Park Avenue. Please park on street.

KINGSTON
Heronswood
7530 N.E. 288th Street

Heronswood is a world-renowned nursery and garden specializing in rare and unusual plants, located on seven acres. The ever-expanding gardens cover many different styles, from shady woodland to sunny rock garden, traditional double perennial borders to a semitropical vegetable garden, arbor plantings, and ponds. Art in the garden includes the work of Little and Lewis, Marcia Donahue, and Mark Bulwinkle. **2005**

Hours: 10 a.m. to 4 p.m.

From Seattle-Bainbridge Ferry (ferries leave every forty minutes from downtown Seattle terminal at Alaskan Way & Marion Street), follow exit, which becomes Highway 305 north. Go north for 7 miles. Once off island (over Agate Pass Bridge), take immediate right at first traffic light. This road heads east to village of Suquamish, where it turns sharply to left and north. From Suquamish, go north 8 miles to next four-way intersection with light (Chevron gas station, new Albertson's shopping center). Go through light towards Hanville, 1 mile north, where N.E. 288th Street "T"s in on left. Turn left onto N.E. 288th Street. Driveway is 0.25 mile on left across from second set of mailboxes. Only our sign "Heronswood, by appointment" and our street address "7530" are visible from road.

McFarlane Gardens
9340 N.E. South Beach

A meditative Zen garden calms the soul with the sound of water burbling and a ceiling of evergreens overhead. A parade of color stimulates the senses, exploding left and right with cascades of exuberant flora. Ruffles of lettuce skirt heirloom tomatoes and invite the picker with sun-drenched scents reminiscent of Italy. Basil, oregano, and thyme vie for attention nearby. A reflecting pool lies at the feet of a bronzed, arched goddess worshipping the sun as she is surrounded by hot colors, cannas, and bananas as another woman sleeps on the rocks nearby. Between the vegetables and the

♿ indicates parts of garden are handicapped accessible

pool is a tranquil rose garden begging you to pause and contemplate the peaceful sounds of running water while you fall under the spell of a demure, angelic creature poised across from you. The other side of the yard holds an English-style cutting garden at the base of the guest house. These descriptions belong to one garden—ours. The garden is a reflection of living spaces with Northwest, Asian, English, Italian, and Mediterranean influences. Somehow, the clear delineations that create the various rooms in our garden make it all work, while a connecting network of paths make it a feast for all senses! **2006** ♿

Hours: 10 a.m. to 3 p.m.

From ferry terminal, turn left at first traffic light onto Winslow Way and go through town to first stop sign. Turn right onto Madison and go to next stop sign, which is Wyatt. Turn left and road will curve left, then fork to right up a hill. Stay straight; road name changes to Blakely Avenue. After 2.5 miles at bottom of hill, turn right onto Country Club Road. Take next right up Fort Ward Hill for 0.65 mile to dead end at South Beach. Turn right and go to first house on right, #9340.

The Skyler Garden
9734 Manitou Place

Gracefully surrounded by waves of cedar pickets, this private third of an acre site sits at the end of a quiet cul-de-sac. Nestled among tall firs, vine maples, rhododendrons, azaleas, and viburnums, these gardens have been a work in progress for more than twenty years. Stroll the pathways through serene surroundings and you will discover endless groupings of hostas, hellebores, hebes, spirea, Daphne, many perennials, and more than eighty-five varieties of ferns. Through the kiwi arbor into the shade garden is a favorite gathering spot for the many birds visiting the feeders and splashing in the small pond. Welcome to our garden. **NEW** ♿

Hours: 10 a.m. to 3 p.m.

From Seattle take the Bainbridge Island Ferry from Coleman Dock on the waterfront (a thirty minute crossing). On Bainbridge Island, from Highway 305, turn east at the Manitou Beach turnoff/traffic light (fourth traffic light upon disembarking ferry). Take the first left onto North Madison. Turn right onto Beach Crest Drive. Turn left onto Manitou Place. Please park in cul-de-sac and walk through the steel gates.

Olympia Area Open Day
Saturday, August 11
PIERCE COUNTY

DuPont
Froggy Bottom
2502 MacArthur Street

This larger-than-average urban village lot contains four distinct gardens with more than 600-feet of stroll paths which lead you through perennial borders, a zonal denial garden, a woodland shade garden, and an Asian-inspired alpine garden with a twist of northwest style centered around waterfalls, ponds, and a stream. This collector's garden is integrated using repeating patterns of yellow, blue, and purple. Even on a cloudy day you don't have to look far to see a splash of gold. Granite obelisks provide punctuation and the right amount of chi. Located adjacent to a wetland and open space near the Nisqually Wildlife Refuge you can usually see bald eagles, great blue herons, and a host of neotropical migrant birds. **NEW** ♿

Hours: 10 a.m. to 4 p.m.

From I-5, take Exit 118 onto Center Drive in DuPont (between Tacoma and Olympia). Turn left at first traffic light onto McNeil Street. Stay on McNeil for 1 mile until you reach Jensen Street, turn left. Jensen Street is a dead-end that turns into MacArthur Street as the road curves to left by an eyebrow cul-de-sac. Our house is third house from end of street on left. We share a driveway with neighbors so please park on street.

THURSTON COUNTY

OLYMPIA

The Hatten Garden
2025 Lakemoor Drive, S.W.

A silver quartzite patio with clamoring ground-covers greets visitors in the kitchen garden. This is just one of the many "rooms" to be explored in this one-third-acre city garden. The year-round garden railroad with its cedar trestles and miniature plantings are captivating at any age. Extensive rhododendrons and evergreens sculpt the property and meandering paths invite the visitor to see more. A unique gathering of herbs, perennials, annuals, and climbing roses flourish among many found treasures that are blended into this charming garden. **NEW** ♿

Hours: 10 a.m. to 4 p.m.

From I-5 take Exit 104 to Highway 101 north/Ocean Beaches. Exit at Black Lake Boulevard (second exit), turn left. At second stoplight turn right onto Ken Lake Drive, S.W. At stop sign turn left onto Lakemoor Drive S.W. Go to 2025 Lakemoor Drive S.W. on left.

The Koi Garden
4817 Palermo Rosa Lane, S.W.

Owner Joyce Hawkins feels the two beautiful large Japanese koi ponds containing seventy-five multi-colored, jewel-like fish are the piece de resistance in her one acre garden. The garden also showcases a wide variety of trees, shrubs, and perennials on raised berms that meander between the ponds, through groupings of evergreen trees and other beautiful garden rooms. Many visitors have commented that they experience a very peaceful, almost spiritual-like feeling while touring this unique garden. **NEW** ♿

Hours: 10 a.m. to 4 p.m.

From I-5, go to Exit 99 (truck stop). Turn west onto 93rd Avenue and go 1.5 miles to stop sign at Littlerock Road. Turn left and go 1.5 miles. Turn left onto Palermo Drive S.W. (this is a small sign, so look for Alden's Taxidermy sign on right and Bears Den sign on left of Lit-

tlerock Road). Go about 0.5 mile, nearly to end of dead-end road, where pavement narrows to one lane, and garden will be on right. Ample parking is available along dead-end road; overflow can utilize 3-acre pasture.

Phillips Garden
124 Foote Street, N.W.

This is a city garden that complements the French/English-style house. A low stone wall surrounds the front garden. Wide borders on either side of the front walk screen the house from the street and provide pleasant year-round views from the windows. A stone path winds through low groundcovers to a vintage bird bath. The rear garden features organic vegetables in raised beds. Nearby, the garden shed echoes the house style. Over the low hedge, a terrace and a small lawn are bordered by trees, shrubs, and flowers. A wisteria trellis shelters a wooden swing, and a fountain provides soothing water sounds. **NEW** ♿

Hours: 10 a.m. to 4 p.m.

From Highway 101, take Black Lake/West Olympia exit. Turn left onto Black Lake Boulevard. Go 1 mile (the street becomes Division Street). Turn right onto Fourth Avenue and continue 9 blocks to Foote Street, N.W., turn left. The Phillips house is in middle of block on right.

From I-5, take the Highway 101 exit to the Black Lake/West Olympia exit. Turn right onto Black Lake Boulevard and proceed as directed above.

Stanford Garden
9137 52nd Lane N.E.

The Stanford Garden is set on three-quarters of an acre overlooking the Puget Sound. The highlight and centerpiece is a 150-foot long "granite outcropping" inspired by the Edinburgh Botanic Garden's Rock Garden and created with 130 tons of granite boulders. This site is surrounded on three sides with borders that create privacy without a fence. The fourth side of the property is bounded by woodland and a dry streambed. The plantings are a combination of perennials, conifers (mostly dwarf), ornamental grasses, and shrubs that are a rich tapestry of color, texture, and form all year. **NEW** ♿

Hours: 10 a.m. to 4 p.m.

From the south, I-5 and Marvin Road/Exit 111, go north on Marvin Road to the second roundabout. Exit the roundabout onto Willamette. Go to the first stop sign, which is 31st Avenue. Turn right and continue to next stop sign, which is Meridian Road. Turn left and go about 0.5 mile to 46th Avenue. Turn left, 46th Avenue will curve to the right and name will change to Hilton Road. Continue to 51st. Turn right and go 1 block. Turn left onto Illahee Lane and go 1 block. Turn right onto 52nd Lane.

From the north, I-5, Nisqually/Exit 114, at the first traffic light, continue straight on Martin Way. At top of hill, you will come to a second light at Meridian Road. Turn right. At roundabout, take first exit which is continuation of Meridian Road, for about 2 miles to 46th Avenue. Turn left and continue as directed above. We are first driveway on right.

TENINO
Golden Leaf Acres
4841 Churchill Road

You are invited to leave the noise of the city and freeway traffic behind and take a trip to the country. The Golden Leaf Acres "makeover" began several years ago when the property was purchased. Large areas of twenty-year-old Douglas firs were cleared to make way for a fenced, one-acre vegetable, berry, and fruit garden, an eighty-foot greenhouse, and ornamental planting areas. A pond was added three years ago. The most recent addition is a large, woodland planting with a seven-foot by fifty-foot cement garden art wall. This garden mixes the beauty of ornamental landscaping with sustainable living vegetable/fruit planting. **NEW** ♿

Hours: 10 a.m. to 4 p.m.

From I-5 north or south, take Exit 101/Tumwater Boulevard. Go east about 1 mile and turn right onto Capitol Boulevard (becomes Old Highway 99). Go 10 miles to Tenino and turn left onto Sussex Avenue (becomes Highway 507). Go 1 mile and turn right onto Churchill Road. Go up hill about 0.25 mile and turn right at third mailbox on right.

Public Gardens
CLARK COUNTY

VANCOUVER
Fort Vancouver Garden
612 East Reserve Street, (360) 816-6200.
www.nps.gov/fova

Fort Vancouver's 1845 Period Garden recreates the flower and vegetable gardens planted by the British Hudson's Bay Company. The original garden was the first formal garden in the Northwest. The National Park Service manages the site organically and plants only heirloom or historic varieties.

Hours: Daylight Savings Time, 9 a.m. to 5 p.m.; otherwise, 9 a.m. to 4 p.m. Closed Thanksgiving, Christmas Eve, Christmas Day, and New Year's Day.

Admission: $3 per person, or $5 per family on Memorial Day and Labor Day

From I-5, take Exit 1-C and follow signs to Fort Vancouver.

From I-205, follow SR14 west to I-5 north and take Exit 1-C; follow signs.

Kaiser Permanente's Salmon Creek Poison Prevention Garden
500 N.E. Multnomah Street,
(503) 813-4820

Opened in 1997, the garden features common garden trees, shrubs, and perennials that are potentially harmful to humans. More than three dozen species are represented, from horse chestnuts to daphne and autumn crocus. All plants are labeled in botanical Latin and English. A plant list is available inside the adjacent Salmon Creek Medical Office.

Hours: Year round, weekdays, 8 a.m. to 5 p.m. (except holidays). Tours led by Master Gardeners by appointment for groups of four or more, April through October.

Admission: Free

From Portland, take I-5 north. Take N.E. 134th Street exit, go 2 blocks east to N.E. 20th, turn left (Poison Prevention Garden is located on campus of Kaiser Permanente's Salmon Creek facility; garden is to left of building.

KING COUNTY

Bainbridge Island

Bloedel Reserve

7571 N.E. Dolphin Drive,
(206) 842-7631, www.bloedelreserve.org

The Bloedel Reserve is a 150-acre former residence, now a public access garden and nature preserve. The primary purpose of the reserve is to provide people with an opportunity to enjoy nature through quiet walks in the gardens and woodlands.

Hours: Year round, Wednesday through Sunday, 10 a.m. to 4 p.m., except federal holidays; reservations required

Admission: $10 adults, $8 seniors, $6 children 5 to 12

Reserve is located about 8 miles north of Winslow (Bainbridge Island Ferry Terminal) off Highway 305. Phone for reservations and directions or visit website.

Bellevue

The Bellevue Botanical Garden

12001 Main Street, (425) 452-2750,
www.bellevuebotanical.org

The Bellevue Botanical Garden comprises fifty-three acres of display gardens, rolling hills, woodlands, meadows, and wetlands offering an ever-changing panorama of greenery and color. A unique combination of horticulture education, scenic beauty, special events, and volunteer opportunities, it has created a focus of community pride.

Hours: Year round, daily, dawn to dusk

Admission: Free

From I-405, exit onto N.E. 8th Avenue east, follow to 120th Street, and turn right. Turn left onto Main Street. Garden is located on right at #12001.

Master Gardener's Urban Demonstration Garden

15416 S.E. 16th Street, (425) 644-9601

Master Gardeners in cooperation with the city of Bellevue's Parks and Recreation Department have transformed an overgrown area into a showcase of urban gardening with the main objective of educating the public. Visitors will see a garden just as they might find in their own yard, only bigger. A steep hill is terraced and planted with drought-tolerant plants and cacti. There are many flower and vegetable gardens as well as fruit trees and shrubs. A large compost area in the back of the garden demonstrates different ways to compost. There is a children's garden and a native plant area. New varieties of plants are tested for our area.

Hours: Year round, daily, staffed by Master Gardeners April through October, Wednesday and Saturday, 9 a.m. to 1 p.m.

Admission: Free

From Highway 520, take 148th Street exit. Turn right and go to S.E. 16th Street. Turn left. Garden is about 1 mile on left.

From I-90, exit at 148th Street. Go north to S.E. 16th Street. Turn right. Garden is about 1 mile on left.

Federal Way

Powellswood, A Northwest Garden

430 South Dash Point Road,
(253) 529-1620, www.powellswood.org

A cultivated paradise hidden in Federal Way's residential suburbs, the three acres of Powellswood are nestled against another thirty-five acres of native successional forest. The garden design itself features eight unique rooms graced with nearly 1,000 varieties of trees, flowering shrubs, and plants. The woodland and shade gardens in particular demonstrate how private landowners can use natural land features to develop stunning landscapes. The garden's perennial borders thrive, the fruit of an extensive soil conservation project. Walking paths, a meandering stream and pond blend gently into the groves and ravines of Redondo's historic upper Cold Creek watershed. A conservatory-style Garden Room offers shelter when the elements threaten. Restore your soul in this peaceful, verdant retreat.

Hours: Special Garden Conservancy Open Day, May 19. Also open Mother's Day weekend, May 13 & 14, 10 a.m. to 5 p.m. Otherwise, open April to mid-October, Tuesday through Thursday, 10 a.m. to 2 p.m. and by appointment.

Admission: $5

From north, take I-5 south to 272nd Street exit and turn right. Turn left onto Pacific Highway south. Turn right onto Dash Point Road. Go 1 mile to #430. Garden is on right.

From south, take I-5 north to 320th Street exit. Turn left. Turn right onto Pacific Highway south. Turn left onto Dash Point Road. Go 1 mile to #430.

Rhododendron Species Botanical Garden

2525 South 336th Street, (253) 661-9377, www.rhodygarden.org

The Rhododendron Species Botanical Garden features one of the most extensive collections of wild rhododendrons in the world. Enjoy more than 10,000 rhododendrons growing in a beautiful twenty-two-acre woodland setting with exotic and unusual companion plants. Year-round features include alpine, pond, and woodland gardens, a hardy fern collection, and a gazebo.

Hours: March through May, daily, except Thursday, 10 a.m. to 4 p.m.; June through February, Saturday through Wednesday, 11 a.m. to 4 p.m.

Admission: $3.50 adults, $2.50 seniors/students

From I-5, take Exit 143/Federal Way/South 320th Street. Turn east onto 320th Street. At Weyerhaeuser Way South, turn right. Enter roundabout, then exit at second right, continuing south. Take second right and follow signs for parking.

ORTING

The Chase Garden

16015 264th Street East, (206) 242-4040, www.chasegarden.org

A PROJECT OF THE GARDEN CONSERVANCY

Recently featured in Starr Ockenga's *Earth on Her Hands: The American Woman in Her Garden*, this naturalistic style garden on four and a half acres has been created and tended by Emmott and Ione Chase since 1960. The area surrounding the house was designed by Rex Zumwalt, evoking the simplicity of a Japanese garden by the use of raked pea gravel, moss-covered boulders, and reflecting pool. A forest of native trees is carpeted with wildflowers. There are perennial shade borders, a rock garden, and a groundcover meadow inspired by the alpine meadows of Mount Rainer. Visitors may enjoy the mountain as part of the panoramic view of the Puyallup River Valley.

Hours: By appointment only April through October. Closed Sunday and Monday.

Admission: $5

From Highway 161/Meridian turn east onto 264th Street about 1 mile south of town of Graham. Continue for 3.5 miles. Watch for driveway on left.

From Seattle, go south on Highway 167. Take Puyallup/Olympia exit onto Highway 512 south. Remain on Highway 512, by-passing Puyallup and take South Hill/Eatonville exit. Turn left at traffic light onto Highway 161/Meridian. Proceed as directed above.

From I-5, take Highway 512 east to Eatonville exit. Turn right at light onto Highway 161/Meridian. Proceed as directed above.

From Olympia, follow signs to Eatonville. Go north from Eatonville via Highway 161/Meridian. Proceed as directed above.

SEATTLE
Streissguth Gardens
1600 Broadway Avenue East,
(206) 329-9148,
www.streissguthgardens.com

We are a small, family maintained garden located on the northwest side of Seattle's Capitol Hill, on a steep hillside offering great views over Lake Union, of downtown Seattle, and of the Olympic Mountains in the distance. We garden slightly less than one acre, in several different pieces. The newer portions of the gardens lie south of the East Blaine stairs and they are now publicly owned, open to visitors at all times. We still maintain these newer gardens for their new owner, the City of Seattle Department of Parks and Recreation.

Hours: Year round, daily, dawn to dusk.

Admission: Free

The gardens are two blocks north of St. Mark's Cathedral on Capitol Hill on a small dead end street. Please park at the corner of 10th Avenue East and East Blaine Street. Go down East Blaine Street steps, 3/4 of a block west. The #49 bus also stops in both directions at this corner. To drive by the garden, follow Tenth Avenue East to traffic light at East Boston Street, and turn west. Go 1 block, and turn south. Follow Broadway Avenue East 3 blocks to East Blaine Street. The garden is on left after East Blaine Street (which is a public staircase on both sides of the street).

University of Washington Botanic Gardens/Washington Park Arboretum
2300 Arboretum Drive East,
(206) 543-8800,
www.uwbotanicgardens.org

Washington Park Arboretum is a dynamic collection of trees and shrubs hardy in the maritime Pacific Northwest. Plant collections are selected and arranged to display their beauty and function in urban landscapes, to demonstrate their natural ecology and diversity, and to conserve important species and cultivated varieties for the future.

Hours: Year round, daily, dawn to dusk

Admission: Free

From I-5, take Exit 168-B/Bellevue/Kirkland east. Take very first exit, Montlake Boulevard/UW. At traffic light, go straight. You are now on Lake Washington Boulevard East. Follow 1 mile to stop sign with left-turn lane. Turn left onto Foster Island Road and follow signs to visitors center.

VASHON ISLAND
The Mukai Farm and Garden
(206) 463-2349

In the midst of her family's prosperous strawberry farm, a first-generation Issei woman created a Japanese-style garden, replete with "islands" and waterfalls surrounded by pools filled with koi and waterlilies. The Mukai family achieved success by being the first to barrel and freeze strawberries in the Puget Sound region. The Garden Conservancy supported Island Landmarks' quest to secure the ownership of the Mukai property, which was accomplished in 2000. Since then the Conservancy has helped develop a strategy and budget for restoration of the gardens and is engaged in efforts to bring additional organizational support to this critical cultural resource.

Hours: Open to the public two times a year: the week of Cherry Blossom, in May and fall celebration in October. Group tours can be arranged with advance notice.

Please call for directions.

PIERCE COUNTY

LAKEWOOD
Lakewold Gardens
12317 Gravelly Lake Drive S.W.,
(253) 584-4106, www.lakewold.org

Lakewold Gardens is a beautiful ten-acre public estate showcasing a year-round display of formal and informal landscape design. Sited to complement the gardens, the Georgian-style manor features a spiral staircase that curves above the marble foyer. A wisteria-covered veranda overlooks Gravelly Lake with vistas of Mount Rainier. Designed as a series of outdoor rooms, the gardens include formal parterres

♿ indicates parts of garden are handicapped accessible

accented by topiary, European statuary, water features, rock and alpine gardens, an English-style knot garden, shade garden, and a newly renovated fern garden. The collections include more than 250 species of rhododendrons, more than thirty varieties of Japanese maples, and many unique trees, shrubs, and ground covers from around the world. Lakewold is a splendid example of noted landscape architect Thomas Church's residential designs.

Hours: April through September, Wednesday through Sunday, 10 a.m. to 4 p.m.; Please phone ahead for fall and winter hours. Guided tours available by appointment.

Admission: $5 adults, $3 seniors/students/military, children under 12 free.

From I-5, take Exit 124/Gravelly Lake Drive. Lakewold is 10 miles south of Tacoma.

WOODLAND
Hulda Klager Lilac Gardens
115 South Pekin Road, (360) 225-8996

The gardens are really an arboretum with many flowers, shrubs, and exotic trees, besides the lilacs. The house has been restored and made into a museum honoring the "Lilac Lady." Also, the woodshed, water tower, and carriage house have all been restored. The Lilac Garden is a nonprofit organization with an approximately 90% volunteer work force, which puts in many hours keeping the gardens as Hulda Klager kept them.

Hours: Year round, daily, 10 a.m. to 4 p.m.

Admission: $2

From I-5, take Exit 21. Coming south, go about 0.5 mile to a stop sign. There will be a sign on street leading to garden. Coming north, turn left at bottom of exit at traffic light. At next light, look straight ahead and there will be a sign pointing to Lilac Garden. Follow signs to garden.

THURSTON COUNTY
LACEY
Closed Loop Park
2418 Hogum Bay Road, (360) 438-6691, http:/gardening.wsu.edu/closedloop

This is an ornamental garden built atop a closed landfill. Located within the Thurston Waste and Recovery Center, the garden was established in 1992 with eighteen inches of soil placed on top of a thick plastic liner. The garden is approximately two and a half acres, featuring ninety peonies, hardy fuchsia, a composting center, water-wise drip irrigation, an enabling garden, and a native plant border. We grow trial plants for Great Plant Picks. Currently the trial plant groups are astrantia, *Sambucus nigra, Berberis thunbergii,* sedum, viburnum, geum, heuchera and tiarella and heucherella.

Hours: Year round, daily, 8 a.m. to 5 p.m. Closed major holidays.

Admission: Free

Take I-5 to Exit 111. Traveling south, turn right, go a half of a block and turn right onto Hogum Bay Road.

Traveling north, turn left, go over freeway and turn right onto Hogum Bay Road. Enter Thurston County Waste and Recovery Center. Garden is on right beyond recycling center.

WEST VIRGINIA

Charleston Area
Open Day
Saturday, June 2

"Her Garden" The Paula Vasale Memorial Garden is also open on this date. See their listing on page 280.

KANAWHA COUNTY

CHARLESTON

Westwind Way Gardens
185 Westwind Way

Our ridge-top house is approached by a long drive passing between two stone pillars. A series of islands planted with bulbs and perennials surround the large trees that line our drive. The house is based on Arts and Crafts architecture with a classic foundation planting of boxwood. The dramatic and unusual view of Yeager Airport and Coonskin Park enhance the extensive terrace and pool area at the back of the house. This area is surrounded by specimen plants and lush beds of perennials. The house and gardens are both recent, but have settled well. **NEW** ♿

Hours: 10 a.m. to 2 p.m.

From Charleston, take I-79 north to Mink Shoals exit. Turn right onto Route 119 (toward Elkview) and go about 1 mile. Turn left onto Crestwood Drive and go to top of mountain and turn left into Quail Pointe Subdivision. Go to end of Quail Pointe development to Westwind Way. Please park at top of Westwind Way entrance and a shuttle will be available.

ELKVIEW

The Fuqua Garden
23 Tyree Circle

The Fuqua Garden is at the end of a secluded cul-de-sac on Tyree Circle and features beautiful stone work in the walks and walls. Upon entering, one will get hints of the amazing woodland border and stream on the left. These become increasingly evident as one wanders down the path, which opens to decks, terraces, and a hot tub area, all providing magnificent woodland vistas of the natural gardens surrounding the stream and pond area. Perennials are used *en masse* as ground cover, highlighting many choice and specimen plants, which are cleverly woven into the landscape. The edges of the woodland have been groomed as a gentle transition from cultivated to natural. **NEW**

Hours: 10 a.m. to 4 p.m.

The garden is 4.3 miles north of Capitol High School on Greenbrier Street. Opposite entrance to Indian Creek Village, turn right on Tyree Circle. Proceed up steep hill to large cul-de-sac at end.

The Garden of Paula & Roger Shafer
49 Upper Pinch Road

Informal plantings of annuals, perennials, bulbs, flowering shrubs, and evergreens complement the country setting of the house. Set back from the road on fifty acres, three colorful gardens attract birds and butterflies. An arch of honeysuckle marks the passage to the entrance garden. Stone paths lead around the house to the very private patio garden where roses provide constant color through the summer months. In use year-round, the patio garden has plants in bloom or berry during all four seasons. **NEW** ♿

Hours: 10 a.m. to 4 p.m.

The garden is about 10 miles north of Charleston. Take Greenbriar Street and follow Route 114 north. Alternately, take I-79 to Big Chimney exit and turn right. At 4-way stop sign, go straight over bridge and turn left at traffic light onto Route 114 north. When Route 114 splits, veer left toward town of Pinch and drive through town. Pass firehouse on right and Pinch Reunion Ground on left. Turn right onto New Hope Road. Just ahead at a 3-way stop sign, turn right onto Upper Pinch Road. The Shafer house is 1 mile ahead on left, just before road for Upper Pinch Estates.

Proceeds shared with Kanawha Garden Club

♿ indicates parts of garden are handicapped accessible

Public Gardens

KANAWHA COUNTY

CHARLESTON

"Her Garden" Paula Vasale Memorial Garden

Greenbrier Street & Airport Road

A public garden of mixed woody and herbaceous perennials designed to be viewed from moving vehicles. Of particular interest are remontant (blooming more than once in a season) bearded iris, hibiscus 'Sweet Caroline', and anemone 'Honorine Jobert'. This garden was designed, funded, and installed by the friends and family of Paula Vasale following her death from breast cancer in June 2001. Maintenance and editing of the garden are provided by the same group. "Her Garden" is funded by the Municipal Beautification Commission and is located on state property through a permit from the West Virginia Department of Highways.

Hours: June 2; 10 a.m. to 4 p.m.

Admission: $5

Take I-77 to Exit 99/Greenbrier Street/State Capitol. Travel north on Greenbrier Street/Route 114 about 1.5 miles to garden at intersection of Airport Road and Greenbrier Street. Park on gravel across Greenbrier Street from garden or pass garden and park on paved lot on left immediately across small concrete bridge.

ACKNOWLEDGMENTS

ALABAMA
Birmingham
  Mrs. John N. Wrinkle (1998–2000, 2002, 2004)
  Mrs. A. Jack Allison (1998–2000, 2002, 2004)

ARIZONA
Greer
  Nadine Stanley (2005)
Phoenix
  Mrs. Scott Crozier (2000–2003)
  Mary Irish (2003–2004)
  Nancy Swanson (1999)
  Mrs. Donald C. Williams (1998–1999)
  Gregory S. Trutza (2001)
Tucson
  Lisa Lucking (2004–2007)
  Elizabeth Przygoda (2004–2007)

CALIFORNIA
Carmel
  Mrs. Lee Meneice (1997–1998)
Los Angeles
  Jeanne Anderson (2005–2007)
  Judy Horton (2001–2006)
  Susan Keirn (2005–2007)
  Joseph Marek (2007)
Pasadena
  Martyn Belmont (2007)
  Kathy Gillespie (2005–2007)
  Judy Horton (2003–2006)
  Elena Shoch (2007)
  Mrs. Donivee Nash (1999–2000, 2002)
Sacramento
  Saul Wiseman (2006–2007)
San Diego
  Lynne & Vernon Blackman (2004)
  Joanne Lee (2007)

Bill & Tamma Nugent (2004)
Susi Torre–Bueno (2003–2005)
San Francisco Bay Area
  Sonny Garcia (1998–2000)
  Charmain Giuliani (1998–2000)
  Laurie Jake (2000–2006)
  Richard G. Turner Jr. (1998–2000)
  Tom Valva (1998–2000)
San Francisco Peninsula
  Mrs. Harvey D. Hinman (1998–2007)
  Joan Sanders (2001–2007)
San Jose
  Alrie Middlebrook (2006)
Sebastopol
  Betsy Flack (2005–2007)

COLORADO
Colorado Springs
  Mrs. Terence Lilly (2000–2004)
  Mrs. Gene Moore (1998–2004)
Denver
  Laurie Brock (2007)
  Mrs. William B. Harvey (2001, 2003 & 2005)
  Mrs. Moses Taylor (1998–1999, 2001, 2003 & 2005)
  Suellen White (2007)

DELAWARE
Wilmington
  Mrs. George P. Bissell Jr. (1998–1999)
  Mrs. Sidney Scott Jr. (1998–1999)

DISTRICT OF COLUMBIA
Joanne S. Lawson (1997–2000)
Mrs. John Macomber (1997–2001)

FLORIDA
Ponte Vedra Beach
  Carolyn Marsh Lindsay (1998 & 2000)

Vero Beach
Christine Hobart (2007)
Mrs. Henry Maresi (2006)
*Mrs. Thomas S. Morse (1998–1999 &
2001)*
Mrs. Bruce Roberts (2002–2004)
Mrs. Henry N. Tifft (1998, 1999, 2001)
Mrs. Stephen Wyer (2002–2004)

GEORGIA

Atlanta
Virginia Almand (1998)
George E. N. de Man (2000)
Benjamin A. Hill (2005)
Mrs. William Huger (1999–2000)
Audrey McMenamy (2005)

HAWAII

Honolulu
Mrs. E. Chipman Higgins (1997–1998)

ILLINOIS

Barrington Hills
Betty Earl (2002–2006)

Chicago
Brooks Hartley–Leonard (2001–2005)
Mrs. Melville C. Hill, Jr. (2004–2007)
*Mrs. Charles E. Schroeder (1997–2000,
2003 & 2005)*
Melissa Shennan (2001–2005)

Hinsdale & Oak Brook
Susan Beard (2001–2004)
Betty Earl (2005–2006)

Western Chicago
Betty Earl (2002–2007)

INDIANA

Indianapolis
Dr. Gilbert S. Daniels (1997–1998)

LOUISIANA

New Orleans
Ann Hobson Haack (1998–2001)

MAINE

Hancock County
Patrick Chassé (2005)

Mrs. George H. P. Dwight (2006–2007)
Mid Coast
Margaret P. Watson (2006–2007)

York County
Mrs. Calvin Hosmer III (2001–2007)

MARYLAND

Annapolis
Mrs. John A. Baldwin (2001)

Baltimore
Nan Paternotte (1997)
Mrs. Frances Huber (1998)
Mrs. Clark MacKenzie (1999)
Mrs. Thomas G. McCausland (2000)

Chestertown
Mrs. Adrian P. Reed (1999)

MASSACHUSETTS

Berkshires
Jytte Brooks (2006–2007)
Cathy Clark (2006)
Mary Jane Emmet (2005–2006)
Diana Felber (2006–2007)
Ian & Madeline Hooper (2007)
Julianna Roosevelt (2005–2006)
Honey Sharp (2005–2007)

Boston
Diane Dalton (2001–2002)
Kevin Doyle (2003–2004)
Mrs. Henry S. Streeter (1997–2000)
Linda Wolcott (2003)

Chatham
*Mrs. Prescott Dunbar (2001–2002, 2004
& 2007)*

Nantucket
Mrs. John A. Baldwin (2006–2007)
*Mrs. Coleman Burke (2002–2003 &
2005–2007)*
Caroline Ellis (2005–2007)

Osterville
Mrs. David Cole (2001)

South Dartmouth
Mrs. Helen Goddard (2002)
Mrs. Thomas S. Morse (1998)

Mrs. Robert G. Walker (1999–2000, 2002)

Worcester
John W. Trexler (1998–1999, 2002 & 2006)

MICHIGAN

Ann Arbor
George Papadalos (1998)
Marie Cochrane (1999)

Grosse Pointe
Mrs. John Ford (1997–1998)
Mrs. Bragaw Vanderzee (1999)

Harbor Springs
Mrs. John Ford (1998)
Mrs. Frank Hightower (2000)

Oakland County
Virginia Berberian (2001)
Norm Bodine (2001–2002)
Lynne Clippert (2000)
Starr Foster (1998–1999)
Lois Gamble (2000)
Mrs. John Knutson (2000–2002)
Suzanne Krueger (2003)
Dr. Alice R. McCarthy (2004–2006)

MINNESOTA

Minneapolis
Mrs. John Winsor (1997)
Mrs. Henry L. Sweatt (1997 & 1999)

MISSOURI

Kansas City
Mrs. George Powell III (1997)
Mrs. Dwight Sutherland (1997)

St. Louis
Mrs. William H. T. Bush (1998, 2001, 2004)
Dr. & Mrs. Tom Ott (2004)

NEW HAMPSHIRE

Monadnock Region
Kris Fenderson (2005)
Mary Liz Lewis (2005)
Mrs. Story Wright (2000, 2002–2003 & 2005)

New London
Mrs. Gusta Teach (2000)
Mrs. John H. Hewitt (2007)

Sea Coast
Beth Hume (2002)

Squam Lake
George Carr (2000)

NEW JERSEY
Joan Kram (2001–2003)
Mrs. Duncan Pitney (1997–2003)
Jeanne Will (2004–2005)

Bergen County
Annie Zusy (2004)

Monmouth County
Jacqueline McMullen (2004)
Barbara Nelson (2007)

NEW YORK

Albany/Schenectady
Joanne Lenden (1998–2001)
Mrs. Henry Ferguson (2000)

Bronx
Marco Polo Stufano (2007)

Cooperstown
Mrs. H. Rodney Hartman (1998)
Patricia Thorpe (1998, 2002 & 2004)

Eastern Long Island
Lalitte Smith (1996–2007)

Lake Champlain
Mrs. James T. Flynn (1999–2002)

Nassau County
Christine Doctor (2004 & 2006)
Judy Goldsmith (2006)

Oneonta
Heleen Heyning (2002)

Onteora
Mr. & Mrs. Alan T. Wenzell (2002)

Remsenburg
Deonne Finkelstein (2006–2007)

Salem & Cambridge
Mrs. Henry Ferguson (2000)

Saratoga Springs
Georgiana Ducas (2000 & 2002)

Bruce Solenski (2000 & 2002)

Syracuse
Michael Brennan (2004–2007)

Tompkins County
Chrys Gardener (2004–2007)
Dan Klein (2005–2006)

Ulster County
James Dinsmore (2006)

NEW YORK & CONNECTICUT
Page Dickey (co–founder)
Jane Havemeyer (1995–2005)
Muffie Knight (1995–2007)
Penelope Maynard (co–founder)
Enid Munroe (1995–2004)
Melissa Orme (1995–2003)
Francis Schell (2004–2007)

NORTH CAROLINA
Asheville
Hunter Stubbs (2001–2006)

Chapel Hill
Taimie Anderson (2001)
Stepheny Houghtlin (2002)

Charlotte
Ann Armstrong (2004 & 2006)
Mary Lindeman Wilson (2002, 2004 & 2006)

Edenton
Samuel Bobbitt Dixon (2005–2006)
Anne Rouse Edwards (2005–2007)

Greensboro
Julia Blizin (2005)
Nancy Cavanaugh (2005)
Mrs. Edwin R. Lyon, Jr. (2004)

Hillsborough
Taimie Anderson (2001)

Raleigh
Taimie Anderson (2001)
Helen Yoest (2006–2007)

OHIO
Akron
Mrs. W. Stuver Parry (1998–1999)

Cincinnati
Ms. Julie Mahlin (2002)
Mrs. William R. Seaman (1999–2000)

Columbus
Mrs. Roger Blair (2000)
Mrs. Robert F. Hoffman Jr. (2000)
Karen K. Meyer (1999)
Connie Page (1998)

Dayton
Mrs. James Woodhull (1997–2002)
Barbara Rion (1997–2002)

Granville
Mrs. James Murr (2001, 2003 & 2005)
Janet Oberleissen (1998)

OKLAHOMA
Tulsa
Brennis O'Neal (2002)

OREGON
Clackamas County
Stephanie Butz (2007)
Y. Sherry Sheng (2007)
Lynn Swanson (2007)

Eugene
Diana Learner (2007)
Pam Perryman (2007)
Rebecca Sams (2006)
Buell Steelman (2006)

Portland
Linda Ernst (2005–2007)
Sally Geist (2006)
Jill Schatz (2002–2007)
Patricia B. Walker (2002–2004)

Salem
Bobbie Dolp (2002–2004)

Washington County
Stephanie Butz (2006)
Sara Cairns (2004)

PENNSYLVANIA
Bucks County
Jack Staub (2000–2003 & 2005–2006)

Philadelphia
Mrs. Frank H. Goodyear (1998–1999)
Mrs. Benjamin H. Heckscher (2001)

Mrs. Morris Lloyd Jr. (2001–2006)
Diane Newbury (2006–2007)
Mrs. Edward Starr III (1998–1999)
Susan Yeager (2006–2007)

Pittsburgh
Bernita Buncher (2000)
Mrs. Joshua C. Whetzel Jr. (1998 & 2000)

State College
Rae Chambers (2001–2002)
Dr. Richard Morgan (2000)

RHODE ISLAND

Little Compton
Mrs. Helen Goddard (2005)

SOUTH CAROLINA

Greenville
Mrs. Nelson B. Arrington, Jr. (1997–1998, 2001 & 2004)
Mrs. Samuel M. Beattie (1997–1998, 2001 & 2004)

TENNESSEE

Chattanooga
Mrs. Halbert Law (1999–2000)
Mrs. E. L. Mitchell (2002)
Mrs. John Stout (1999–2000)

Knoxville
Jim McDonough (2007)

Memphis
Mrs. Albert M. Austin III (1999)
Barbara Keathley, ASLA (2001 & 2003)
Mrs. David B. Martin (1999)

Nashville
Mr. Bob Brackmann (2000–2003)
Mrs. Robert C. H. Mathews, Jr. (2000–2003)
Mr. Ben Page (2000–2003)

TEXAS

Austin
James deGrey David (1998–1999)
Deborah Hornickel (2000, 2002–2003 & 2006)
Jennifer Staub Meyers (1998–1999)
Dr. Gordon L. White (1998–1999)

Dallas
Susan Gregory (2006)
Peter Schaar (2002–2007)

El Paso
Mrs. Sam Davis (2006–2007)
Maria Woody (2006–2007)

Fort Worth
Ginger Bason (2005 & 2007)

Galveston
Steven Creitz (2006)
Brian Davis (2006)

Houston
Joanne Seale Wilson (2002–2004)
Mrs. J. Taft Symonds (1998–2004)
Mrs. Sellers J. Thomas Jr. (1998–2004)

VERMONT

Lake Champlain
Robin Coleburn (2006)
Mrs. James T. Flynn (1999–2001)
Marcia Pierce (2003)

Manchester
Mrs. A. V. S. Olcott (1998–2005)

Upper Valley/Woodstock
Mrs. John H. Hewitt (2007)
Patsy Highberg (2005)
William Noble (2005)

VIRGINIA

Arlington
Tom Mannion (2002–2003)

Charlottesville
Candy Crosby (2007)
Mrs. Terrence D. Daniels (2004)
Mrs. Mario di Valmarana (1997, 2004 & 2007)

Middleburg
Mrs. Charles H. Seilheimer Jr. (1997)

Richmond
Mrs. Robert A. Bristow II (1997)

WASHINGTON

Bainbridge Island
Karla Waterman (2003–2007)

Bellevue
  Jane Whiteley (2004)

Clark County
  Jill Schatz (2005)

Olympia
  Tam Crocker (2007)

Seattle
  Barbara Flynn (1999)
  Keith Geller (2002–2003)
  Mrs. Bruce McIvor (2000, 2003–2006)
  Nicole Nelson (2004)

West Virginia

Charleston
  Mrs. Herbert Jones (1997)
  Marion Jones (2007)
  Mr. Bill Mills (2005)
  Mrs. & Mrs. James Rufus Thomas II
  (1998–2000, 2002–2003)

Wisconsin

Lake Country
  Mrs. Anthony Meyer (2000)
  Mrs. Henry Quadracci (2000)

Milwaukee
  Mrs. William Allis (1998–1999, 2002)
  Mrs. Robert W. Braeger (1998–1999,
  2002)

Canada

British Columbia

Qualicum Beach
  Jim Cadwaladr (2004)

Victoria
  Valerie Murray (2004)

Vancouver
  Cheryl Cooper (2004)

Y

Z

NOTES

Notes

NOTES

NOTES

NOTES

NOTES

JOIN THE GARDEN CONSERVANCY

If you enjoyed Open Days this year, why not consider becoming a member of the Garden Conservancy? Your support enables us to preserve America's exceptional gardens and to open them to the public. Members enjoy the following benefits:

- a subscription to our quarterly newsletter
- free admission to selected Garden Conservancy Preservation Projects
- invitations to Garden Conservancy-sponsored special events
- discounts on purchases of the National *Open Days Directory* and admission tickets
- a personalized membership card and an automobile decal
- gifts of $100 or more are acknowledged in our newsletter and annual report
- gifts of $1,500 or more include membership in the Society of Fellows and you will be invited to attend garden-study tours and special events

Please enroll me as a member of the Garden Conservancy:

☐ $35 Individual ☐ $100 Friend ☐ $1,500 Fellow ☐ $10,000 Chairman's Circle
☐ $50 Family ☐ $250 Sponsor ☐ $2,500 President's Circle/Sustainer
☐ $50 Organization ☐ $500 Patron ☐ $5,000 President's Circle/Benefactor

Open Days Discount Admission Tickets make garden visiting easier and never expire. Use them at any Open Day garden (private only), anywhere. One book includes 6 tickets.

Membership contribution $ _____

Directories ($10.95 members, $15.95 nonmembers) $ _____

East edition ($5) $ _____

West edition ($5) $ _____

Ticket Books—a $30 value ($15 members, $25 nonmembers) $ _____

Add $4.50 for shipping & handling when ordering a National Directory $ _____

Add $1.95 for each additional Regional Directory $ _____

Total enclosed $ _____

Please charge my credit card account: MasterCard _____ VISA _____

Account Number: _____ Exp. ___ /___

Name _____

Address _____

City/Town _____ State _____ Zip _____

Phone _____ Email _____

Make checks payable to: The Garden Conservancy P.O. Box 219, Cold Spring, NY 10516, or fax to (845) 265-5392. You may also call our toll-free line (888) 842-2442 or visit www.gardenconservancy.org.

The Garden Conservancy, Inc. is a tax-exempt organization under section 501(c)(3) of the Internal Revenue Code. Membership contributions are fully tax deductible. Purchases of The Garden Conservancy's *Open Days Directory* and/or ticket books do not constitute a charitable contribution and are not tax deductible.

Notes

WITH OUR COMPLIMENTS

Discounted admission tickets are a great way to save on Open Days visits. Just complete and return the free admission ticket offer below and we'll send you one free Open Days admission ticket. You may also complete this form and redeem it at any Open Days admission table on that day. Incomplete forms will not be accepted.

Admission tickets do not expire and may be used at any time during an Open Day to enter a private garden. However, they are not valid at Public Gardens listed in the *Directory*.

Admission to each private garden is $5. Garden Conservancy members may purchase a book of 6 discounted admission tickets for $15 (that's 50% off!). Non members may purchase a book of tickets for $25. To order tickets, use the form on the opposite page or call our toll-free order line at 1-888-842-2442. You may also purchase tickets on-line at www.opendaysprogram.org.

To redeem, please complete and return to:

The Garden Conservancy
Post Office Box 219
Cold Spring, NY 10516

Photocopies of this form will not be accepted.

Name _____

Address _____

City/Town _____ State ____ Zip code _____

Please provide your e-mail address if you would like to be reminded about upcoming Open Days in your area and to receive invitations to special events. The above information is collected for the use of the Garden Conservancy and will not be shared with third parties.

E-mail _____